Selected American Prose, 1841-1900

focused on America; it enforced the process of national self-discovery that became the principal motivation for literature after the Civil War. The most visible product of that self-discovery was the vast literature of local color, much of it nostalgic and sentimental but much of it overlapping with and contributing to realism. From his desk at the *Atlantic* and later from the Easy Chair of *Harper's*, William Dean Howells directed both movements with the clear perception that they were closely linked.

Insofar as it was colored, local color literature was romantic; insofar as it was local, it was likely to be realistic to a considerable degree, the Midwestern and New England strains more so than the Far Western and Southern. The literary exploitation of the American regions may be said to have begun with Harriet Beecher Stowe's *Pearl of Orr's Island* in 1862. It got a great thrust into popularity with Bret Harte's first mining camp stories in 1868, and through the 1870's and 1880's there came into every corner of the continent eager writers with notebooks in their hands and their eyes sharp for something picturesque, theatrical, or "authentic."

At its best and most realistic, local color fiction was written by people who like Mark Twain knew their native regions from childhood up; at its worst it was written by tourists. Strong influences upon it lingered from the romantic antiquarianism of Scott and the *couleur locale* of Hugo and Mérimée, and in the South nostalgia for the antebellum feudal life resulted in such sectional pieties as the stories of John Esten Cooke, Thomas Nelson Page, Maurice Thompson, George Cary Eggleston, and others.

Bret Harte, who received credit for starting the whole local color movement and even for inventing the short story which was its principal form, was guilty in less pietistic ways of romanticizing his materials. For one thing, he didn't know them well; his geography and his lingo were both synthetic; for another, he wrote about the mining camps when they were almost as dead as the feudal South. By 1868 the bulk of the mining excitement as well as most of the miners had been over across the mountain on the Comstock Lode for ten years. Nevertheless there was a streak of realism here: these stories treated prostitutes, drunks, card sharps, thieves, and murderers unabashedly, and if Harte sentimentalized them, as he surely did, he sentimentalized them for humor and for effects of Dickensian paradox, and not to gloss over their sins. "The Idyll of Red Gulch," to take a single example, suggests that a man may get hog-drunk, and may have an illegitimate child by a prostitute, and still be a rather likeable fellow capable of stirring the maidenly feelings of a pure schoolteacher. That was not exactly going as far as Maupassant's "Boule de Suif," but it was going a considerable distance in American fiction in 1869. Only John de Forest, with his portraits of Madame LaRue and Colonel Carter in *Miss Ravenel's Conversion*, had gone as far.

The common man and woman—though not necessarily drunk—dominated local color fiction. Yankee, Hoosier, Pike, Cracker, gave American readers a multiple image of themselves. After her early start, Harriet Beecher Stowe returned to her New England milieu in a series of books that are oddly snug and homely after the reforming zeal of *Uncle Tom's Cabin* and the unfortunate scandalmongering of *Lady Byron Vindicated*. Up and down New England, other writers, mainly women, painted other domestic and community genre pieces: Celia Thaxter of the isolated fisher families on the Isles of Shoals, Sarah Orne Jewett of fishermen and farmers on the Maine coast, Mary Wilkins Freeman of the shrivelled old-maid-haunted towns from which the men had drifted off to California or the Civil War or just "down country" and never returned.

Nowadays the standard texts omit many once-famous names. The rather touristy Tennessee mountain stories of Mary Noailles Murfree ("Charles Egbert Craddock") can probably be spared; so can Mary Hartwell Catherwood, Constance Fenimore Woolson, Alice French ("Octave Thanet"), Margaret Deland, and many more. They justify themselves as the solid base of a pyramid from which the higher tiers of writers could arise. Much of Cable's fiction (not his social criticism) seems rather posturing and affected now; if one wants Creoles and Cajuns, those of Kate Chopin seem more alive and less stapled to a rococo stage set. As for the Negro, whose muffled spirituals had been noticed in 1867 by Thomas Wentworth Higginson, he came into literature under the best of guides: Joel Chandler Harris began telling his humorous animal fables in the Atlanta *Constitution* in 1879, and Mark Twain gave the Negro himself a heroic and human dignity in Nigger Jim. These, certainly, cannot be spared. To the shrinking list of the enduring and worthy one would like to add the name of Mary Hallock Foote, both writer and illustrator. Her mining camps in California, Colorado, and Idaho are almost the only real ones in local color fiction—very much more real than those of Bret Harte. By no means a major figure, she is too honest to be totally lost.

Midwestern local color, which began in 1871 with Edward Eggleston's *The Hoosier Schoolmaster*, John Hay's *Pike County Ballads*, and the first volume of Will Carleton's rustic poems, will not be lost, though its worth is often less than that of Mary Foote or Kate Chopin, and much less than that of Miss Jewett and Mrs. Freeman. What Eggleston started in Indiana had the secret of growth and change in it: a method that was sober and honest, and a local society that was typical rather than picturesque. Eggleston's method was simple enough: to apply to his own Indiana backwoods some of the theories of Hippolyte Taine ("the artist of originality will work courageously with the materials he finds in his own environment"), in the realistic spirit of Dutch painting, using as a tool the carefully studied local dialect. From the beginning, Eggleston's purpose was close to that of a social historian. Out of his example came a whole Midwestern school: Nicholson and Tarkington, Garland and Dreiser, Lewis and Sandburg, the "Chicago realists." And continuing the tradition of the folksy Carleton was a succession of versifiers, from Riley and Eugene Field and the Sweet Singer of Michigan to Edgar Guest, who may be neither realistic nor literary but who appear to be immortal.

Midwestern writers had the advantage of dealing with a nascent culture, a backwoods freehold society just coming into adolescence. Mark Twain and Howells both endowed it in several books with an aura of golden youth; it came to look, later on when pessimism and disillusion about the present had soured some of its sons, like an ideal civilization: happy, almost classless, peaceable, just, and equalitarian. Its lacks they could charitably overlook; for its pattern was a representative and apparently dominant one. New England was in decline; if Indiana was, as Maurice Thompson said in *Hoosier Mosaics*, like a boy whose voice was changing, New England had already crossed the line dividing the maiden from the old maid. The South was defeated and bitter with Reconstruction, the West had only the hit-and-run societies of the mining camps and cow towns, the overtaken Indians and Spaniards, and the socially eccentric Mormons. But Eggleston's Indiana, or Howells' Ohio, or Mark Twain's Missouri, were in many ways the flowering of the democratic ideal, and much of that ideal, with its scientific and pragmatic biases, was entangled with the philosophy of literary realism. Only if one defines it by its excesses should the term local color have a pejorative sound. Even its excesses, its celebration of picturesque setting and its dialectal contortions and phonetic misspellings, were stigmata of a partially realistic impulse. The differences existed, and were no less real for being picturesque or difficult to pronounce.

In a country supposedly lacking both in a tradition and in usable literary materials, the local colorists came suddenly upon riches. They had to invent nothing, but could simply record what had grown unseen. Available to them, by the end of the Civil War, was a surprising amount of factual information on the continent, a literature of travel and exploration. Available also—unavoidable actually—was a lively current of oral and newspaper humor, in which could be discerned the outlines of several regional subcultures, several typical American "characters," and several varieties of the American language. Explicit in the literature of travel and exploration was a scientific attitude toward the natural environment; implicit in the humor was a democratic, even though comic, view of man. Both attitudes and both bodies of tradition were indispensable to realism as to local color. No one curious about realism's native roots can afford to neglect them.

"Once," says George R. Stewart, "from eastern ocean to western ocean, the land stretched away without names." It is an obvious but striking thought: what a slow accumulation of painfully won facts, what a perennial slaying of the dragons of ignorance, error, and fantasy, before we are at the point of seeing the world with even partial objectivity. The realism of a new nation begins with its maps, its catalogues of birds, animals, and plants, its information on soils, topography, rivers, mountains, weather, its acquaintance with its tribes of wild men. And new facts demand new eyes. The exploration of a new continent demands both the poetic capacity for wonder and the prosaic capacity for seeing straight, and to counteract Currier and Ives prints and the dime novels published by the Beadle brothers there was by the 1860's a solid body of real information in the books of explorers and travelers.

Actually the link between travel and fiction is close, especially in America where the adventurous new was always close at hand. Irving in *Astoria* and *The Adventures of Captain Bonneville* had made vicarious excursions into the West; Melville's *Typee* and *Omoo* were published as fiction but can hardly be distinguished in type from such true-life adventures as Parkman's *The Oregon Trail*, undertaken as preparation for the writing of history, or Major J. W. Powell's *Exploration of the Colorado River of the West*, published in 1875 as a scientific report. And note that Mark Twain and Howells eased into the writing of fiction by almost imperceptible degrees from the writing of travel narratives, and that the fact and condition of habitual travel inform the largest part of the fiction of Henry James.

We should not, that is, mistake the local color period's interest in place as a merely fictional one. Consider the monographs and reports of the Hayden, Wheeler, King, and Powell surveys in the 1860's and '70's. They contained some of the most reliable information on the new West and were besides among the most beautifully printed and illustrated books of their times. Editions were large, printings were often repeated, and the congressional frank distributed copies to correspondents and libraries the country wide. Hayden's presentation of paintings by Thomas Moran and photographs by William Henry Jackson electrified Congress and led to the creation of Yellowstone National Park; Powell's exploration of the Colorado was made graphic on the stereopticon slides in thousands of parlors whose tables also showed *Scribner's, Harper's Illustrated Weekly,* and the other magazines specializing in local description. The excitement of place was fanned by such compendia as L. P. Brockett's *Our Western Empire; or, The New West Beyond the Mississippi* (1881), and by *Picturesque America,* celebrating every corner of the continent and utilizing the brightest names among writers and illustrators, which William Cullen Bryant edited in 1874. The public that made these publications successful was the public that devoured local color.

The writings of John Burroughs, beginning with *Wake Robin* in 1871, fitted neatly into the local excitement of the period. So did the later-published outdoor exuberances of John Muir, based on Yosemite Valley. But the closest link between the fictional and the nonfictional literature of place was probably the *Mountaineering in the Sierra Nevada* of Clarence King. King had been a geologist with Whitney's Geological Survey of California, and later conducted his own Survey of the Fortieth Parallel, whose authorization Henry Adams called America's first modern act of legislation. Even in his light-hearted chapters of personal adventure, King spoke with the authority of one who knew. Some of his pieces appeared in the same issues of the *Overland* and the *Atlantic* that were featuring the early mining camp stories of Bret Harte; and what made King's personal-experience narratives instantly attractive was precisely what made Harte's fiction attractive: an authentically described, picturesque locality, and within that frame, characters of a local coloration—Pikes, already figures of fiction and of humor as well as matters of fact.

The factual literature of place helped focus American eyes on the local, but it was from oral and journalistic humor that writers learned the native language and the native tone of voice. Laughter and low life and the prose lingo and the idiosyncratic yokel were by no means a new combination, but in America they took distinctive forms. Some of the qualities of native humor and the humorous character extend unbroken from the revolutionary broadsides and almanacs to the resiny wit of Will Rogers and the fables of James Thurber. By the time any regional variant of humor found its way into print it was fully developed, and thereafter changed little. Harold W. Thompson uses the "pivotal" work of Mark Twain and Lincoln to separate the humor springing from frontier conditions and that based upon immigrant strains and immigrant dialects, and the division is useful for our purposes; except for the comic Irishman Teague O'Regan in H. H. Brackenridge's *Modern Chivalry* (1792-1815), and the not-so-comic Germans and Scandinavians of Hamlin Garland's stories, the new immigrant can be almost ignored in a discussion of local color or its backgrounds.

Native humor, like the local color of a later period, emerged first in New England and in two Yankee characters, the peddler or trickster, closely related to folk-tale tricksters throughout the world, and the cracker-barrel philosopher, who made his public bow as Major Jack Downing, the creation of a Maine newspaper man named Seba Smith, in 1830. Jack Downing had his imitator and rival in Sam Slick, whose comments were begun by T. C. Halliburton in 1836, and the type came to a kind of climax when James Russell Lowell's Hosea Biglow arose to denounce the Mexican War in 1846. These three were all closer to rural life, and freer of the more grotesque misspellings, than their successors of Civil War times: Charles Farrar Brown (Artemus Ward), Henry Wheeler Shaw (Josh Billings), Major Charles H. Smith (Bill Arp), and David Ross Locke (Petroleum V. Nasby). The most successful literary use of the type was in Alfred Noyes Westcott's *David Harum* (1898).

The texture of this humor is skillfully mixed. It is deceptively folksy and at the same time very artful; though its language is unsophisticated, its wit is as sharp as an ice pick. Even within the language itself the contrast of textures appears, for with all its disregard of grammatical niceties, Lowell thought the folk speech of Massachusetts "fuller of metaphor and of phrases that suggest lively images than that of any other people I have seen." "God," as William Dean Howells would say later, "apparently meant [the languages] for the common people." And metaphor of the kind Lowell meant (compare Benjamin Franklin's remark about his birth, that he was launched in Boston but his keel was laid in Nantucket) is a by-product of the risible local imagination. It tickles a hearer with recognitions; at points like these, native expression and a native audience begin to meet.

Nearly simultaneously with the peddler and the rustic philosopher appeared other humorous types with a conformation peculiarly American. The frontiersman, who had received an affectionate and at least partially realistic treatment in Cooper's *The Pioneers* in 1823, quickly showed a comic and fantastic side, as Ring-Tailed Roarer or Game Cock of the Wilderness. His full-length portrait appeared in *A Narrative of the Life of David Crockett, of the State of Tennessee* (1834), in the succession of plays based on Crockett stories, and in the floating legends of Mike Fink, Daniel Boone, Kit Carson. He had a part in Robert Montgomery Bird's *Nick of the Woods* (1837), and he was made immortal in the raftsmen chapter of *Huckleberry Finn*.

The tall tale, utilizing both trickster and ring-tailed roarer, but developing no single humorous character of its own, is a third variety of native humor. It began in 1835 with Augustus Longstreet's *Georgia Scenes*, and proceeded through a notable succession of yarns, many of them collected in the best legendary fashion around a central figure, some of them isolated performances such as T. B. Thorpe's "The Big Bear of Arkansas." Among the "cycle" tales were W. T. Thompson's Major Jones stories, and Johnson J. Hooper's *Some Adventures of Simon*

Suggs (1845), whose hero's motto, "It's good to be shifty in a new country," defines the trickster in his shabbiest frontier form and makes plain his relationship to Mark Twain's King and Duke. Joseph G. Baldwin's *Flush Times of Alabama and Mississippi* (1853) presented in Ovid Bolus, Esq., a characteristic braggart, a *miles gloriosus* in American dress. The most uproarious —the "broadest" as well as the tallest of the tall tales—were George W. Harris' *Sut Lovingood's Yarns* (collected in 1867), many of them contributed to W. T. Porter's sporting magazine *The Spirit of the Times*, which from 1831 to 1856 was a mine of what might be called impolite literature.

"Realistic" seems hardly the word to apply to these grotesqueries and pranks. Sometimes the itch for humorous effect led their authors to distort them out of all resemblance to the real. Yet Longstreet in introducing *Georgia Scenes* had called his sketches no more than "fanciful combinations of real incidents and characters," and even in the tallest Dogpatch shenanigans of Sut Lovingood there is a considerable faithfulness to local customs and local character, and the jawbreaking phonetic spellings are less in the interest of humor than of a faithful transcription of folk speech.

Working in his brother Orion's print shop, young Sam Clemens read the exchanges, heard the yarning on river boats, attended minstrel shows and theatricals. His first sketch, "The Dandy Frightening the Squatter," was completely in the tradition; his first big success, "The Notorious Jumping Frog of Calaveras County," was distinguished from the type only by the fact of genius. Standard tricks of the humorists (the parody set piece, as in the Duke's soliloquy in *Huckleberry Finn*, or the handbill for a gladiatorial combat in *The Innocents Abroad*, and the parodied mortuary poetry that in the hands of Emmeline Grangerford strongly suggests John Phoenix' elegy for Jeames Hambrick) were in his repertory. He drew constantly on the fable and the oral yarn, both folkloristic rather than "literary" forms. Mark Twain was never very good at the formal short story, but he was a master of the fable; and it is significant that in "How to Tell a Story," his one real excursion into literary theory, he should outline the artful form of the humorous story and the character of its teller.

Something must be said of language. Despite notable efforts such as Noah Webster's *Spelling Book* (1783-1785), which normalized the American spellings that differed from the English, and his *American Dictionary of the English Language* (1828), which enriched the mother tongue with 5000 new Americanisms, the American language in its several dialects was at the end of the Civil War exactly where the American common man was: it could be used humorously but not seriously. In *The American Democrat* (1838) James Fenimore Cooper spanked his countrymen for their provincial perversions and mispronunciations of words—such practices as "clerk" instead of "clark," "cucumber" instead of "cowcumber," and the use of the Dutch term "boss" in place of the good English "master." Forty years later the *Atlantic*, under Howells of all people, gave R. G. White space to attack Bartlett's *American Glossary*, and incidentally the whole notion of an American language, in no less than eight articles.

Until after the war linguistic toryism was rather more the rule than the exception, though Jack Downing, Sam Slick, Davy Crockett, and the crackers of *Georgia Scenes* were all lifting into view a lingo more colorfully and vulgarly American than what Cooper protested. Through the 1830's, 1840's, and 1850's the corrupted and altered language of New England and the backwoods Midwest and Southwest made its way underground, and when local colorists found the regions, they found the dialects already broken to literary use by the humorists. Their literary discovery actually reversed the process of differentiation; the unification following the Civil War, and the greater communication among sections, meant a blurring of regional differences. Artemus Ward's lingo fused New England and Hoosier and Pike; Mark Twain continued the blending, and for him, as for Lincoln, the vernacular became an instrument capable of every demand made on it—a language flexible, delicate, powerful, evocative, and with a quality of living speech, a power of change and enrichment, an experimental exuberance and metaphorical daring, that English had not had since the days of Elizabeth. One result of the linguistic agonies of the local color movement was thus to make the dialects familiar and hasten the amalgamation of the national tongue.

Of the native tradition we have been summarizing, Mark Twain was the triumphant consummation. He perfected its language, refined its characteristic forms, enriched it with a Breughel-like swarm of characters who leap magically to life on the page and continue to impress us as revealing American types. Their unmistakable rightness justifies the realist creed of writing from experience. Pore lost Dauphin or Duke of Bilgewater, Boggs or Shepherdson or Grangerford or Nigger Jim, Mark had "known them on the river" of his boyhood and youth where his real authority as a writer lay. There is a magic, an incandescence, in the writing that reflects this part of his life— in *Tom Sawyer*, in sections of the *Autobiography*, in *Life on the Mississippi*, most of all in *Huckleberry Finn*. This is realism enlarged and transfigured. And though it took a long time for literary historians to lift Twain from among the mere funny men, there was never any doubt, from the time of "The Notorious Jumping Frog" on, that he had the indispensable "chorus in the hearts of his audience."

His contradictions are obvious and do not much matter. A democrat to the bone, he grew to hate the damned human race; and yet while he was publicly despising it, he could come back upon Andrew Lang with the hot democratic doctrine that he wrote "for the belly and members" and had no wish to "cultivate the cultivated classes." Though he drew most of his characters from the shirt-sleeved mass, he would never have subscribed to Howells' belief that "the sincere observer of man will not desire to look upon his heroic or occasional phases, but will seek him in his habitual moods of vacancy and tiresomeness." Mark had lived in too theatrical an atmosphere to be content with the commonplace; and when he took hold of the vacant and tiresome, he made them hilarious. Factualist he might be on occasion, but no slave of facts. He advised Kipling to get his facts first and then do with them what he would; his real complaint against Cooper was that Cooper told *unintentional* lies.

Systematic realist Mark Twain was not; there was at least as much Tom Sawyer as Huck Finn in him. Actually he was something very rare. Like Lincoln, he demonstrated the validity of Whitman's "archetypal figure," the voice of an emergent people. He was born lucky, close to America's heart, and he was in touch with myth.

. Against him we may place the different, almost opposite figure of Henry James; the two, as Henry Seidel Canby has said, are the opposite faces of a coin. The one expressed at the highest level the natively and vulgarly American, the other deliberately studied the American in contact with the Europe of his ancestors. Both were deeply involved in the American character, for while Twain almost unconsciously expressed it, James spent much of his life trying to define it. James' Daisy Miller and Isabel Archer, Christopher Newman and Madame Merle, belong in the American gallery along with Huck and Colonel Sellers, but they are Americans of another persuasion.

James had no interest—indeed no belief—in an American culture or society, and hunted his subjects in the traditional and complex society of Europe. Though he accepted, and enlarged, the conflict of American innocence and European decadence, he was no mouthpiece for American morals as against European manners. He merely recorded the struggle. He paid no attention to dialect, linguistic realism, but was content to distinguish his American characters by an occasional "I guess" or by the statement, undemonstrated, that they spoke with an American accent. By and large, the characters he wrote of would have deplored Americanese quite as strenuously as Fenimore Cooper or the cultural tories. He did not justify his "super-subtle fry" by claiming to have "known them on the Riviera"; he said only that if they did not exist they ought to, and thereby tacitly admitted that he was not above improving on nature.

If James was left undernourished by his deracination, he was also liberated from the cant, vulgarity, bombast, and half-educated yawping of self-conscious and aggressive nativism. Cultivating the character of detached observer, he defined an area and a method for the art of prose fiction, and gave realism still another possibility.

James equated fiction with history, as Eggleston had; he also found the novelist to be brother to the painter, and this perception allowed him, as Howells had not always done, to make a place for the artist himself as a filter through which experience was screened. Less bound than many of his contemporaries by positivist and materialist ideas, he conceived reality to be not a demonstrable and unchanging phenomenon but a world of appearances subtly different when viewed through different eyes. The fictional devices most closely associated with his name, the limitation of point of view, and the "registers," "ficelles," and other inventions, apply as technique what James held as theory. And the characteristic rebellion of realism, first against the aristocratic, romantic, and sentimental, and later against narrow and limiting Victorian conventions of art and morals, is present in James much more than in Howells. He meant it when he said that there was no valid limitation upon a novelist's subject matter except taste. Taste was relative, part of the subtle personalizing that all his fictions took on from the character of their observer-narrators or point of view personages, but on occasion it could permit James to treat situations of a marked ugliness. There is hardly a situation in naturalist fiction more unsavory, though there are many more bluntly revealed, than the one Maisie knew.

Much of James' practice could be subsumed under the rubric of a refined impressionism, but he had learned too much from Flaubert and Turgenev to be less than honest in his presentation of the world he knew. His artistic integrity was unparalleled, and his influence has been, ultimately, enormous; our fiction now is far closer to his than to that of Twain or Howells. His greatest weakness emphasizes his antithetical relationship to Twain, for the gift that Twain most lacked, the power of logical analysis, James possessed spectacularly; and the gift that Twain most had, the incomparable power of giving life to everything he touched, James did not possess in high degree.

His pragmatic brother William protested that Henry's characters were all made "wholly out of impalpable materials, air, and the prismatic interferences of light, ingeniously focussed by mirrors upon empty space." Those would seem to be destructive words indeed to throw at a presumed realist; yet the moral and psychological meanings that for James lay "beneath the vast smug surface of life" were perhaps quite as real as the surface itself.

Of Howells one damaging judgment has been made so often that it has nearly wiped out, for modern readers, a sensitive and honest writer. Howells tells us that from early youth he hankered after the "cleanly respectabilities." He won them, became a man of the world, the dean of American letters, a one-man literary movement. But he never lost the friendliness, the hopefulness, or the aspiration toward gentility that his Ohio boyhood and youth had given him, and these were in a way his blind spots. It has been suggested that his position as editor and professional writer in the New England dominated by convention and the female audience put obstacles in the path of his realism, but there is little evidence that he tried very hard to break the obstacles down. Through an extremely long writing career, from 1860 to 1924, he pursued the middle way of realism, avoiding in the beginning the "slop, silly slop" of sentiment, and trying through his late years to escape the harsh, shocking, and angry views that arose from the scientific determinism of Taine and the "experimental novel" of Zola, and that found their demonstration in the industrial ugliness of a changed America.

Still, he grew all his life, and grew in the direction of, if not entirely into, the harsher and more critical attitudes of the naturalists. When Garland and Crane burst out in forms of realism more violent (and probably more "distorted") than Howells' own, he encouraged them as enthusiastically as he had encouraged Twain and James and De Forest and Harte. His celebrated plea for the Haymarket anarchists was an act of real courage; and after 1886 his books, especially *A Hazard of New Fortunes*, admitted the bleak and dark and ugly into their pages. Yet conviction came hard, and five years later, when he was defending realism against R. L. Stevenson, F. Marion Crawford, Andrew Lang, and other advocates of romance, he could still assert that "whoever struck a note so profoundly tragic in American fiction" as Dostoevski had struck in *Crime and Punishment* "would do a false and mistaken thing." Even after the Haymarket affair he could still come back to "the more smiling aspects of life, which are the more American." And yet two years after his remarks about Dostoevski, he could go "sedately mad" over Stephen Crane's *Maggie*.

Even in Howells, realism was an approximation. "The truthful treatment of material" would do for a theory, so long as the material was not restricted by the young-girl audience or by the cleanly respectabilities or by a woundable but not killable frontier optimism; and when reality as Howells knew it refused to be bound within the restricting theory, theory went out. Gordon Haight has remarked that despite Howells' contention that novels should deal with the commonplace and not the catastrophic, "three plots turn on train wrecks, three on fires; two characters are removed by brain fever, a number by sudden sickness; two commit suicide with poison; one hero is shot, another knocked down by a horsecar, and two others killed by locomotives." His own theories bound him tighter than he was content to be bound.

Others would be bound far less. Garland and Crane both thought of themselves as realists, even Howellsian realists, but neither could have kept within the limitations Howells proposed. Garland's stories, truthful to the hardships of the Midwest frontier, were of no very smiling aspect of life, yet as Howells himself acknowledged, they justified themselves as honest portraiture. Howells' theories might have sanctioned "The Return of a Private," and—rather surprisingly—"Among the Corn Rows," where unhappiness literally forces a breach of public morals, but "Under the Lion's Paw," or any of Garland's Populist propaganda novels, could hardly have been called "truthful treatment of material" any more than Garland's Far Western romances could. Evidently Garland didn't quite know what he was doing, or else theory among Midwest democrats is always more hopeful than practice, for *Crumbling Idols*, published three years after *Criticism and Fiction*, is full of optimism and the nativist faith in an organic art that would come by some process of social evolution. Garland's stories were at first bleakly realistic and even naturalistic, then reformist, and finally conventionally romantic; but his theory of Veritism was no more than a fervent, hortatory warming-over of Howells, Emerson, Whitman, Taine, and the French and Norwegian genre painters, a pastiche of simplifications and stereotypes with only one fresh perception in it: that in the Midwest the native stock was already more German and Scandinavian than English, and that one must expect from it a different kind of literature. In a short time would come Dreiser, Sandburg, Rölvaag, and others to corroborate that observation.

Organic art was all Garland's cry. The novel of the slums, he said, would be written by one who had grown up there. He forgot Crane's *Maggie*, which he had helped to launch. But then Crane was hard to catalogue. A slum novel by a visitor to the Bowery, a war novel by one who never saw battle, western stories by one who had only passed through, challenged the doctrine of experience so dear to local colorists and nativists as well as realists, and so clearly sound for Twain or for Garland. Evidently Crane's bright impressionism was another way, another emphasis, another trick by which the observable (or imaginable) world could be captured. And the reality that one captured could be made to cast a shadow longer than itself, could carry in itself symbolic extensions of meaning, as it had already begun to do in Howells himself, especially in *A Hazard of New Fortunes*, and as it had done almost stealthily in the *Trois Contes* of Flaubert. The fact was, realism's own well-groomed idols were crumbling; the theoretical statement that in *Criticism and Fiction* and *Crumbling Idols* seemed like an announcement of victory was really an obituary—or more accurately, a prelude to change.

The generation that came on after 1890 would keep insisting that it wished to treat material truthfully, but its "truthful" meant something much more aggressive than it had to Howells.

It meant for some a vigorous attack on Victorian convention and a long-overdue loosening of restrictions on writers. It meant for some the repudiation of James's "taste," as well as of the individual who could will to exercise it. It meant a new image of man, stripped of his divinity and often of his dignity as well. *Maggie* introduced a new figure to American readers: the protagonist as victim. Moral choice was no longer held to be possible. The Silas Laphams and Huckleberry Finns and Isabel Archers who could rise to a moral crisis by an act of the ethical will were soon to be replaced by the Sister Carries and the Jennie Gerhardts, "waifs among forces," or by the McTeagues and the Wolf Larsens, evolutionary throwbacks and Nietzschean supermen, bubbles in the meaningless yeast of life.

In its pessimism, its frequently antidemocratic ideas, its seizure of the sinister horn of the evolutionary dilemma, this naturalism was a long way from the kind of realism that had developed organically through travel and humor and local color until it could fix, briefly, the vanishing face of the older and simpler America. Around 1890 the nation turned a corner; industrialism corroborated what Spencer's survival of the fittest threatened. For Henry Adams and Mark Twain, and to some extent even for Howells, the century washed out in a sense of failure and lost hope, and it is a fact that our fiction has never recovered the buoyancy and optimism and confidence in our more smiling destiny that it had until the end of the 1880's.

The faith in progress, growth, cultural flowering, the freshness of the new world, and the serene belief in American innocence, are somehow inextricable from the literary philosophy that we have here called realism, and that called itself by the same name. They all went out together, and the naturalism which came in to replace realism as the dominant movement in serious fiction was actually not so much a continuation as a repudiation. Frank Norris, insisting that Zola was really the "very head" of the romanticists, knew exactly where he stood with regard to Howells' kind of realism, which dealt with the type of normal life. This old-fashioned method, Norris protested, "notes only the surface of things . . . it goes no further than the Realist himself can actually see, or actually hear." [He might have been commenting on the limited points of view so lovingly focused down by Henry James.] "Realism is minute; it is the drama of a broken teacup, the tragedy of a walk down the block, the excitement of an afternoon call, the adventure of an invitation to dinner."

Perhaps it is. José Ortega y Gasset finds all novels divisible into those which are devoted to incident and those which are devoted to character. But one must insist on the capacity for the reconciliation or mixture of incompatibilities, for there was a strong realist impulse even in the Norris who fancied himself a romantic. He wrote some of the silliest fiction of his day (try *Blix*, or *Moran of the Lady Letty*), and much of the way through *McTeague* he could not restrain himself from convulsing that mass of Darwinian muscle. But when he wrote of Owgoost's visit to the theater, or Trina's family on a picnic (the drama of wet pants, the tragedy of a spoiled afternoon?), he was doing everyday life with a touch that Howells and all his tribe would have applauded.

Like almost everyone we have considered except Eggleston, who was more social historian than novelist, Norris was hopelessly mixed, a "romantic realist" in the best sense of those weasel words. His writing was only an approximation of his intention; his theory was an attempt to rationalize a temperament. But if we are to judge realism by its intention, as we set out to do, then the generation of Crane, Garland, Norris, Dreiser, and London was something else: Crane an impressionist, almost an imagist; Garland a romantic, alternately angry and sentimental; Dreiser the most thoroughgoing of naturalists; and Norris what William Dean Howells would somewhat caustically have called an Effectist.

W. S.

CONTENTS

Selected American Prose, 1841-1900

I   The Native Roots of Realism:
Travel and Humor

No brief summary can adequately introduce a student to the extensive travel literature which precedes, underlies, and accompanies the realistic movement in America. For the travel literature of the nineteenth century, which means primarily that of the West, an indispensable bibliographical work is Henry R. Wagner's *The Plains and the Rockies: A Bibliography of Original Narratives of Travel and Adventure, 1800-1865,* rev. and enl. by Charles R. Camp, 1937. Best source of the narratives themselves is Reuben Gold Thwaites, *Early Western Travels, 1748-1846,* 32 vols., 1904-1907. A stimulating study of the explorations that culminated in the Lewis and Clark expedition is Bernard DeVoto, *The Course of Empire,* 1952. For a selected bibliography of significant accounts of the Gold Rush see Carl Wheat, *Books of the California Gold Rush,* 1949. Worth special mention because Longfellow and others drew on it, not always with safety, for details of Indian life, is Henry Roe Schoolcraft's *Historical and Statistical Information Respecting the History, Condition, and Prospects of the Indian Tribes of the United States,* 6 vols., 1851-1857. See also, for the germs of some of Bret Harte's stories, Louise Amelia Knapp Smith Clappe, *The Shirley Letters,* 1854-1855, perhaps the very best account of life in a gold camp. There has been no adequate study of the Pacific Railroad Surveys, though they represent the beginning of accurate modern knowledge of the West. The work of the Hayden, King, Wheeler, and especially Powell surveys is treated at some length in Wallace Stegner, *Beyond the Hundredth Meridian: John Wesley Powell and the Second Opening of the West,* 1954. Among the literary and journalistic travelers' accounts, see especially Bayard Taylor, *Eldorado,* 1850; Samuel Bowles, *Across the Continent,*

1865, and *The Switzerland of America*, 1869; and Mark Twain, *Roughing It*, 1874. An illuminating study of early painters, photographers, and illustrators is Robert Taft, *Artists and Illustrators of the Old West; 1850-1900*, 1953, and also his *Photography and the American Scene*, 1938.

The pioneering studies in American folklore and humor are those of Constance Rourke in *American Humor: A Study of the National Character*, 1931, and *The Roots of American Culture*, 1942. Extremely useful are Walter Blair's several books, especially *Native American Humor, 1800-1900*, 1937, a collection with a good bibliography; and *Horse Sense in American Humor*, 1942. Franklin J. Meine, *Tall Tales of the Southwest: An Anthology of Southern and Southwestern Humor, 1830-1860*, 1930, is a good selection of yarns from *Georgia Scenes* to Sut Lovingood. The social backgrounds of western humor and their influence on Mark Twain are effectively presented in Bernard DeVoto, *Mark Twain's America*, 1932. For other discussions of Mark Twain's relation to the humorous tradition see Dixon Wecter, *Sam Clemens of Hannibal*, 1952; Minnie Brashear, *Mark Twain, Son of Missouri*, 1934, and Delancey Ferguson, *Mark Twain: Man and Legend*, 1943. The best study of George Horatio Derby is George R. Stewart, *John Phoenix, Esq., the Veritable Squibob*, 1937. For Clarence King, see *Clarence King Memoirs*, 1904, Wallace Stegner, *supra*, and Harry Crosby, *So Deep a Trail*, unpublished Stanford University dissertation, 1953. Josh Billings has been collected in *Josh Billings: His Works, Complete*, 1888, revised as *The Complete Works of Josh Billings*, 1919. The only life is that by Cyril Clemens, *Josh Billings; Yankee Humorist*, 1932. Joel Chandler Harris' Uncle Remus stories have been much reprinted. The standard biography is that by Julia C. Harris, his daughter-in-law: *The Life and Letters of Joel Chandler Harris*, 1918. The bulk of the Harris papers is in the library of Emory University in Atlanta, the Mark Twain papers are in the library of the University of California at Berkeley.

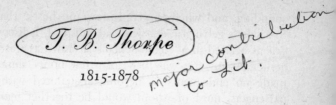

T. B. Thorpe

major contribution to lit.

1815-1878

THE BIG BEAR OF ARKANSAS

(1841)

A steamboat on the Mississippi frequently, in making her regular trips, carries between places varying from one to two thousand miles apart; and as these boats advertise to land passengers and freight at "all intermediate landings," the heterogeneous character of the passengers of one of these up-country boats can scarcely be imagined by one who has never seen it with his own eyes. Starting from New Orleans in one of these boats, you will find yourself associated with men from every state in the Union, and from every portion of the globe; and a man of observation need not lack for amusement or instruction in such a crowd, if he will take the trouble to read the great book of character so favourably opened before him. Here may be seen jostling together the wealthy Southern planter, and the pedlar of tin-ware from New England—the Northern merchant, and the Southern jockey—a venerable bishop, and a desperate gambler—the land speculator, and the honest farmer—professional men of all creeds and characters—Wolvereens, Suckers, Hoosiers, Buckeyes, and Corn-crackers, beside a "plentiful sprinkling" of the half-horse and half-alligator species of men, who are peculiar to "old Mississippi," and who appear to gain a livelihood simply by going up and down the river. In the pursuit of pleasure or business, I have frequently found myself in such a crowd.

On one occasion, when in New Orleans, I had occasion to take a trip of a few miles up the Mississippi, and I hurried on board the well-known "high-pressure-and-beat-every-thing" steamboat *Invincible*, just as the last note of the last bell was

3

sounding; and when the confusion and bustle that is natural to a boat's getting under way had subsided, I discovered that I was associated in as heterogeneous a crowd as was ever got together. As my trip was to be of a few hours' duration only, I made no endeavours to become acquainted with my fellow passengers, most of whom would be together many days. Instead of this, I took out of my pocket the "latest paper," and more critically than usual examined its contents; my fellow passengers at the same time disposed themselves in little groups. While I was thus busily employed in reading, and my companions were more busily employed in discussing such subjects as suited their humours best, we were startled most unexpectedly by a loud Indian whoop, uttered in the "social hall," that part of the cabin fitted off for a bar; then was to be heard a loud crowing, which would not have continued to have interested us—such sounds being quite common in that place of spirits—had not the hero of these windy accomplishments stuck his head into the cabin and hallooed out, "Hurra for the Big Bar of Arkansaw!" and then might be heard a confused hum of voices, unintelligible, save in such broken sentences as "horse," "screamer," "lightning is slow," &c. As might have been expected, this continued interruption attracted the attention of every one in the cabin; all conversation dropped, and in the midst of this surprise the "Big Bar" walked into the cabin, took a chair, put his feet on the stove, and looking back over his shoulder, passed the general and familiar salute of "Strangers, how are you?" He then expressed himself as much at home as if he had been at "the Forks of Cypress," and "perhaps a little more so." Some of the company at this familiarity looked a little angry, and some astonished; but in a moment every face was wreathed in a smile. There was something about the intruder that won the heart on sight. He appeared to be a man enjoying perfect health and contentment: his eyes were as sparkling as diamonds, and good-natured to simplicity. Then his perfect confidence in himself was irresistibly droll. "Perhaps," said he, "gentlemen," running on without a person speaking, "perhaps you have been to New Orleans often; I never made *the first visit before*, and I don't intend to make another in a crow's life. I am thrown away in that ar place, and useless, that ar a fact. Some of the gentlemen thar called me *green*—well, perhaps I am, said I, *but I arn't so at home*; and if I ain't off my trail much, the heads of them perlite chaps themselves wern't much the hardest; for according to my notion, they were real *know-nothings*, green as a pumpkin-vine—couldn't, in farming, I'll bet, raise a crop of turnips: and as for shooting, they'd miss a barn if the door was swinging, and that, too, with the best rifle in the country. And then they talked to me 'bout hunting, and laughed at my calling the principal game in Arkansaw poker, and high-low-jack. 'Perhaps,' said I, 'you prefer chickens and rolette'; at this they laughed harder than ever, and asked me if I lived in the woods, and didn't know what *game* was? At this I rather think I laughed. 'Yes,' I roared, and says, 'Strangers, if you'd asked me *how we got our meat* in Arkansaw, I'd a told you at once, and given you a list of varmints that would make a caravan, beginning with the bar, and ending off with the cat; that's *meat* though, not game.' Game, indeed, that's what city folks call it; and with them it means chippen-birds and shite-pokes; maybe such trash live in my diggens, but I arn't noticed them yet: a bird any way is too trifling. I never did shoot at but one, and I'd never forgiven myself for that, had it weighed less than forty pounds. I wouldn't draw a rifle on any thing less than that; and when I meet with another wild turkey of the same weight I will drap him."

"A wild turkey weighing forty pounds!" exclaimed twenty voices in the cabin at once.

"Yes, strangers, and wasn't it a whopper? You see, the thing was so fat that it couldn't fly far; and when he fell out of the tree, after I shot him, on striking the ground he bust open behind, and the way the pound gobs of tallow rolled out of the opening was perfectly beautiful."

"Where did all that happen?" asked a cynical-looking Hoosier.

"Happen! happened in Arkansaw: where else could it have

happened, but in the creation state, the finishing-up country—a state where the *sile* runs down to the centre of the 'arth, and government gives you a title to every inch of it? Then its airs —just breathe them, and they will make you snort like a horse. It's a state without a fault, it is."

"Excepting mosquitoes," cried the Hoosier.

"Well, stranger, except them; for it ar a fact that they are rather *enormous*, and do push themselves in somewhat troublesome. But, stranger, they never stick twice in the same place; and give them a fair chance for a few months, and you will get as much above noticing them as an alligator. They can't hurt my feelings, for they lay under the skin; and I never knew but one case of injury resulting from them, and that was to a Yankee: and they take worse to foreigners, any how, than they do to natives. But the way they used that fellow up! first they punched him until he swelled up and busted; then he super-a-ted, as the doctor called it, until he was as raw as beef; then he took the ager, owing to the warm weather, and finally he took a steamboat and left the country. He was the only man that ever took mosquitoes to heart that I know of. But mosquitoes is natur, and I never find fault with her. If they ar large, Arkansaw is large, her varmints ar large, her trees ar large, her rivers ar large, and a small mosquito would be of no more use in Arkansaw than preaching in a cane-brake."

This knock-down argument in favour of big mosquitoes used the Hoosier up, and the logician started on a new track, to explain how numerous bear were in his "diggins," where he represented them to be "about as plenty as blackberries, and a little plentifuler."

Upon the utterance of this assertion, a timid little man near me inquired if the bear in Arkansaw ever attacked the settlers in numbers.

"No," said our hero, warming with the subject, "no, stranger, for you see it ain't the natur of bar to go in droves; but the way they squander about in pairs and single ones is edifying. And then the way I hunt them the old black rascals know the crack of my gun as well as they know a pig's squealing. They grow thin in our parts, it frightens them so, and they do take the noise dreadfully, poor things. That gun of mine is perfect *epidemic among bar*; if not watched closely, it will go off as quick on a warm scent as my dog Bowie-knife will: and then that dog—whew! why the fellow thinks that the world is full of bar, he finds them so easy. It's lucky he don't talk as well as think; for with his natural modesty, if he should suddenly learn how much he is acknowledged to be ahead of all other dogs in the universe, he would be astonished to death in two minutes. Strangers, the dog knows a bar's way as well as a horse-jockey knows a woman's: he always barks at the right time, bites at the exact place, and whips without getting a scratch. I never could tell whether he was made expressly to hunt bar, or whether bar was made expressly for him to hunt: any way, I believe they were ordained to go together as naturally as Squire Jones says a man and woman is, when he moralizes in marrying a couple. In fact, Jones once said, said he, 'Marriage according to law is a civil contract of divine origin; it's common to all countries as well as Arkansaw, and people take to it as naturally as Jim Doggett's Bowie-knife takes to bar.' "

"What season of the year do your hunts take place?" inquired a gentlemanly foreigner, who, from some peculiarities of his baggage, I suspected to be an Englishman, on some hunting expedition, probably at the foot of the Rocky Mountains.

"The season for bar hunting, stranger," said the man of Arkansaw, "is generally all the year round, and the hunts take place about as regular. I read in history that varmints have their fat season, and their lean season. That is not the case in Arkansaw, feeding as they do upon the *spontenacious* productions of the sile, they have one continued fat season the year round: though in winter things in this way is rather more greasy than in summer, I must admit. For that reason bar with us run in warm weather, but in winter, they only waddle. Fat, fat! it's an enemy to speed; it tames everything that has plenty of it. I have seen wild turkeys, from its influence, as gentle as chickens. Run a bar in this fat condition, and the way it improves the critter for eating is amazing; it sort of mixes the ile up with the meat, until you can't tell t'other from which. I've done this often. I recollect one perty morning in particular, of putting an old fellow on the stretch, and considering the weight he carried, he run well. But the dogs soon tired him down, and when I came up with him wasn't he in a beautiful sweat—I might say fever; and then to see his tongue sticking out of his mouth a feet, and his sides sinking and opening like a bellows, and his cheeks so fat he couldn't look cross. In this fix I blazed at him, and pitch me naked into a briar patch if the steam didn't come out of the bullet-hole ten foot in a straight line. The fellow, I reckon, was made on the high-pressure system, and the lead sort of bust his biler."

"That column of steam was rather curious, or else the bear must have been *warm*," observed the foreigner, with a laugh.

"Stranger, as you observe, that bar was WARM, and the blowing off of the steam show'd it, and also how hard the varmint had been run. I have no doubt if he had kept on two miles farther his insides would have been stewed; and I expect to meet with a varmint yet of extra bottom, who will run himself into a skinfull of bar's grease: it is possible, much onlikelier things have happened."

"Whereabouts are these bears so abundant?" inquired the foreigner, with increasing interest.

"Why, stranger, they inhabit the neighbourhood of my settlement, one of the prettiest places on old Mississippi—a perfect location, and no mistake; a place that had some defects until the river made the 'cut-off' at 'Shirt-tail bend,' and that remedied the evil, as it brought my cabin on the edge of the river—a great advantage in wet weather, I assure you, as you can now roll a barrel of whiskey into my yard in high water from a boat, as easy as falling off a log. It's a great improvement, as toting it by land in a jug, as I used to do, *evaporated* it too fast, and it became expensive. Just stop with me, stranger, a month or two, or a year if you like, and you will appreciate my place. I can give you plenty to eat; for beside hog and hominy, you can have bar-ham, and bar-sausages, and a mattrass of bar-skins to sleep on, and a wildcat-skin, pulled off hull, stuffed with corn-shucks, for a pillow. That bed would put you to sleep if you had the rheumatics in every joint in your body. I call that ar bed a *quietus*. Then look at my land— the government ain' got another such a piece to dispose of. Such timber, and such bottom land, why you can't preserve any thing natural you plant in it unless you pick it young, things thar will grow out of shape so quick. I once planted in those diggins a few potatoes and beets: they took a fine start, and after that an ox team couldn't have kept them from growing. About that time I went off to old Kentuck on bisiness, and did not hear from them things in three months, when I accidentally stumbled on a fellow who had stopped at my place, with an idea of buying me out. 'How did you like things?' said I. 'Pretty well,' said he; 'the cabin is convenient, and the timber land is good; but that bottom land ain't worth the first red cent.' 'Why?' said I. ' 'Cause,' said he. ' 'Cause what?' said I. ' 'Cause it's full of cedar stumps and Indian mounds,' said he, *'and it can't be cleared'.* 'Lord,' said I, 'them ar "cedar stumps" is beets, and them ar "Indian mounds" ar tater hills.' As I expected, the crop was overgrown and useless: the sile is too rich, *and planting in Arkansaw is dangerous.* I had a good-sized sow killed in that same bottom land. The old thief stole an ear of corn, and took it down where she slept at night to eat. Well, she left a grain or two on the ground, and lay down on them: before morning the corn shot up, and the percussion killed her dead. I don't plant any more: natur intended Arkansaw for a hunting ground, and I go according to natur."

The questioner who thus elicited the description of our hero's settlement, seemed to be perfectly satisfied, and said no more; but the "Big Bar of Arkansaw" rambled on from one thing to another with a volubility perfectly astonishing, occasionally disputing with those around him, particularly with a "live Sucker" from Illinois, who had the daring to say that our Arkansaw friend's stories "smelt rather tall."

In this manner the evening was spent; but conscious that

my own association with so singular a personage would probably end before morning, I asked him if he would not give me a description of some particular bear hunt; adding that I took great interest in such things, though I was no sportsman. The desire seemed to please him, and he squared himself round towards me, saying, that he could give me an idea of a bar hunt that was never beat in this world, or in any other. His manner was so singular, that half of his story consisted in his excellent way of telling it, the great peculiarity of which was, the happy manner he had of emphasizing the prominent parts of his conversation. As near as I can recollect, I have italicized them, and given the story in his own words.

"Stranger," said he, "in bar hunts I *am numerous*, and which particular one, as you say, I shall tell, puzzles me. There was the old she devil I shot at the Hurricane last fall—then there was the old hog thief I popped over at the Bloody Crossing, and then—Yes, I have it! I will give you an idea of a hunt, in which the greatest bar was killed that ever lived, *none excepted*; about an old fellow that I hunted, more or less, for two or three years; and if that ain't a particular bar hunt, I ain't got one to tell. But in the first place, stranger, let me say, I am pleased with you, because you ain't ashamed to gain information by asking, and listening, and that's what I say to Countess's pups every day when I'm home; and I have got great hopes of them ar pups, because they are continually *nosing* about; and though they stick it sometimes in the wrong place, they gain experience any how, and may learn something useful to boot. Well, as I was saying about this big bar, you see when I and some more first settled in our region, we were drivin to hunting naturally; we soon liked it, and after that we found it an easy matter to make the thing our business. One old chap who had pioneered 'afore us, gave us to understand that we had settled in the right place. He dwelt upon its merits until it was affecting, and showed us, to prove his assertions, more marks on the sassafras trees than I ever saw on a tavern door 'lection time. 'Who keeps that ar reckoning?' said I. 'The bar,' said he. 'What for?' said I. 'Can't tell,' said he;

'but so it is: the bar bite the bark and wood too, at the highest point from the ground they can reach, and you can tell, by the marks,' said he, 'the length of the bar to an inch.' 'Enough,' said I; 'I've learned something here a'ready, and I'll put it in practice.'

"Well, stranger, just one month from that time I killed a bar, and told its exact length before I measured it, by those very marks; and when I did that, I swelled up considerable— I've been a prouder man ever since. So I went on, larning something every day, until I was reckoned a buster, and allowed to be decidedly the best bar hunter in my district; and that is a reputation as much harder to earn than to be reckoned first man in Congress, as an iron ramrod is harder than a toadstool. Did the varmints grow over-cunning by being fooled with by green-horn hunters, and by this means get troublesome, they send for me as a matter of course; and thus I do my own hunting, and most of my neighbours'. I walk into the varmints though, and it has become about as much the same to me as drinking. It is told in two sentences—a bar is started, and he is killed. The thing is somewhat monotonous now—I know just how much they will run, where they will tire, how much they will growl, and what a thundering time I will have in getting them home. I could give you this history of the chase with all particulars at the commencement, I know the signs so well—*Stranger, I'm certain*. Once I met with a match though, and I will tell you about it; for a common hunt would not be worth relating.

"On a fine fall day, long time ago, I was trailing about for bar, and what should I see but fresh marks on the sassafras trees, about eight inches above any in the forests that I knew of. Says I, 'them marks is a hoax, or it indicates the d——t bar that was ever grown.' In fact, stranger, I couldn't believe it was real, and I went on. Again I saw the same marks, at the same height, and *I knew the thing lived*. That conviction came home to my soul like an earthquake. Says I, 'here is something a-purpose for me: that bar is mine, or I give up the hunting business.' The very next morning what should I see but a number of buzzards hovering over my cornfield. 'The rascal has been there,' said I, 'for that sign is certain:' and, sure enough, on examining, I found the bones of what had been as beautiful a hog the day before, as was ever raised by a Buckeye. Then I tracked the critter out of the field to the woods, and all the marks he left behind, showed me that he was *the bar*.

"Well, stranger, the first fair chase I ever had with that big critter, I saw him no less than three distinct times at a distance: the dogs run him over eighteen miles and broke down, my horse gave out, and I was as nearly used up as a man can be, made on *my* principle, *which is patent*. Before this adventure, such things were unknown to me as possible; but, strange as it was, that bar got me used to it before I was done with him; for he got so at last, that he would leave me on a long chase *quite easy*. How he did it, I never could understand. That a bar runs at all, is puzzling; but how this one could tire down and bust up a pack of hounds and a horse, that were used to overhauling everything they started after in no time, was past my understanding. Well, stranger, that bar finally got so sassy, that he used to help himself to a hog off my premises whenever he wanted one; the buzzards followed after what he left, and so between *bar and buzzard*, I rather think I was *out of pork*.

"Well, missing that bar so often took hold of my vitals, and I wasted away. The thing had been carried too far, and it reduced me in flesh faster than an ager. I would see that bar in every thing I did: *he hunted me*, and that, too, like a devil, which I began to think he was. While in this fix, I made preparations to give him a last brush, and be done with it. Having completed every thing to my satisfaction, I started at sunrise, and to my great joy, I discovered from the way the dogs run, that they were near him; finding his trail was nothing, for that had become as plain to the pack as a turnpike road. On we went, and coming to an open country, what should I see but the bar very leisurely ascending a hill, and the dogs close at his heels, either a match for him in speed, or else he did not care to get out of their way—I don't know which. But wasn't he a beauty, though? I loved him like a brother.

"On he went, until he came to a tree, the limbs of which formed a crotch about six feet from the ground. Into this crotch he got and seated himself, the dogs yelling all around it; and there he sat eyeing them as quiet as a pond in low water. A green-horn friend of mine, in company, reached shooting distance before me, and blazed away, hitting the critter in the centre of his forehead. The bar shook his head as the ball struck it, and then walked down from that tree as gently as a lady would from a carriage. 'Twas a beautiful sight to see him do that—he was in such a rage that he seemed to be as little afraid of the dogs as if they had been sucking pigs; and the dogs warn't slow in making a ring around him at a respectful distance, I tell you; even Bowie-knife, himself, stood off. Then the way his eyes flashed—why the fire of them would have singed a cat's hair; in fact that bar was in a *wrath all over*. Only one pup came near him, and he was brushed out so totally with the bar's left paw, that he entirely disappeared; and that made the old dogs more cautious still. In the mean time, I came up, and taking deliberate aim as a man should do, at his side, just back of his foreleg, *if my gun did not snap*, call me a coward, and I won't take it personal. Yes, stranger, *it snapped*, and I could not find a cap about my person. While in this predicament, I turned round to my fool friend—says I, 'Bill,' says I, 'you're an ass—you're a fool—you might as well have tried to kill that bar by barking the tree under his belly, as to have done it by hitting him in the head. Your shot has made a tiger of him, and blast me, if a dog gets killed or wounded when they come to blows, I will stick my knife into your liver, I will—' my wrath was up. I had lost my caps, my gun had snapped, the fellow with me had fired at the bar's head, and I expected every moment to see him close in with the dogs, and kill a dozen of them at least. In this thing I was mistaken, for the bar leaped over the ring formed by the dogs, and giving a fierce growl, was off—the pack, of course, in full cry after him. The run this time was short, for coming to the edge of a lake the varmint jumped in, and swam to a little island in the lake, which it reached just a moment before the dogs. 'I'll have him now,' said I, for I had found my caps in the *lining of my coat*—so, rolling a log into the lake, I paddled myself across to the island, just as the dogs had cornered the bar in a thicket. I rushed up and fired—at the same time the critter leaped over the dogs and came within three feet of me, running like mad; he jumped into the lake, and tried to mount the log I had just deserted, but every time he got half his body on it, it would roll over and send him under; the dogs, too, got around him, and pulled him about, and finally Bowie-knife clenched with him, and they sunk into the lake together. Stranger, about this time, I was excited, and I stripped off my coat, drew my knife, and intended to have taken a part with Bowie-knife myself, when the bar rose to the surface. But the varmint staid under—Bowie-knife came up alone, more dead than alive, and with the pack came ashore. 'Thank God', said I, 'the old villain has got his deserts at last.' Determined to have the body, I cut a grape-vine for a rope, and dove down where I could see the bar in the water, fastened my queer rope to his leg, and fished him, with great difficulty, ashore. Stranger, may I be chawed to death by young alligators, if the thing I looked at wasn't a *she bar, and not the old critter after all*. The way matters got mixed on that island was onaccountably curious, and thinking of it made me more than ever convinced that I was hunting the devil himself. I went home that night and took to my bed—the thing was killing me. The entire team of Arkansaw in bar-hunting, acknowledged himself used up, and the fact sunk into my feelings like a snagged boat will in the Mississippi. I grew as cross as a bar with two cubs and a sore tail. The thing got out 'mong my neighbours, and I was asked how come on that individu-al that never lost a bar when once started? and if that same individ-u-al didn't wear telescopes when he turned a she bar, of ordinary size, into an old he one, a little larger than a horse? 'Perhaps,' said I, 'friends'— getting wrathy—'perhaps you want to call somebody a liar,'

'Oh, no,' said they, 'we only heard such things as being *rather common* of late, but we don't believe one word of it; oh, no,' —and then they would ride off and laugh like so many hyenas over a dead nigger. It was too much, and I determined to catch that bar, go to Texas, or die,—and I made my preparations accordin'. I had the pack shut up and rested. I took my rifle to pieces and iled it. I put caps in every pocket about my person, *for fear of the lining.* I then told my neighbours, that on Monday morning—naming the day—I would start THAT BAR, and bring him home with me, or they might divide my settlement among them, the owner having disappeared. Well, stranger, on the morning previous to the great day of my hunting expedition, I went into the woods near my house, taking my gun and Bowie-knife along, just *from habit,* and there sitting down also from habit, what should I see, getting over my fence, but *the bar!* Yes, the old varmint was within a hundred yards of me, and the way he walked *over that fence*—stranger, he loomed up like a *black mist,* he seemed so large, and he walked right towards me. I raised myself, took deliberate aim, and fired. Instantly the varmint wheeled, gave a yell, and *walked through the fence* like a falling tree would through a cobweb. I started after, but was tripped up by my inexpressibles, which either from habit, or the excitement of the moment, were about my heels, and before I had really gathered myself up, I heard the old varmint groaning in a thicket near by, like a thousand sinners, and by the time I reached him he was a corpse. Stranger, it took five niggers and myself to put that carcase on a mule's back, and old long-ears waddled under the load, as if he was foundered in every leg of his body, and with a common whopper of a bar, he would have trotted off, and enjoyed himself. 'Twould astonish you to know how big he was: I made a *bed-spread of his skin,* and the way it used to cover my bar mattress, and leave several feet on each side to tuck up, would have delighted you. It was in fact a creation bar, and if it had lived in Samson's time, and had met him, in a fair fight, it would have licked him in the twinkling of a dice-box. But, strangers, I never like the way I hunted, and *missed him.* There is something curious about it, I could never understand,—and I never was satisfied at his giving in so easy at last. Prehaps, he had heard of my preparations to hunt him the next day, so he jist come in, like Capt. Scott's coon, to save his wind to grunt with in dying; but that ain't likely. My private opinion is, that that bar was an *unhuntable bar, and died when his time come.*"

When the story was ended, our hero sat some minutes with his auditors in a grave silence; I saw there was a mystery to him connected with the bear whose death he had just related, that had evidently made a strong impression on his mind. It was also evident that there was some superstitious awe connected with the affair,—a feeling common with all "children of the wood," when they meet with any thing out of their everyday experience. He was the first one, however, to break the silence, and jumping up, he asked all present to "liquor" before going to bed,—a thing which he did, with a number of companions, evidently to his heart's content.

Long before day, I was put ashore at my place of destination, and I can only follow with the reader, in imagination, our Arkansas friend, in his adventures at the "Forks of Cypress" on the Mississippi.

John Phoenix

[GEORGE HORATIO DERBY]

1823-1861

MELANCHOLY ACCIDENT—
DEATH OF A YOUNG MAN
(1853)

Mr. Mudge has just arrived in San Diego from Arkansas; he brings with him four yoke of oxen, seventeen American cows, nine American children, and Mrs. Mudge. They have encamped in the rear of our office, pending the arrival of the new coasting steamer.

Mr. Mudge is about thirty-seven years of age, his hair is light, not a "sable silvered," but a *yaller*, gilded; you can see some of it sticking out of the top of his hat; his costume is the national costume of Arkansas, coat, waistcoat, and pantaloons of homespun cloth, dyed a brownish yellow, with a decoction of the bitter barked butternut—a pleasing alliteration; his countenance presents a determined, combined with a sanctimonious expression, and in his brightly gleaming eye—a red eye we think it is—we fancy a spark of poetic fervor may be distinguished.

Mr. Mudge called on us yesterday. We were eating watermelon. Perhaps the reader may have eaten watermelon; if so, he knows how difficult a thing it is to speak, when the mouth is filled with the luscious fruit, and the slippery seed and sweet though embarrassing juice is squizzling out all over the chin and shirt-bosom. So at first we said nothing, but waved with our case knife toward an unoccupied box, as who should say sit down. Mr. Mudge accordingly seated himself, and removing his hat (whereat all his hair sprang up straight like a Jack in the box), turned that article of dress over and over in his hands, and contemplated its condition with alarming seriousness.

"Take some melon, Mr. Mudge?" said we, as with a sudden bolt we recovered our speech and took another slice ourself. "No, I thank you," replied Mr. Mudge, "I wouldn't choose any, now."

There was a solemnity in Mr. Mudge's manner that arrested our attention; we paused, and holding a large slice of watermelon dripping in the air, listened to what he might have to say.

"Thar was a very serious accident happened to us," said Mr. Mudge, "as we wos crossin the plains. 'Twas on the bank of the Peacus river. Thar was a young man named Jeames Hambrick along, and another young feller, he got to fooling with his pistil, and he shot Jeames. He was a good young man and hadn't a enemy in the company; we buried him thar on the Peacus river we did, and as we went off, these here lines sorter passed through my mind." So saying, Mr. Mudge rose, drew from his pocket—his waistcoat pocket—a crumpled piece of paper, and handed it over. Then he drew from his coat-tail pocket a large cotton handkerchief with a red ground and a yellow figure, slowly unfolded it, blew his nose—an awful blast it was—wiped his eyes, and disappeared. We publish Mr. Mudge's lines, with the remark that any one who says they have no poets or poetry in Arkansas would doubt the existence of William Shakespeare:

DIRGE ON THE DETH OF JEAMES HAMBRICK

By Mr. Orion W. Mudge, Esq.

It was on June the tenth
our hearts were very sad

for it was by an awful accident
we lost a fine young lad

Jeames Hambrick was his name
and alas it was his lot
to you I tell the same
he was accidently shot

on the peacus river side
the sun was very hot
and its there he fell and died
where he was accidently shot

on the road his character good
without a strain or blot
and in our opinions growed
until he was accidently shot

a few words only he spoke
for moments he had not
and only then he seemed to choke
I was accidently shot

we wraped him in a blanket good
for coffin we had not
and there we buried him where he stood
when he was accidently shot

and as we stood around his grave
our tears the ground did blot
we prayed to god his soul to save
he was accidently shot

This is all, but I writ at the time a epitaff which I think is
short and would do to go over his grave:—

EPITAFF

here lies the body of Jeames Hambrick
who was accidently shot
on the bank of the peacus river
by a young man

he was accidently shot with one of the large size colt's revolv-
ers with no stopper for the cock to rest on it was one of the

old fashion kind brass mounted and of such is the kingdom of
heaven

truly yourn

ORION W. MUDGE ESQ

Josh Billings

[HENRY WHEELER SHAW]

1818-1885

ESSA ON THE MUEL

(1858)

The mule is haf hoss, and haf Jackass, and then kums to a full
stop, natur diskovering her mistake. Tha weigh more, akordin
tu their heft, than enny other kreetur, except a crowbar. Tha
cant hear enny quicker, nor further than the hoss, yet their
ears are big enuff for snow shoes. You kan trust them with
enny one whose life aint worth enny more than the mules.
The only wa tu keep them into a paster, is tu turn them into
a medder jineing, and let them jump out. Tha are reddy for
use, just as soon as they will du tu abuse. Tha haint got enny
friends, and will live on huckel berry brush, with an ockasional
chanse at Kanada thissels. Tha are a modern invenshun, i dont
think the Bible deludes tu them at tall. Tha sel for more
money than enny other domestik animile. Yu kant tell their
age by looking into their mouth, enny more than you kould
a Mexican cannons. Tha never hav no dissease that a good
club won't heal. If tha ever die tha must kum rite tu life again,
for i never herd nobody sa "ded mule." Tha are like sum men,

very korrupt at harte; ive known them tu be good mules for 6 months, just tu git a good chanse to kick sumbody. I never owned one, nor never mean to, unless there is a United Staits law passed, requiring it. The only reason why tha are pashunt, is bekause tha are ashamed ov themselfs. I have seen eddicated mules in a sirkus. Tha kould kick, and bite, tremenjis. I would not sa what I am forced tu say, again the mule, if his birth want an outrage, and man want tu blame for it. Enny man who is willing tu drive a mule, ought to be exempt by law from running for the legislatur. Tha are the strongest creeturs on earth, and heaviest, ackording tu their sise; I herd tell ov one who fell oph from the tow path, on the Eri kanawl, and sunk as soon as he touched bottom, but he kept rite on towing the boat tu the next stashun, breathing thru his ears, which stuck out ov the water about 2 feet 6 inches; i didn't see this did, but an auctioneer told me ov it, and i never knew an auctioneer tu lie unless it was absolutely convenient.

George Washington Harris

1814-1869

from SUT LOVINGOOD'S YARNS

MRS. YARDLEY'S QUILTING

(1867)

"Thar's one durn'd nasty muddy job, an' I is jis' glad enuf tu take a ho'n ur two, on the straingth ove hit."

"What have you been doing, Sut?"

"Helpin tu salt ole Missis Yardley down."

"What do you mean by that?"

"Fixin her fur rotten cumfurtably, kiverin her up wif sile, tu keep the buzzards frum cheatin the wurms."

"Oh, you have been helping to bury a woman."

"That's hit, by golly! Now why the devil can't I 'splain mysef like yu? I ladles out my words at randum, like a calf kickin at yaller-jackids; yu jis' rolls em out tu the pint, like a feller a-layin bricks—every one fits. How is it that bricks fits so clost enyhow? Rocks won't ni du hit."

"Becaze they'se all ove a size," ventured a man with a wen over his eye.

"The devil yu say, hon'ey-head! haint reapin-mersheens ove a size? I'd like tu see two ove em fit clost. You wait ontil yu sprouts tuther ho'n, afore yu venters tu 'splain mix'd questions. George, did yu know ole Missis Yardley?"

"No."

"Well, she wer a curious 'oman in her way, an' she wore shiney specks. Now jis' listen: Whenever yu see a ole 'oman ahine a par ove *shiney* specks, yu keep yer eye skinn'd; they am dang'rus in the extreme. Thar is jis' no knowin what they ken du. I hed one a-stradil ove me onst, fur kissin her gal. She went fur my har, an' she went fur my skin, ontil I tho't she ment tu kill me, an' wud a-dun hit, ef my hollerin hadent fotch ole Dave Jordan, a *bacheler*, tu my aid. He, like a durn'd fool, cotch her by the laig, an' drug her back'ards ofen me. She jis' kivered him, an' I run, by golly! The nex time I seed him he wer bald headed, an' his face looked like he'd been a-fitin wild-cats.

"Ole Missis Yardley wer a great noticer ove littil things, that nobody else ever seed. She'd say right in the middil ove sumbody's serious talk: 'Law sakes! thar goes that yaller slut ove a hen, a-flingin straws over her shoulder; she' arter settin now, an' haint laid but seven aigs. I'll disapint *her*, see ef I don't; I'll put a punkin in her nes', an' a feather in her nose. An' bless my soul! jis' look at that cow wif the wilted ho'n, a-flingin up dirt an' a-smellin the place whar hit cum frum, wif the rale ginuine still-wurim twis' in her tail, too; what upon the face ove the yeath kin she be arter now, the ole fool? watch her, Sally. An' sakes alive! jis' look at that ole sow; she's a-gwine in a fas' trot, wif her empty bag a-floppin agin her sides. Thar, she hes stop't, an's a-listenin! she's arter no good, sich kerryin on means no good.'

"An' so she wud gabble, no odds who wer a-listenin. She looked like she mout been made at fust 'bout four foot long, an' the common thickness ove wimen when they's at tharsefs, an' then had her har tied tu a stump, a par ove steers hitched to her heels, an' then straiched out a-mos' two foot more— mos' ove the straichin cumin outen her laigs an' naik. Her stockins, a-hangin on the clothes-line tu dry, looked like a par ove sabre scabbards, an' her naik looked like a dry beef shank smoked, an' mout been ni ontu es tough. I never felt hit my-sef, I didn't, I jis' jedges by looks. Her darter Sal wer bilt at fust 'bout the laingth ove her mam, but wer never straiched eny by a par ove steers, an' she wer fat enuf tu kill; she wer taller lyin down than she wer a-standin up. Hit wer her who gin me the 'hump shoulder.' Jis' look at me; haint I'se got a tech ove the dromedary back thar bad? haint I humpy? Well, a-stoopin tu kill that squatty lar-stan ove a gal is what dun hit tu me. She wer the fairest-lookin gal I ever seed. She allers wore thick woolin stockins 'bout six inches too long fur her laig; they rolled down over her garders, lookin like a par ove life presarvers up thar. I tell yu she wer a tarin gal enyhow. Luved kissin, wrastlin, an' biled cabbige, an' hated tite clothes, hot weather, an' suckit-riders. B'leved strong in married folk's ways, cradles, an' the remishun ove sins, an' didn't b'leve in corsets, fleas, peaners, nur the fashun plates.

"What caused the death of Mrs. Yardley, Sut?"

"Nuffin, only her heart stop't beatin 'bout losing a nine di-munt quilt. True, she got a skeer'd hoss tu run over her, but she'd a-got over that ef a quilt hadn't been mix'd up in the catastrophy. Yu see quilts wer wun ove her speshul gifts; she run strong on the bed-kiver question. Irish chain, star ove Texas, sun-flower, nine dimunt, saw teeth, checker board, an' shell quilts; blue, an' white, an' yaller an' black coverlids; an' callicker-cumfurts reigned triumphan' 'bout her hous'. They

wer packed in drawers, layin in shelfs full, wer hung four dub-
bil on lines in the lof, packed in chists, piled on cheers, an' wer
everywhar, even ontu the beds, an' wer changed every bed-
makin. She told everybody she cud git tu listen tu hit that she
ment tu give every durn'd one ove them tu Sal when she got
married. Oh, lordy! what es fat a gal es Sal Yardley cud ever du
wif half ove em, an' sleeping wif a husbun at that, is more nor
I ever cud see through. Jis' think ove her onder twenty layer
ove quilts in July, an' yu in thar too. Gewhillikins! George,
look how I is sweatin' now, an' this is December. I'd 'bout es
lief be shet up in a steam biler wif a three hundred pound bag
ove lard, es to make a bisiness ove sleepin wif that gal—
'twould kill a glass-blower.

"Well, tu cum tu the serious part ove this conversashun, that
is how the old quilt-mersheen an' coverlidloom cum tu stop
operashuns on this yeath. She hed narrated hit thru the neighborhood that nex Saterday she'd gin a quiltin—three quilts
an' one cumfurt tu tie. 'Goblers, fiddils, gals, an' whisky,' wer
the words she sent tu the men-folk, an' more tetchin ur wake-
nin words never drap't ofen an 'oman's tongue. She sed tu the
gals, 'Sweet toddy, huggin, dancin, an' huggers in 'bundance.'
Them words struck the gals rite in the pit ove the stumick,
an' spread a ticklin sensashun bof ways, ontil they scratched
thar heads wif one han, an' thar heels wif tuther.

"Everybody, he an' she, what wer baptized b'levers in the
righteousnes ove quiltins wer thar, an' hit jis' so happen'd that
everybody in them parts, frum fifteen summers tu fifty winters,
wer unannamus b'levers. Strange, warn't hit? Hit wer the big-
ges' quiltin ever Missis Yardley hilt, an' she hed hilt hundreds;
everybody wer thar, 'scept the constibil an' suckit-rider, two
dam easily-spared pussons; the numbers ni ontu even too; jis'
a few more boys nur gals; that made hit more exhitin, fur hit
gin the gals a chance tu kick an' squeal a littil, wifout runnin
eny risk ove not gittin kissed at all, an' hit gin reasonabil
grouns fur a few scrimmages amung the he's. Now es kissin an'
fitin am the pepper an' salt ove all soshul getherins, so hit wer
more espishully wif this ove ours. Es I swung my eyes over the

crowd, George, I thought quiltins, managed in a morril an' sensibil way, truly am good things—good fur free drinkin, good fur free eatin, good fur free huggin, good fur free dancin, good fur free fitin, an' goodest ove all fur poperlatin a country fas'.

"Thar am a fur-seein wisdum in quiltins, ef they has proper trimmins: 'vittils, an' sperrits in 'bundance.' One holesum quiltin am wuf three old pray'rmeetins on the poperlashun pint, purtickerly ef hits hilt in the dark ove the moon, an' runs intu the night a few hours, an' April ur May am the time chosen. The moon don't suit quiltins whar everybody is well acquainted an' already fur along in courtin. She dus help pow'ful tu begin a courtin match onder, but when hit draws ni ontu a head, nobody wants a moon but the old mammys.

"The mornin cum, still, saft, sunshiney; cocks crowin, hens singin, birds chirpin, tuckeys gobblin—jis' the day tu sun quilts, kick, kiss, squeal, an' make love.

"All the plow-lines an' clothes-lines wer straiched tu every post an' tree. Quilts purvailed. Durn my gizzard ef two acres roun that ar house warn't jis' one solid quilt, all out a-sunnin, an' tu be seed. They dazzled the eyes, skeered the hosses, gin wimen the heart-burn, an' perdominated.

"To'ards sundown the he's begun tu drap in. Yearnis' needil-drivin cummenced tu lose groun; threads broke ofen, thimbils got los', an' quilts needed anuther roll. Gigglin, winkin, whisperin, smoofin ove har, an' gals a-ticklin one anuther, wer a-gainin every inch ove groun what the needils los'. Did yu ever notis, George, at all soshul getherins, when the he's begin tu gather, that the young she's begin tu tickil one anuther an' the ole maids swell thar tails, roach up thar backs, an' sharpen thar nails ontu the bed-posts an' door jams, an' spit an' groan sorter like cats a-courtin? Dus hit mean *rale* rath, ur is hit a dare tu the he's, sorter kivered up wif the outside signs ove danger? I honestly b'leve that the young shes' ticklin means, 'Cum an' take this job ofen our hans.' But that swelling I jis' don't onderstan; dus yu? Hit looks skeery, an' I never tetch one ove em when they am in the swellin way. I may be mistaken'd 'bout the ticklin bisiness too; hit may be

dun like a feller chaws poplar bark when he haint got any terbacker, a-sorter better nur nun make-shif. I dus know one
thing tu a certainty: that is, when the he's take hold the ticklin quits, an' ef yu gits one ove the old maids out tu herself,
then she subsides an' is the smoofes, sleekes, saft thing yu ever
seed, an' dam ef yu can't hear her purr, jis' es plain!

"But then, George, gals an' ole maids haint the things tu
fool time away on. Hits widders, by golly, what am the rale
sensibil, steady-goin, never-skeerin, never-kickin, willin, sper-
rited, smoof pacers. They cum clost up tu the hoss-block,
standin still wif thar purty silky years playin, an' the naik-veins
a-throbbin, an' waits fur the word, which ove course yu gives,
arter yu finds yer feet well in the stirrup, an' away they moves
like a cradil on cushioned rockers, ur a spring buggy runnin
in damp san'. A tetch ove the bridil, an' they know yu wants
em tu turn, an' they dus hit es willin es ef the idear wer thar
own. I be dod rabbited ef a man can't 'propriate happiness by
the skinful ef he is in contack wif sumbody's widder, an' is
smart. Gin me a willin widder, the yeath over: what they don't
know, haint worth larnin. They hes all been tu Jamakey an'
larnt how sugar's made, an' know how tu sweeten wif hit; an'
by golly, they is always ready to use hit. All yu hes tu du is tu
find the spoon, an' then drink cumfort till yer blind. Nex tu
good sperrits an' my laigs, I likes a twenty-five year old widder,
wif roun ankils, an' bright eyes, honestly an' squarly lookin
intu yurn, an' sayin es plainly es a partrige sez 'Bob White,'
'Don't be afraid ove me; I hes been thar; yu know hit ef yu
hes eny sense, an' thar's no use in eny humbug, ole feller—
cum ahead!'

"Ef yu onderstands widder nater, they ken save yu a power
ove troubil, onsartinty, an' time, an' ef yu is interprisin yu gits
mons'rous well paid fur hit. The very soun ove thar littil shoe-
heels speak full trainin, an' hes a knowin click as they tap the
floor; an' the rustil ove thar dress sez, 'I dar yu tu ax me.'

"When yu hes made up yer mind tu court one, jis' go at hit
like hit wer a job ove rail-maulin. Ware yer workin close, use
yer common, everyday moshuns an' words, an' abuv all, fling

away yer cinament ile vial an' burn all yer love songs. No use in tryin tu fool em, fur they sees plum thru yu, a durn'd sight plainer than they dus thru thar veils. No use in a pasted shut; she's been thar. No use in borrowin a cavortin fat hoss; she's been thar. No use in cloves, tu kill whisky breff; she's been thar. No use in buying clost curtains fur yer bed, fur she has been thar. Widders am a speshul means, George, fur ripenin green men, killin off weak ones, an makin 'ternally happy the soun ones.

"Well, es I sed afore, I flew the track an' got ontu the widders. The fellers begun tu ride up an' walk up, sorter slow, like they warn't in a hurry, the durn'd 'saitful raskils, hitchin thar critters tu enything they cud find. One red-comb'd, long-spurr'd, dominecker feller, frum town, in a red an' white grid-iron jackid an' patent leather gaiters, hitched his hoss, a wild, skeery, wall-eyed devil, inside the yard palins, tu a cherry tree lim'. Thinks I, that hoss hes a skeer intu him big enuf tu run intu town, an' perhaps beyant hit, ef I kin only tetch hit off; so I sot intu thinkin.

"One aind ove a long clothes-line, wif nine dimunt quilts ontu hit, wer tied tu the same cherry tree that the hoss wer. I tuck my knife and socked hit thru every quilt, 'bout the middil, an' jis' below the rope, an' tied them thar wif bark, so they cudent slip. Then I went tu the back aind, an' ontied hit frum the pos', knottin in a hoe-handil, by the middil, tu keep the quilts frum slippin off ef my bark strings failed, an' laid hit on the groun. Then I went tu the tuther aind: thar wer 'bout ten foot tu spar, a-lyin on the groun arter tyin tu the tree. I tuck hit atwix Walleye's hine laigs, an' tied hit fas' tu bof stir-rups, an' then cut the cherry tree lim' betwix his bridil an' the tree, almos' off. Now, mine yu thar were two ur three uther ropes full ove quilts atween me an' the hous', so I were pruty well hid frum thar. I jis' tore off a palin frum the fence, an' tuck hit in bof hans, an' arter raisin hit 'way up yander, I fotch hit down, es hard es I cud, flatsided to'ards the groun, an' hit acksidentally happen'd tu hit Wall-eye, 'bout nine inches ahead ove the root ove his tail. Hit landed so hard that hit made my hans tingle, an' then busted intu splinters. The first things I did, wer tu feel ove mysef, on the same spot whar hit hed hit the hoss. I cudent help duin hit tu save my life, an' I swar I felt sum ove Wall-eye's sensashun, jis' es plain. The fust thing he did, wer tu tare down the lim' wif a twenty-foot jump, his head to'ards the hous'. Thinks I, now yu hev dun hit, yu durn'd wall-eyed fool! tarin down that lim' wer the beginin ove all the troubil, an' the hoss did hit hissef; my conshuns felt clar es a mountin spring, an' I wer in a frame ove mine tu observe things es they happen'd, an' they soon begun tu happen purty clost arter one anuther rite then, an' thar, an' tharabouts, clean ontu town, thru hit, an' still wer a-happenin, in the woods beyant thar ni ontu eleven mile frum ole man Yardley's gate, an' four beyant town.

"The fust line ove quilts he tried tu jump, but broke hit down; the nex one he ran onder; the rope cotch ontu the ho'n ove the saddil, broke at bof ainds, an' went along wif the hoss, the cherry tree lim' an' the fust line ove quilts, what I hed proverdensally tied fas' tu the rope. That's what I calls foresight, George. Right furnint the frunt door he cum in contack wif old Missis Yardley hersef, an' anuther ole 'oman; they wer a-holdin a nine dimunt quilt spread out, a-'zaminin hit, an' a-praisin hits perfeckshuns. The durn'd onmanerly, wall-eyed fool run plum over Missis Yardley, frum ahine, stompt one hine foot through the quilt, takin hit along, a-kickin ontil he made hits corners snap like a whip. The gals screamed, the men hollered wo! an' the ole 'oman wer toted intu the hous' limber es a wet string, an' every word she sed wer, 'Oh, my preshus nine dimunt quilt!'

"Wall-eye busted thru the palins, an' Dominicker sed 'im, made a mortal rush fur his bitts, wer too late fur them, but in good time fur the strings ove flying quilts, got tangled amung em, an' the gridiron jackid patren wer los' tu my sight amung star an' Irish chain quilts; he went frum that quiltin at the rate ove thuty miles tu the hour. Nuffin lef on the lot ove the hole consarn, but a nine biler hat, a par ove gloves, an' the jack ove hearts.

"What a onmanerly, suddin way ove leavin places sum folks hev got, enyhow.

"Thinks I, well, that fool hoss, tarin down that cherry tree lim', hes dun sum good, enyhow; hit hes put the ole 'oman outen the way fur the balance ove the quiltin, an' tuck Dominicker outen the way an' outen danger, fur that gridiron jackid wud a-bred a scab on his nose afore midnite! hit wer morrily boun tu du hit.

"Two months arterwards, I tracked the route that hoss tuck in his kalamatus skeer, by quilt rags, tufts ove cotton, bunches ove har (human an' hoss), an' scraps ove a gridiron jackid stickin ontu the bushes, an' plum at the aind ove hit, whar all signs gin out, I foun a piece ove watch chain an' a hosses head. The places what know'd Dominicker, know'd im no more.

"Well, arter they'd tuck the ole 'oman up stairs an' camfired her tu sleep, things begun tu work agin. The widders broke the ice, an' arter a littil gigilin, goblin, an' gabblin, the kissin begun. *Smack!*—'Thar, now,' a widder sed that. *Pop!*—'Oh, don't!' *Pfip!*—'Oh, yu quit! *Plosh!*—'Go *way* yu awkerd critter, yu kissed me in the eye!' anuther widder sed that. *Bop!* 'Now yu ar satisfied, I recon, big mouf!' *Vip!*—'That haint fair!' *Spat!*—'Oh, lordy! May, cum pull Bill away; he's a-tanglin my har'. *Thut!*—'I jis' d-a-r-e yu tu du that agin!' a widder sed that, too. Hit sounded all 'roun that room like poppin co'n in a hot skillet, an' wer pow'ful sujestif.

"Hit kep on ontil I be durn'd ef *my* bristils didn't begin tu rise, an' sumthin like a cold buckshot wud run down the marrow in my backbone 'bout every ten secons, an' then run up agin, tolerabil hot. I kep a swallerin wif nuthin tu swaller, an' my face felt swell'd; an' yet I wer fear'd tu make a bulge. Thinks I, I'll ketch one out tu herself torreckly, an' then I guess we'll rastil. Purty soon Sal Yardley started fur the smoke-'ous, so I jis' gin my head a few short shakes, let down one ove my wings a-trailin, an' sirkiled roun her wif a side twis' in my naik, steppin sidewise, an' a-fetchin up my hinmos' foot wif a sorter jerkin slide at every step. Sez I, 'Too coo-took a-too.'' She onderstood hit, an' stopt, sorter spreadin her shoulders. An' jis' es I hed pouch'd out my mouf, an' wer a-reachin forrid wif hit, fur the article hitsef, sunthin interfared wif me, hit did. George, wer yu ever ontu yer hans an' knees, an' let a hell-tarin big, mad ram, wif a ten-yard run, but yu yearnis'ly, jis onst, right squar ontu the pint ove yer back-bone?"

"No, you fool; why do you ask?"

"Kaze I wanted tu know ef yu cud hev a realizin' noshun ove my shock. Hits scarcely worth while tu try to make yu onderstan the case by words only, onles yu hev been tetched in that way. Gr-eat golly! the fust thing I felt, I tuck hit tu be a back-ackshun yeathquake; an' the fust thing I seed wer my chaw'r terbacker a-flying over Sal's head like a skeer'd bat. My mouf wer pouch'd out, ready fur the article hitsef, yu know, an' hit went outen the roun hole like the wad outen a pop-gun—thug! an' the fust think I know'd, I wer a flying over Sal's head too, an' a-gainin on the chaw'r terbacker fast. I wer straitened out strait, toes hinemos', middil finger-nails foremos', an' the fust thing I hearn wer, 'Yu dam Shanghi!' Great Jerus-a-lam! I lit ontu my all fours jis' in time tu but the yard gate ofen hits hinges, an' skeer loose sum more hosses—kep on in a four-footed gallop, clean acrost the lane afore I cud straiten up, an' yere I cotch up wif my chaw'r terbacker, stickin flat agin a fence-rail. I hed got so good a start that I thot hit a pity tu spile hit, so I jis' jump'd the fence an' tuck thru the orchurd. I tell yu I dusted these here close, fur I tho't hit wer arter me.

"Arter runnin a spell, I ventered tu feel roun back thar, fur sum signs ove what hed happened tu me. George, arter two pow'ful hardtugs, I pull'd out the vamp an' sole ove one ove ole man Yardley's big brogans, what he hed los' amung my coat-tails. Dre'ful! dre'ful! Arter I got hit away frum thar, my flesh went fas' asleep, frum abuv my kidneys tu my knees; about now, fur the fust time, the idear struck me, what hit wer that hed interfar'd wif me, an' los' me the kiss. Hit wer ole Yardley hed kicked me. I walked fur a month like I wer straddlin a thorn hedge. Sich a shock, at sich a time, an' on sich a place—jis' think ove hit! hit am tremenjus, haint hit? The place feels num, right now."

"Well, Sut, how did the quilting come out?"

"How the hell du yu 'speck me tu know? I warn't thar eny more."

Clarence King

1842-1901

from MOUNTAINEERING IN THE SIERRA NEVADA

THE NEWTYS OF PIKE

(1872)

Our return from Mount Tyndall to such civilization as flourishes around the Kaweah outposts was signalized by us chiefly as to our *cuisine*, which offered now such bounties as the potato, and once a salad, in which some middle-aged lettuce became the vehicle for a hollow mockery of dressing. Two or three days, during which we dined at brief intervals, served to completely rest us, and put in excellent trim for further campaigning all except Professor Brewer, upon whom a constant toothache wore painfully,—my bullet-mould failing even upon the third trial to extract the unruly member.

It was determined we should ride together to Visalia, seventy miles away, and, the more we went, the impatienter became my friend, till we agreed to push ahead through day and night, and reached the village at about sunrise in a state of reeling sleepiness quite indescribably funny.

At evening, when it became time to start back for our mountain camp, my friend at last yielded consent to my project of climbing the Kern Sierras to attempt Mount Whitney; so I parted from him, and, remaining at Visalia, outfitted myself with a pack-horse, two mounted men, and provisions enough for a two weeks' trip.

I purposely avoid telling by what route I entered the Sierras, because there lingers in my breast a desire to see once more that lovely region, and failing, as I do, to confide in the people, I fear lest, if the camp I am going to describe should be recognized, I might, upon revisiting the scene, suffer harm, or even come to an untimely end. I refrain, then, from telling by what road I found myself entering the region of the pines one lovely twilight evening, two days after leaving Visalia. Pines, growing closer and closer, from sentinels gathered to groups, then stately groves, and at last, as the evening wore on, assembled in regular forest, through whose open tops the stars shone cheerfully.

I came upon an open meadow, hearing in front the rush of a large brook, and directly reached two campfires, where were a number of persons. My two hirelings caught and unloaded the pack-horse, and set about their duties, looking to supper and the animals, while I prospected the two camps. That just below me, on the same side of the brook, I found to be the bivouac of a company of hunters, who, in the ten minutes of my call, made free with me, hospitably offering a jug of whiskey, and then went on in their old eternal way of making bear-stories out of whole cloth.

I left them with a belief that my protoplasm and theirs must be different, in spite of Mr. Huxley, and passed across the brook to the other camp. Under noble groups of pines smouldered a generous heap of coals, the ruins of a mighty log. A little way from this lay a confused pile of bedclothes, partly old and half-bald buffalo-robes, but, in the main, thick strata of what is known to irony as comforters, upon which, outstretched in wretched awkwardness of position, was a family, all with their feet to the fire, looking as if they had been blown over in one direction, or knocked down by a single bombshell. On the extremities of this common bed, with the air of having gotten as far from each other as possible, the mother and father of the Pike family reclined; between them were two small children—a girl and boy—and a huge girl, who, next the old man, lay flat upon her back, her mind absorbed in the simple amusement of waving one foot (a cowhide eleven) slowly across the fire, squinting, with half-shut eye, first at the vast shoe and thence at the fire, alternately hiding bright places and darting the foot quickly in the direction of any new display of heightening flame. The mother was a bony sister, in the yellow, shrunken, of sharp visage, in which were prominent two cold eyes and a positively poisonous mouth; her hair, the color of faded hay, tangled in a jungle around her head. She rocked jerkily to and fro, removing at intervals a clay pipe from her mouth in order to pucker her thin lips up to one side, and spit with precision upon a certain spot in the fire, which she seemed resolved to prevent from attaining beyond a certain faint glow.

I have rarely felt more in difficulty for an overture to conversation, and was long before venturing to propose, "You seem to have a pleasant camp-spot here." The old woman sharply, and in almost a tone of affront, answered, "They's wus, and then again they's better."

"Doos well for our hogs," inserted the old man. "We've a band of pork that make out to find feed."

"Oh! how many have you?" I asked.

"Nigh three thousand."

"Won't you set?" asked Madame; then, turning, "You, Susan, can't you try for to set up, and not spread so? Hain't you no manners, say?"

At this the massive girl got herself somewhat together, and made room for me, which I declined, however.

"Prospecting?" inquired Madame.

"I say huntin'," suggested the man.

"Maybe he's a cattle-feller," interrupted the little girl.

"Goin' somewhere, ain't yer?" was Susan's guess.

I gave brief account of myself, evidently satisfying the social requirements of all but the old woman, who at once classified me as not up to her standard. Susan saw this, so did her father, and it became evident to me in ten minutes' conversation that they two were always at one, and made it their business to be in antagonism to the mother. They were then allies of mine from nature, and I felt at once at home. I saw too that Susan, having slid back to her horizontal position when I declined to share her rightful ground, was watching with subtle solicitude that fated spot in the fire, opposing sympathy and squints accurately aligned by her shoe to the dull spot in the embers, which slowly went out into blackness before the well-directed fire of her mother's saliva.

The shouts which I heard proceeding from the direction of my camp were easily translatable into summons for supper. Mr. Newty invited me to return later and be sociable, which I promised to do, and, going to my camp, supped quickly and left the men with orders about picketing the animals for the night, then, strolling slowly down to the camp of my friends, seated myself upon a log by the side of the old gentleman. Feeling that this somewhat formal attitude unfitted me for partaking to the fullest degree the social ease around me, and knowing that my buckskin trousers were impervious to dirt, I slid down in a reclined posture with my feet to the fire, in absolute parallelism with the rest of the family.

The old woman was in the exciting *dénouement* of a coon-story, directed to her little boy, who sat clinging to her skirt and looking in her face with absorbed curiosity. "And when Johnnie fired," she said, "the coon fell and busted open." The little boy had misplaced his sympathies with the raccoon, and having inquired plaintively, "Did it hurt him?" was promptly snubbed with the reply, "Of course it hurt him. What do you suppose coons is made for?" Then turning to me she put what was plainly enough with her a test-question: "I allow you have killed your coon in your day?" I saw at once that I must forever sink beneath the horizon of her standards, but, failing in real experience or accurate knowledge concerning the coon, knew no subterfuges would work with her. Instinct had taught her that I had never killed a coon, and she had asked me thus ostentatiously to place me at once and forever before the family in my true light. "No, ma'am," I said; "now you speak of it,

I realize that I never have killed a coon." This was something of a staggerer to Susan and her father, yet as the mother's pleasurable dissatisfaction with me displayed itself by more and more accurate salivary shots at the fire, they rose to the occasion, and began to palliate my past. "Maybe," ventured Mr. Newty, "that they don't have coon round the city of York"; and I felt that I needed no self-defence when Susan firmly and defiantly suggested to her mother that perhaps I was in better business.

Driven in upon herself for some time, the old woman smoked in silence, until Susan, seeing that her mother gradually quenched a larger and larger circle upon the fire, got up and stretched herself, and giving the coals a vigorous poke swept out of sight the quenched spot, thus readily obliterating the result of her mother's precise and prolonged expectoration; then flinging a few dry boughs upon the fire illumined the family with the ruddy blaze, and sat down again, leaning upon her father's knee with a faint light of triumph in her eye.

I ventured a few platitudes concerning pigs, not penetrating the depths of that branch of rural science enough to betray my ignorance. Such sentiments as "A little piece of bacon well broiled for breakfast is very good," and "Nothing better than cold ham for lunch," were received by Susan and her father, in the spirit I meant—of entire good-will toward pork generically. I now look back in amusement at having fallen into this weakness, for the Mosaic view of pork has been mine from infancy, and campaigning upon government rations has, in truth, no tendency to dim this ancient faith.

By half past nine the gates of conversation were fairly open, and our part of the circle enjoyed itself socially,—taciturnity and clouds of Virginia plug reigning supreme upon the other. The two little children crept under comforters somewhere near the middle of the bed, and subsided pleasantly to sleep. The old man at last stretched sleepily, finally yawning out, "Susan, I do believe I am too tired out to go and see if them corral bars are down. I guess you'll have to go. I reckon there ain't no bears round to-night." Susan rose to her feet, stretched herself with her back to the fire, and I realized for the first time her amusing proportions. In the region of six feet, tall, square-shouldered, of firm iron back and heavy mould of limb, she yet possessed that suppleness which enabled her as she rose to throw herself into nearly all the attitudes of the Niobe children. As her yawn deepened, she waved nearly down to the ground, and then, rising upon tiptoe, stretched up her clinched fists to heaven with a groan of pleasure. Turning to me, she asked, "How would you like to see the hogs?" The old man added, as an extra encouragement, "Pootiest band of hogs in Tulare County! There's littler of the real sissor-bill nor Mexican racer stock than any band I have ever seen in the State. I driv the original outfit from Pike County to Oregon in '51 and '52." By this time I was actually interested in them, and joining Susan we passed out into the forest.

The full moon, now high in the heavens, looked down over the whole landscape of clustered forest and open meadow with tranquil silvery light. It whitened measurably the fine spiry tips of the trees, fell luminous upon broad bosses of granite which here and there rose through the soil, and glanced in trembling reflections from the rushing surface of the brook. Far in the distance moonlit peaks towered in solemn rank against the sky.

We walked silently on four or five minutes through the woods, coming at last upon a fence which margined a wide circular opening in the wood. The bars, as her father had feared, were down. We stepped over them, quietly entered the enclosure, put them up behind us, and proceeded to the middle, threading our way among sleeping swine to where a lonely tree rose to the height of about two hundred feet. Against this we placed our backs, and Susan waved her hand in pride over the two acres of tranquil pork. The eye, after accustoming itself to the darkness, took cognizance of a certain ridgyness of surface which came to be recognized as the objects of Susan's pride.

Quite a pretty effect was caused by the shadow of the forest, which, cast obliquely downward by the moon, divided the corral into halves of light and shade.

The air was filled with heavy breathing, interrupted by here and there a snore, and at times by crescendos of tumult, caused by forty or fifty pigs doing battle for some favorite bedplace.

I was informed that Susan did not wish me to judge of them by dark, but to see them again in the full light of day. She knew each individual pig by its physiognomy, having, as she said, "growed with 'em."

As we strolled back toward the bars a dusky form disputed our way,—two small, sharp eyes and a wild crest of bristles were visible in the obscure light. "That's Old Arkansas," said Susan; "he's eight year old come next June, and I never could get him to like me." I felt for my pistol, but Susan struck a vigorous attitude, ejaculating, "S-S-oway, Arkansas!" She made a dash in his direction; a wild scuffle ensued, in which I heard the dull thud of Susan's shoe, accompanied by, "Take that, dog-on-you!" a cloud of dust, one shrill squeal, and Arkansas retreated into the darkness at a business-like trot.

When quite near the bars the mighty girl launched herself into the air, alighting with her stomach across the topmost rail, where she hung a brief moment, made a violent muscular contraction, and alighted upon the ground outside, communicating to it a tremor quite perceptible from where I stood. I climbed over after her, and we sauntered under the trees back to camp.

The family had disappeared, a few dry boughs, however, thrown upon the coals, blazed up, and revealed their forms in the corrugated topography of the bed.

I bade Susan good night, and before I could turn my back she kicked her number-eleven shoes into the air, and with masterly rapidity turned in, as Minerva is said to have done, in full panoply. *God of Wisdom —strong*

I fled precipitately to my camp, and sought my blankets, lying awake in a kind of half-revery, in which Susan and Arkansas, the old woman and her coons, were the prominent figures. Later I fell asleep, and lay motionless until the distant roar of swine awoke me before sunrise next morning.

Seated upon my blankets, I beheld Susan's mother drag forth the two children, one after another, by the napes of their necks, and, shaking the sleep out of them, propel them spitefully toward the brook; then taking her pipe from her mouth she bent low over the sleeping form of her huge daughter, and in a high, shrill, nasal key, screeched in her ear, "Yew Suse!"

No sign of life on the part of the daughter.

"Susan, *are* you a-going to get up?"

Slight muscular contraction of the lower limbs.

"Will you hear me, *Susan?*"

"Marm," whispered the girl, in low, sleepy tones.

"Get up and let the *hogs* out!"

The idea had at length thrilled into Susan's brain, and with a violent suddenness she sat bolt upright, brushing her green-colored hair out of her eyes, and rubbing those valuable but bleared organs with the ponderous knuckles of her forefingers.

By this time I started for the brook for my morning toilet, and the girl and I met upon opposite banks, stooping to wash our faces in the same pool. As I opened my dressing-case her lower jaw fell, revealing a row of ivory teeth rounded out by two well-developed "wisdoms," which had all that dazzling grin one sees in the show-windows of certain dental practitioners. It required but a moment to gather up a quart or so of water in her broad palms, and rub it vigorously into a small circle upon the middle of her face, the moisture working outward to a certain high-water mark, which, along her chin and cheeks, defined the limits of former ablution; then, baring her large red arms to the elbow, she washed her hands, and stood resting them upon her hips, dripping freely, and watching me with intense curiosity.

When I reached the towel process, she herself twisted her body after the manner of the Belvidere torso, bent low her head, gathered up the back breadths of her petticoat, and wiped her face vigorously upon it, which had the effect of tracing concentric streaks irregularly over her countenance.

I parted my hair by the aid of a small dressing-glass, which so fired Susan that she crossed the stream with a mighty jump, and stood in ecstasy by my side. She borrowed the glass, and then my comb, rewashed her face, and fell to work diligently upon her hair.

All this did not so limit my perception as to prevent my watching the general demeanor of the family. The old man lay back at his ease, puffing a cloud of smoke; his wife, also emitting volumes of the vapor of "navy plug," squatted by the camp-fire, frying certain lumps of pork, and communicating an occasional spiral jerk to the coffee-pot, with the purpose, apparently, of stirring the grounds. The two children had gotten upon the back of a contemplative ass, who stood by the upper side of the bed quietly munching the corner of a comforter.

My friend was in no haste. She squandered much time upon the arrangement of her towy hair, and there was something like a blush of conscious satisfaction when she handed me back my looking-glass and remarked ironically, "O no, I guess not,—no, sir."

I begged her to accept the comb and glass, which she did with maidenly joy.

This unusual toilet had stimulated with self-respect Susan's every fibre, and as she sprung back across the brook and approached her mother's camp-fire, I could not fail to admire the magnificent turn of her shoulders and the powerful, queenly poise of her head. Her full, grand form and heavy strength reminded me of the statues of Ceres; yet there was withal a very unpleasant suggestion of fighting trim, a sort of prize-ring manner of swinging the arms, and hitching of the shoulders. She suddenly spied the children upon the jackass, and with one wide sweep of her right arm projected them over the creature's head, and planted her left eleven firmly in the ribs of the donkey, who beat a precipitate retreat in the direction of the hog-pens, leaving her executing a *pas seul*,—a kind of slow, stately jig, something between the minuet and the *juba*, accompanying herself by a low-hummed air and a vigorous beating of time upon her slightly lifted knee.

It required my Pike County friends but ten minutes to swallow their pork and begin the labors of the day.

The mountaineers' camp was not yet astir. These children of the forest were well chained in slumber; for, unless there is some special programme for the day, it requires the leverage of a high sun to arouse their faculties, dormant enough by nature, and soothed into deepest quiet by whiskey. About eight o'clock they breakfasted, and by nine had engaged my innocent camp-men in a game of social poker.

I visited my horses, and had them picketed in the best possible feed, and congratulated myself that they were recruiting finely for the difficult ride before me.

Susan, after a second appeal from her mother, ran over to the corral and let out the family capital, who streamed with exultant grunt through the forest, darkening the fair green meadow gardens, and happily passing out of sight.

When I had breakfasted I joined Mr. Newty in his trip to the corral, where we stood together for hours, during which I had mastered the story of his years since, in 1850, he left his old home in Pike of Missouri.

It was one of those histories common enough through this wide West, yet never failing to startle me with its horrible lesson of social disintegration, of human retrograde.

That brave spirit of Westward Ho! which has been the pillar of fire and cloud leading on the weary march of progress over stretches of desert, lining the way with graves of strong men; of new-born lives; of sad, patient mothers, whose pathetic longing for the new home died with them; of the thousand old and young whose last agony came to them as they marched with eyes strained on after the sunken sun, and whose shallow barrows scarcely lift over the drifting dust of the desert; that restless spirit which has dared to uproot the old and plant the new, kindling the grand energy of California, laying foundations for a State to be, that is admirable, is poetic, is to fill an immortal page in the story of America; but when, instead of urging on to wresting from new lands something better than old can give, it degenerates into mere weak-minded restlessness, killing the power of growth, the ideal of home, the faculty of repose, it results in that race of perpetual emigrants who roam as dreary waifs over the West, losing possessions, love of life, love of God, slowly dragging from valley to valley till they fall by the wayside, happy if some chance stranger performs for them the last rites,—often less fortunate, as blanched bones and fluttering rags upon too many hillsides plainly tell.

The Newtys were of this dreary brotherhood. In 1850, with a small family of that authentic strain of high-bred swine for which Pike County is widely known, as Mr. Newty avers, they bade Missouri and their snug farm good by, and, having packed their household goods into a wagon drawn by two spotted oxen, set out with the baby Susan for Oregon, where they came after a year's march, tired, and cursed with a permanent discontent. There they had taken up a rancho, a quarter-section of public domain, which at the end of two years was "improved" to the extent of the "neatest little worm fence this side of Pike," a barn, and a smoke-house. "In another year," said my friend, "I'd have dug for a house, but we tuck ager and the second baby died." One day there came a man who "let on that he knowd" land in California much fairer and more worthy tillage than Oregon's best, so the poor Newtys harnessed up the wagon and turned their backs upon a home nearly ready for comfortable life, and swept south with pigs and plunder. Through all the years this story had repeated itself, new homes gotten to the edge of completion, more babies born, more graves made, more pigs, who replenished as only the Pike County variety may, till it seemed to me the mere multiplication of them must reach a sufficient dead weight to anchor the family; but this was dispelled when Newty remarked: "These yer hogs is awkward about moving, and I've pretty much made my mind to put 'em all into bacon this fall, and sell out and start for Montana."

Poor fellow! at Montana he will probably find a man from Texas who in half an hour will persuade him that happiness lies there.

As we walked back to their camp, and when Dame Newty hove in sight, my friend ventured to say, "Don't you mind the old woman and her coons. She's from Arkansas. She used to say no man could have Susan who couldn't show coonskins enough of his own killing to make a bedquilt, but she's over that mostly." In spite of this assurance my heart fell a trifle when, the first moment of our return, she turned to her husband and asked, "Do you mind what a dead-open-and-shut on coons our little Johnny was when he was ten years old?" I secretly wondered if the dead-open-and-shut had anything to do with his untimely demise at eleven, but kept silence.

Regarding her as a sad product of the disease of chronic emigration, her hard thin nature, all angles and stings, became to me one of the most depressing and pathetic spectacles, and the more when her fever-and-ague boy, a mass of bilious lymph, came and sat by her, looking up with great haggard eyes as if pleading for something, he knew not what, but which I plainly saw only death could bestow.

Noon brought the hour of my departure. Susan and her father talked apart a moment, then the old man said the two would ride along with me for a few miles, as he had to go in that direction to look for new hog-feed.

I despatched my two men with the pack-horse, directing them to follow the trail, then saddled my Kaweah and waited for the Newtys. The old man saddled a shaggy little mountain pony for himself, and for Susan strapped a sheepskin upon the back of a young and fiery mustang colt.

While they were getting ready, I made my horse fast to a stake and stepped over to bid good by to Mrs. Newty. I said to her, in tones of deference, "I have come to bid you good by, madam, and when I get back this way I hope you will be kind enough to tell me one or two really first-rate coon-stories. I am quite ignorant of that animal, having been raised in countries where they are extremely rare, and I would like to know more of what seems to be to you a creature of such interest." The wet, gray eyes relaxed, as I fancied, a trifle of their asperity; a faint kindle seemed to light them for an instant as she asked, "You never see coons catch frogs in a spring branch?"

"No, Madame," I answered.

"Well, I wonder! Well, take care of yourself, and when you come back this way stop along with us, and we'll kill a yearlin' and I'll tell you about a coon that used to live under grandfather's barn." She actually offered me her hand, which I grasped and shook in a friendly manner, chilled to the very bone with its damp coldness.

Mr. Newty mounted, and asked me if I was ready. Susan stood holding her prancing mustang. To put that girl on her horse after the ordinary plan would have required the strength of Samson, or the use of a step-ladder, neither of which I possessed; so I waited for events to develop themselves. The girl stepped to the left side of her horse, twisted one hand in the mane, laying the other upon his haunches, and, crouching for a jump, sailed through the air, alighting upon the sheepskin. The horse reared, and Susan, twisting herself around, came right side up with her knee upon the sheepskin, shouting, as she did so, "I guess you don't get me off, sir!" I jumped upon Kaweah, and our two horses sprang forward together, Susan waving her hand to her father, and crying, "Come along after, old man!" and to her mother, "Take care of yourself!" which is the Pike County for *Au revoir!* Her mustang tugged at the bit, and bounded wildly into the air. We reached a stream bank at full gallop, the horses clearing it at a bound, sweeping on over the green floor, and under the magnificent shadow of the forest. Newty, following us at an humble trot, slopped through the creek, and when I last looked he had nearly reached the edge of the wood.

I could but admire the unconscious excellence of Susan's riding, her firm, immovable seat, and the perfect coolness with which she held the fiery horse. This quite absorbed me for five minutes, when she at last broke the silence by the laconic inquiry, "Does yourn buck?" To which I added the reply that he had only occasionally been guilty of that indiscretion. She then informed me that the first time she had mounted the colt he had "nearly bucked her to pieces; he had jumped and jounced till she was plum tuckered out" before he had given up. Gradually reining the horses down and inducing them to walk, we rode side by side through the most magnificent forest of the Sierras, and I determined to probe Susan to see whether there were not, even in the most latent condition, some germs of the appreciation of nature. I looked from base to summit of the magnificent shafts, at the green plumes which traced themselves against the sky, the exquisite fall of purple shadows and golden light upon trunks, at the labyrinth of glowing flowers, at the sparkling whiteness of the mountain brook, and up to the clear matchless blue that vaulted over us, then turned to Susan's plain, honest face, and gradually introduced the subject of trees. Ideas of lumber and utilitarian notions of fencerails were uppermost in her mind; but I briefly penetrated what proved to be only a superficial stratum of the materialistic, and asked her point-blank if she did not admire their stately symmetry. A strange, new light gleamed in her eye as I described to her the growth and distribution of forests, and the marvellous change in their character and aspects as they approached the tropics. The palm and the pine, as I worked them up to her, really filled her with delight, and prompted numerous interested and intelligent queries, showing that she thoroughly comprehended my drift.

In the pleasant hour of our chat I learned a new lesson of the presence of undeveloped seed in the human mind.

Mr. Newty at last came alongside and remarked that he must stop about here; "but," he added, "Susan will go on with you about half a mile, and come back and join me here after I have taken a look at the feed." As he rode out into the forest a little way, he called me to him, and I was a little puzzled at what seemed to be the first traces of embarrassment I had seen in his manner.

"You'll take care of yourself, now, won't you?" he asked. I tried to convince him that I would.

A slight pause.

"You'll take care of yourself, won't you?"

He might rely on it, I was going to say.

He added, "Thet—thet—thet man what gits Susan *has half the hogs!*"

Then turning promptly away, he spurred the pony, and his words as he rode into the forest were, "Take good care of yourself!"

Susan and I rode on for half a mile, until we reached the brow of a long descent, which she gave me to understand was her limit.

We shook hands and I bade her good by, and as I trotted off these words fell sweetly upon my ear, "Say, you'll take good care of yourself, won't you, say?"

I took pains not to overtake my camp-men, wishing to be alone; and as I rode for hour after hour the picture of this family stood before me in all its deformity of outline, all its poverty of detail, all its darkness of future, and I believe I thought of it too gravely to enjoy as I might the subtle light of comedy which plays about these hard, repulsive figures.

In conversation I had caught the clew of a better past. Newty's father was a New-Englander, and he spoke of him as a man of intelligence and, as I should judge, of some education. Mrs. Newty's father had been an Arkansas judge, not perhaps the most enlightened of men, but still very far in advance of herself. The conspicuous retrograde seemed to me an example of the most hopeless phase of human life. If, as I suppose, we may all sooner or later give in our adhesion to the Darwinian view of development, does not the same law which permits such splendid scope for the better open up to us also possible gulfs of degradation, and are not these chronic emigrants whose broken-down wagons and weary faces greet you along the dusty highways of the far West melancholy examples of beings who have forever lost the conservatism of home and the power of improvement?

A Story of Evasion

Mark Twain

[SAMUEL L. CLEMENS]

1835-1910

from ROUGHING IT

THE STORY OF THE OLD RAM
(1872)

Every now and then, in these days, the boys used to tell me I ought to get one Jim Blaine to tell me the stirring story of his grandfather's old ram—but they always added that I must not mention the matter unless Jim was drunk at the time—just comfortably and sociably drunk. They kept this up until my curiosity was on the rack to hear the story. I got to haunting Blaine; but it was of no use, the boys always found fault with his condition; he was often moderately but never satisfactorily drunk. I never watched a man's condition with such absorbing interest, such anxious solicitude; I never so pined to see a man uncompromisingly drunk before. At last, one evening I hurried to his cabin, for I learned that this time his situation was such that even the most fastidious could find no fault with it—he was tranquilly, serenely, symmetrically drunk—not a hiccup to mar his voice, not a cloud upon his brain thick enough to obscure his memory. As I entered, he was sitting upon an empty powder-keg, with a clay pipe in one hand and the other raised to command silence. His face was round, red, and very serious; his throat was bare and his hair tumbled; in general appearance and costume he was a stalwart miner of the period. On the pine table stood a candle, and its dim light revealed "the boys" sitting here and there on bunks, candle-boxes, powder-kegs, etc. They said:

"Sh—! Don't speak—he's going to commence."

I found a seat at once, and Blaine said:

"I don't reckon them times will ever come again. There never was a more bullier old ram than what he was. Grandfather fetched him from Illinois—got him of a man by the name of Yates—Bill Yates—maybe you might have heard of him; his father was a deacon—Baptist—and he was a rustler, too; a man had to get up ruther early to get the start of old Thankful Yates; it was him that put the Greens up to j'ining teams with my grandfather when he moved west. Seth Green was prob'ly the pick of the flock; he married a Wilkerson—Sarah Wilkerson—good cretur, she was—one of the likeliest heifers that was ever raised in old Stoddard, everybody said that knowed her. She could heft a bar'l of flour as easy as I can flirt a flapjack. And spin? Don't mention it! Independent? Humph! When Sile Hawkins come a-browsing around her, she let him know that for all his tin he couldn't trot in harness alongside of *her*. You see, Sile Hawkins was—no, it warn't Sile Hawkins, after all—it was a galoot by the name of Filkins—I disremember his first name; but he *was* a stump—come into pra'r-meeting drunk, one night, hooraying for Nixon, becuz he thought it was a primary; and old Deacon Ferguson up and scooted him through the window and he lit on old Miss Jefferson's head, poor old filly. She was a good soul—had a glass eye and used to lend it to old Miss Wagner, that hadn't any, to receive company in; it warn't big enough, and when Miss Wagner warn't noticing, it would get twisted around in the socket, and look up, maybe, or out to one side, and every which way, while t'other one was looking as straight ahead as a spy-glass. Grown people didn't mind it, but it 'most always made the children cry, it was so sort of scary. She tried packing it in raw cotton, but it wouldn't work, somehow—the cotton would get loose and stick out and look so kind of awful that the chil-

dren couldn't stand it no way. She was always dropping it out,
and turning up her old deadlight on the company empty, and
making them oncomfortable, becuz *she* never could tell when
it hopped out, being blind on that side, you see. So somebody
would have to hunch her and say, 'Your game eye has fetched
loose, Miss Wagner, dear'—and then all of them would have
to sit and wait till she jammed it in again—wrong side before,
as a general thing, and green as a bird's egg, being a bashful
cretur and easy sot back before company. But being wrong
side before warn't much difference, anyway, becuz her own
eye was sky-blue and the glass one was yaller on the front side,
so whichever way she turned it it didn't match nohow. Old
Miss Wagner was considerable on the borrow, she was. When
she had a quilting, or Dorcas S'iety at her house she gen'ally
borrowed Miss Higgins's wooden leg to stump around on; it
was considerable shorter than her other pin, but much *she*
minded that. She said she couldn't abide crutches when she
had company, becuz they were so slow; said when she had
company and things had to be done, she wanted to get up and
hump herself. She was as bald as a jug, and so she used to
borrow Miss Jacops's wig—Miss Jacops was the coffin-peddler's
wife—a ratty old buzzard, he was, that used to go roosting
around where people was sick, waiting for 'em; and there that
old rip would sit all day, in the shade, on a coffin that
he judged would fit the can'idate; and if it was a slow customer
and kind of uncertain, he'd fetch his rations and a blanket
along and sleep in the coffin nights. He was anchored out that
way, in frosty weather, for about three weeks, once, before old
Robbins's place, waiting for him; and after that, for as much
as two years, Jacops was not on speaking terms with the old
man, on account of his disapp'inting him. He got one of his
feet froze, and lost money, too, becuz old Robbins took
a favorable turn and got well. The next time Robbins got sick,
Jacops tried to make up with him, and varnished up the same
old coffin and fetched it along; but old Robbins was too many
for him; he had him in, and 'peared to be powerful weak; he
bought the coffin for ten dollars and Jacops was to pay it back

and twenty-five more besides if Robbins didn't like the coffin after he'd tried it. And then Robbins died, and at the funeral he bursted off the lid and riz up in his shroud and told the parson to let up on the performances, becuz he could *not* stand such a coffin as that. You see he had been in a trance once before, when he was young, and he took the chances on another, cal'lating that if he made the trip it was money in his pocket, and if he missed fire he couldn't lose a cent. And, by George, he sued Jacops for the rhino and got judgment; and he set up the coffin in his back parlor and said he 'lowed to take his time, now. It was always an aggravation to Jacops, the way that miserable old thing acted. He moved back to Indiany pretty soon—went to Wellsville—Wellsville was the place the Hogadorns was from. Mighty fine family. Old Maryland stock. Old Squire Hogadorn could carry around more mixed licker, and cuss better than 'most any man I ever see. His second wife was the Widder Billings—she that was Becky Martin; her dam was Deacon Dunlap's first wife. Her oldest child, Maria, married a missionary and died in grace— et up by the savages. They et *him*, too, poor feller—biled him. It warn't the custom, so they say, but they explained to friends of his'n that went down there to bring away his things, that they'd tried missionaries every other way and never could get any good out of 'em—and so it annoyed all his relations to find out that that man's life was fooled away just out of a dern'd experiment, so to speak. But mind you, there ain't anything ever reely lost; everything that people can't understand and don't see the reason of does good if you only hold on and give it a fair shake; Prov'dence don't fire no blank ca'tridges, boys. That there missionary's substance, unbeknowns to himself, actu'ly converted every last one of them heathens that took a chance at the barbecue. Nothing ever fetched them but that. Don't tell *me* it was an accident that he was biled. There ain't no such a thing as an accident. When my Uncle Lem was leaning up agin a scaffolding once, sick, or drunk, or suthin, an Irishman with a hod full of bricks fell on him out of the third story and broke the old man's back in two places.

People said it was an accident. Much accident there was about
that. He didn't know what he was there for, but he was there
for a good object. If he hadn't been there the Irishman would
have been killed. Nobody can ever make me believe anything
different from that. Uncle Lem's dog was there. Why didn't
the Irishman fall on the dog? Becuz the dog would 'a' seen
him a-coming and stood from under. That's the reason the dog
warn't app'inted. A dog can't be depended on to carry out a
special prov'dence. Mark my words, it was a put-up thing. Ac-
cidents don't happen, boys. Uncle Lem's dog—I wish you
could 'a' seen that dog. He was a reg'lar shepherd—or ruther
he was part bull and part shepherd—splendid animal; belonged to Parson Hagar before Uncle Lem got him. Parson
Hagar belonged to the Western Reserve Hagars; prime family;
his mother was a Watson; one of his sisters married a Wheeler;
they settled in Morgan County, and he got nipped by the machinery in a carpet factory and went through in less than a
quarter of a minute; his widder bought the piece of carpet that
had his remains wove in, and people come a hundred mile to
'tend the funeral. There was fourteen yards in the piece. She
wouldn't let them roll him up, but planted him just so—full
length. The church was middling small where they preached
the funeral, and they had to let one end of the coffin stick out
of the window. They didn't bury him—they planted one end,
and let him stand up, same as a monument. And they nailed
a sign on it and put—put on—put on it—sacred to—the
m-e-m-o-r-y—of fourteen y-a-r-d-s—of three-ply—car - - - pet—
containing all that was—m-o-r-t-a-l—of—of—W-i-l-l-i-a-m—
W-h-e—"

Jim Blaine had been growing gradually drowsy and drowsier
—his head nodded, once, twice, three times—dropped peace-
fully upon his breast, and he fell tranquilly asleep. The tears
were running down the boys' cheeks—they were suffocating
with suppressed laughter—and had been from the start,
though I had never noticed it. I perceived that I was "sold."
I learned then that Jim Blaine's peculiarity was that whenever

he reached a certain stage of intoxication, no human power could keep him from setting out, with impressive unction, to tell about a wonderful adventure which he had once had with his grandfather's old ram—and the mention of the ram in the first sentence was as far as any man had ever heard him get, concerning it. He always maundered off, interminably, from one thing to another, till his whisky got the best of him, and he fell asleep. What the thing was that happened to him and his grandfather's old ram is a dark mystery to this day, for nobody has ever yet found out.

Joel Chandler Harris

1848-1908

from UNCLE REMUS, HIS SONGS AND SAYINGS

THE WONDERFUL TAR-BABY STORY
(1880)

"Didn't the fox *never* catch the rabbit, Uncle Remus?" asked the little boy the next evening.

"He come mighty nigh it, honey, sho's you born—Brer Fox did. One day atter Brer Rabbit fool 'im wid dat calamus root, Brer Fox went ter wuk en got 'im some tar, en mix it wid some turkentime, en fix up a contrapshun wat he call a Tar-Baby, en he tuck dish yer Tar-Baby en he sot 'er in de big road, en den he lay off in de bushes fer to see wat de news wuz gwineter be. En he didn't hatter wait long, nudder, kaze bimeby here come Brer Rabbit pacin' down de road—lippity-clippity, clippity-lippity—dez ez sassy ez a jay-bird. Brer Fox, he lay low. Brer Rabbit come prancin' 'long twel he spy de Tar-Baby, en den he fotch up on his behime legs like he wuz 'stonished. De Tar-Baby, she sot dar, she did, en Brer Fox, he lay low.

"'Mawnin'!' sez Brer Rabbit, sezee—'nice wedder dis mawnin',' sezee.

"Tar-Baby ain't sayin' nothin', en Brer Fox, he lay low.

"'How duz yo' sym'tums seem ter segashuate?' sez Brer Rabbit, sezee.

"Brer Fox, he wink his eye slow, en lay low, en de Tar-Baby, she ain't sayin' nothin'.

"'How you come on, den? Is you deaf?' sez Brer Rabbit, sezee. 'Kaze if you is, I kin holler louder,' sezee.

"Tar-Baby stay still, en Brer Fox, he lay low.

"'Youer stuck up, dat's w'at you is,' says Brer Rabbit, sezee, 'en I'm gwineter kyore you, dat's w'at I'm a gwineter do,' sezee.

"Brer Fox, he sorter chuckle in his stummuck, he did, but Tar-Baby ain't sayin' nothin'.

"'I'm gwineter larn you howter talk ter 'specttubble fokes ef hit's de las' ack,' sez Brer Rabbit, sezee. 'Ef you don't take off dat hat en tell me howdy, I'm gwineter bus' you wide open,' sezee.

"Tar-Baby stay still, en Brer Fox, he lay low.

"Brer Rabbit keep on axin' 'im, en de Tar-Baby, she keep on sayin' nothin', twel present'y Brer Rabbit draw back wid his fis', he did, en blip he tuck 'er side er de head. Right dar's whar he broke his merlasses jug. His fis' stuck, en he can't pull loose. De tar hilt 'im. But Tar-Baby, she stay still, en Brer Fox, he lay low.

"'Ef you don't lemme loose, I'll knock you agin,' sez Brer Rabbit, sezee, en wid dat he fotch 'er a wipe wid de udder han', en dat stuck. Tar-Baby, she ain't sayin' nothin', en Brer Fox, he lay low.

"'Tu'n me loose, fo' I kick de natal stuffin' outen you,' sez Brer Rabbit, sezee, but de Tar-Baby, she ain't sayin' nothin'. She des hilt on, en den Brer Rabbit lose de use er his feet in de same way. Brer Fox, he lay low. Den Brer Rabbit squall out dat ef de Tar-Baby don't tu'n 'im loose he butt 'er cranksided. En den he butted, en his head got stuck. Den Brer Fox, he sa'ntered fort', lookin' des ez innercent ez one er yo' mammy's mockin'-birds.

"'Howdy, Brer Rabbit,' sez Brer Fox, sezee. 'You look sorter stuck up dis mawnin',' sezee, en den he rolled on de groun', en laughed en laughed twel he couldn't laugh no mo'. 'I speck you'll take dinner wid me dis time, Brer Rabbit. I done laid in some calamus root, en I ain't gwineter take no skuse,' sez Brer Fox, sezee."

Here Uncle Remus paused, and drew a two-pound yam out of the ashes.

"Did the fox eat the rabbit?" asked the little boy to whom the story had been told.

"Dat's all de fur de tale goes," replied the old man. "He mout, en den agin he moutent. Some say Jedge B'ar come 'long en loosed 'im—some say he didn't. I hear Miss Sally callin'. You better run 'long."

MR. FOX GOES A-HUNTING, BUT
MR. RABBIT BAGS THE GAME
(1880)

"Atter Brer Fox hear 'bout how Brer Rabbit done Brer Wolf," said Uncle Remus, scratching his head with the point of his awl, "he 'low, he did, dat he better not be so brash, en he sorter let Brer Rabbit 'lone. Dey wuz all time seein' one nudder, en 'bunnunce er times Brer Fox could er nab Brer Rabbit, but eve'y time he got de chance, his mine 'ud sorter rezume 'bout Brer Wolf, en he let Brer Rabbit 'lone. Bimeby dey 'gun ter git kinder familious wid wunner nudder like dey useter, en it got so Brer Fox'd call on Brer Rabbit, en dey'd set up en smoke der pipes, dey would, like no ha'sh feelin's 'd ever rested 'twixt um.

"Las', one day Brer Fox come 'long all rig out, en ax Brer Rabbit fer ter go huntin' wid 'im, but Brer Rabbit, he sorter feel lazy, en he tell Brer Fox dat he got some udder fish fer ter fry. Brer Fox feel mighty sorry, he did, but he say he b'leeve he try his han' enny how, en off he put. He wuz gone all day, en he had a monstus streak er luck, Brer Fox did, en he bagged a sight er game. Bimeby, to'rds de shank er de evenin', Brer Rabbit sorter stretch hisse'f, he did, en 'low hit's mos' time fer Brer Fox fer ter git 'long home. Den Brer Rabbit, he went'n mounted a stump fer ter see ef he could year Brer Fox comin'. He ain't bin dar long, twel sho' nuff, yer come Brer Fox thoo de woods, singing like a nigger at a frolic. Brer Rabbit, he lipt down off'n de stump, he did, en lay down in de road en make like he dead. Brer Fox he come 'long, he did, en see Brer Rabbit layin' dar. He tu'n 'im over, he did, en 'zamine 'im, en say, sezee:

" 'Dish yer rabbit dead. He look like he bin dead long time. He dead, but he mighty fat. He de fattes' rabbit w'at I ever see, but he bin dead too long. I feard ter take 'im home,' sezee.

"Brer Rabbit ain't sayin' nuthin'. Brer Fox, he sorter lick his chops, but he went on en lef' Brer Rabbit layin' in de road. Dreckly he wuz outer sight, Brer Rabbit, he jump up, he did, en run roun' thoo de woods en git befo Brer Fox agin. Brer Fox, he come up, en dar lay Brer Rabbit, periently cole en stiff. Brer Fox, he look at Brer Rabbit, en he sorter study. Atter while he onslung his game-bag, en say ter hisse'f, sezee:

" 'Deze yer rabbits gwine ter was'e. I'll des 'bout leave my game yer, en I'll go back'n git dat udder rabbit, en I'll make fokes b'leeve dat I'm ole man Hunter fum Huntsville,' sezee.

"En wid dat he drapt his game en loped back up de road atter de udder rabbit, en w'en he got outer sight, ole Brer Rabbit, he snatch up Brer Fox game en put out fer home. Nex' time he see Brer Fox, he holler out:

" 'What you kill de udder day, Brer Fox?' sezee.

"Den Brer Fox, he sorter koam his flank wid his tongue, en holler back:

" 'I kotch a han'ful er hard sense, Brer Rabbit,' sezee.

"Den ole Brer Rabbit, he laff, he did, en up en 'spon',
sezee:

" 'Ef I'd a know'd you wuz atter dat, Brer Fox, I'd a loant
you some er mine,' sezee."

Mark Twain

1835-1910

HOW TO TELL A STORY
(1895)

*The Humorous Story an American Development.—Its
Difference from Comic and Witty Stories.*

I do not claim that I can tell a story as it ought to be told. I
only claim to know how a story ought to be told, for I have
been almost daily in the company of the most expert story-
tellers for many years.

There are several kinds of stories, but only one difficult
kind—the humorous. I will talk mainly about that one. The
humorous story is American, the comic story is English, the
witty story is French. The humorous story depends for its effect upon the *manner* of the telling; the comic story and the
witty story upon the *matter*.

The humorous story may be spun out to great length, and
may wander around as much as it pleases, and arrive nowhere
in particular; but the comic and witty stories must be brief
and end with a point. The humorous story bubbles gently
along, the others burst.

The humorous story is strictly a work of art—high and delicate art—and only an artist can tell it; but no art is necessary

in telling the comic and the witty story; anybody can do it. The art of telling a humorous story—understand, I mean by word of mouth, not print—was created in America, and has remained at home.

The humorous story is told gravely; the teller does his best to conceal the fact that he even dimly suspects that there is anything funny about it; but the teller of the comic story tells you beforehand that it is one of the funniest things he has ever heard, then tells it with eager delight, and is the first person to laugh when he gets through. And sometimes, if he has had good success, he is so glad and happy that he will repeat the "nub" of it and glance around from face to face, collecting applause, and then repeat it again. It is a pathetic thing to see.

Very often, of course, the rambling and disjointed humorous story finishes with a nub, point, snapper, or whatever you like to call it. Then the listener must be alert, for in many cases the teller will divert attention from that nub by dropping it in a carefully casual and indifferent way, with the pretense that he does not know it is a nub.

Artemus Ward used that trick a good deal; then when the belated audience presently caught the joke he would look up with innocent surprise, as if wondering what they had found to laugh at. Dan Setchell used it before him, Nye and Riley and others use it to-day.

But the teller of the comic story does not slur the nub; he shouts it at you—every time. And when he prints it, in England, France, Germany, and Italy, he italicizes it, puts some whooping exclamation-points after it, and sometimes explains it in a parenthesis. All of which is very depressing, and makes one want to renounce joking and lead a better life.

Let me set down an instance of the comic method, using an anecdote which has been popular all over the world for twelve or fifteen hundred years. The teller tells it in this way:

The Wounded Soldier

In the course of a certain battle a soldier whose leg had been shot off appealed to another soldier who was hurrying by to carry him to the rear, informing him at the same time of the loss which he had sustained; whereupon the generous son of Mars, shouldering the unfortunate, proceeded to carry out his desire. The bullets and cannon-balls were flying in all directions, and presently one of the latter took the wounded man's head off—without, however, his deliverer being aware of it. In no long time he was hailed by an officer, who said:

"Where are you going with that carcass?"

"To the rear, sir—he's lost his leg!"

"His leg, forsooth?" responded the astonished officer; "you mean his head, you booby."

Whereupon the soldier dispossessed himself of his burden, and stood looking down upon it in great perplexity. At length he said:

"It is true, sir, just as you have said." Then after a pause he added, "*But he* TOLD *me* IT WAS HIS LEG! ! ! ! !"

Here the narrator bursts into explosion after explosion of thunderous horse-laughter, repeating that nub from time to time through his gaspings and shriekings and suffocatings.

It takes only a minute and a half to tell that in its comic-story form; and isn't worth the telling, after all. Put into the humorous-story form it takes ten minutes, and is about the funniest thing I have ever listened to—as James Whitcomb Riley tells it.

He tells it in the character of a dull-witted old farmer who has just heard it for the first time, thinks it is unspeakably funny, and is trying to repeat it to a neighbor. But he can't remember it; so he gets all mixed up and wanders helplessly round and round, putting in tedious details that don't belong in the tale and only retard it; taking them out conscientiously and putting in others that are just as useless; making minor mistakes now and then and stopping to correct them and explain how he came to make them; remembering things which he forgot to put in in their proper place and going back to put them in there; stopping his narrative a good while in order to try to recall the name of the soldier that was hurt, and finally remembering that the soldier's name was not mentioned, and remarking placidly that the name is of no real importance, anyway—better, of course, if one knew it, but not essential, after all—and so on, and so on, and so on.

The teller is innocent and happy and pleased with himself, and has to stop every little while to hold himself in and keep from laughing outright; and does hold in, but his body quakes in a jelly-like way with interior chuckles; and at the end of the ten minutes the audience have laughed until they are ex hausted, and the tears are running down their faces.

The simplicity and innocence and sincerity and unconscious-ness of the old farmer are perfectly simulated, and the result is a performance which is thoroughly charming and delicious. This is art—and fine and beautiful, and only a master can compass it; but a machine could tell the other story.

To string incongruities and absurdities together in a wan-dering and sometimes purposeless way, and seem innocently unaware that they are absurdities, is the basis of the American art, if my position is correct. Another feature is the slurring of the point. A third is the dropping of a studied remark appar-ently without knowing it, as if one were thinking aloud. The fourth and last is the pause.

Artemus Ward dealt in numbers three and four a good deal. He would begin to tell with great animation something which he seemed to think was wonderful; then lose confi-dence, and after an apparently absent-minded pause add an incongruous remark in a soliloquizing way; and that was the remark intended to explode the mine—and it did.

For instance, he would say eagerly, excitedly, "I once knew a man in New Zealand who hadn't a tooth in his head"—here his animation would die out; a silent, reflective pause would follow, then he would say dreamily, and as if to himself, "and yet that man could beat a drum better than any man I ever saw."

The pause is an exceedingly important feature in any kind of story, and a frequently recurring feature, too. It is a dainty thing, and delicate, and also uncertain and treacherous; for it must be exactly the right length—no more and no less—or it fails of its purpose and makes trouble. If the pause is too short the impressive point is passed, and the audience have had time to divine that a surprise is intended—and then you can't surprise them, of course.

On the platform I used to tell a negro ghost story that had a pause in front of the snapper on the end, and that pause was the most important thing in the whole story. If I got it the right length precisely, I could spring the finishing ejaculation with effect enough to make some impressible girl deliver a startled little yelp and jump out of her seat—and that was what I was after. This story was called "The Golden Arm," and was told in this fashion. You can practise with it yourself —and mind you look out for the pause and get it right.

The Golden Arm

Once 'pon a time dey wuz a monsus mean man, en he live 'way out in de prairie all 'lone by hisself, 'cep'n he had a wife. En bimeby she died, en he tuck en toted her way out dah in de prairie en buried her. Well, she had a golden arm—all solid gold, fum de shoulder down. He wuz pow'ful mean—pow'ful; en dat night he couldn't sleep, caze he want dat golden arm so bad.

When it come midnight, he couldn't stan' it no mo'; so he git up, he did, en tuck his lantern en shoved out thoo de storm en dug her up en got de golden arm; en he bent his head down 'gin de win', en plowed en plowed en plowed thoo de snow. Den all on a sudden he stop (make a considerable pause here, and look startled, and take a listening attitude) en say: "My lan', what's dat!"

En he listen—en listen—en de win' say (set your teeth together and imitate the wailing and wheezing singsong of the wind), "Bzzz-z-zzz"—en den, way back yonder whah de grave is, he hear a *voice!*—he hear a voice all mix' up in de win'— can't hardly tell 'em 'part— "Bzzz-zzz—W-h-o—g-o-t—m-y —g-o-l-d-e-n *arm?*—zzz—zzz—W-h-o g-o-t m-y g-o-l-d-e-n *arm?*" (You must begin to shiver violently now.)

En he begin to shiver en shake, en say, "Oh, my! *Oh*, my

lan'!" en de win' blow de lantern out, en de snow en sleet blow in his face en mos' choke him, en he start a-plowin' knee-deep towards home mos' dead, he so sk'yerd—en pooty soon he hear de voice agin, en (pause) it 'us comin' *after* him! "Bzzz—zzz—zzz—W-h-o—g-o-t—m-y—g-o-l-d-e-n—*arm?*"

When he git to de pasture he hear it agin—closter now, en *a-comin'!*—a-comin' back dah in de dark en de storm—(repeat the wind and the voice). When he git to de house he rush up-stairs en jump in de bed en kiver up, head and years, en lay dah shiverin' en shakin'—en den way out dah he hear it *agin!*—en a-*comin'*! En bimeby he hear (pause—awed, listening attitude)—pat—pat—pat—*hit's a-comin' up-stairs!* Den he hear de latch, en he *know* it's in de room!

Den pooty soon he know it's a-*stannin' by de bed!* (Pause.) Den—he know it's a-*bendin' down over him*—en he cain't skasely git his breath! Den—den—he seem to feel someth'n *c-o-l-d*, right down 'most agin his head! (Pause.)

Den de voice say, *right at his year*— "W-h-o—g-o-t—m-y—g-o-l-d-e-n *arm?*" (You must wail it out very plaintively and accusingly; then you stare steadily and impressively into the face of the farthest-gone auditor—a girl, preferably—and let that awe-inspiring pause begin to build itself in the deep hush. When it has reached exactly the right length, jump suddenly at that girl and yell, "*You've* got it!")

If you've got the *pause* right, she'll fetch a dear little yelp and spring right out of her shoes. But you *must* get the pause right; and you will find it the most troublesome and aggravating and uncertain thing you ever undertook.)

II Local Color

A summary view of the local color movement may be obtained from Arthur Hobson Quinn, *American Fiction: An Historical and Critical Survey*, 1936; Carl Van Doren, *The American Novel, 1789-1939*, 1940; Fred Lewis Pattee, *The Development of the American Short Story*, 1923; and Spiller, *et al.*, *Literary History of the United States*, 1948, II, 843-877. A convenient anthology of representative stories from all the regions is Harry R. Warfel and G. Harrison Orians, *American Local-Color Stories*, 1941. An excellent discussion of the California school is Franklin Walker, *San Francisco's Literary Frontier*, 1939; still the best treatment of Bret Harte is George R. Stewart, *Bret Harte: Argonaut and Exile*, 1931. On the Indiana school, see Meredith Nicholson, *The Hoosiers*, 1900. The Chicago school is dealt with in Harry Hansen, *Midwest Portraits*, 1923. For the extensive and sometimes aggressively regional literature of the South and its several sections, see Edwin A. Alderman, *et al.*, *Library of Southern Literature*, 17 vols., 1907-1923, which includes both an author bibliography and a biographical dictionary of authors; Montrose J. Moses, *The Literature of the South*, 1910; and Carl Holliday, *A History of Southern Literature*, 1906. The regional bibliographies in Spiller, *et al.*, *Literary History of the United States*, III, 304-325, are indispensable.

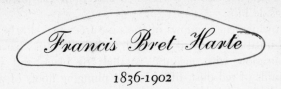

Francis Bret Harte

1836-1902

from THE LUCK OF ROARING CAMP
AND OTHER SKETCHES

THE IDYLL OF RED GULCH
(1870)

Sandy was very drunk. He was lying under an azalea bush in
pretty much the same attitude in which he had fallen some
hours before. How long he had been lying there he could not
tell, and didn't care; how long he should lie there was a matter
equally indefinite and unconsidered. A tranquil philosophy,
born of his physical condition, suffused and saturated his moral
being.

The spectacle of a drunken man, and of this drunken man
in particular, was not, I grieve to say, of sufficient novelty in
Red Gulch to attract attention. Earlier in the day some local
satirist had erected a temporary tombstone at Sandy's head,
bearing the inscription, "Effects of McCorkle's whiskey—kills
at forty rods," with a hand pointing to McCorkle's saloon. But
this, I imagine, was, like most local satire, personal; and was a
reflection upon the unfairness of the process rather than a
commentary upon the impropriety of the result. With this
facetious exception, Sandy had been undisturbed.

A wandering mule, released from his pack, had cropped the
scant herbage beside him and sniffed curiously at the prostrate
man; a vagabond dog, with that deep sympathy which the
species have for drunken men, had licked his dusty boots and
curled himself up at his feet, and lay there, blinking one eye
in the sunlight, with a simulation of dissipation that was in-

genious and dog-like in its implied flattery of the unconscious man beside him.

Meanwhile, the shadows of the pine trees had slowly swung around until they crossed the road, and their trunks barred the open meadow with gigantic parallels of black and yellow. Little puffs of red dust, lifted by the plunging hoofs of passing teams, dispersed in a grimy shower upon the recumbent man. The sun sank lower and lower, and still Sandy stirred not. And then the repose of this philosopher was disturbed, as other philosophers have been, by the intrusion of an unphilosophical sex.

"Miss Mary," as she was known to the little flock that she had just dismissed from the log schoolhouse beyond the pines, was taking her afternoon walk. Observing an unusually fine cluster of blossoms on the azalea bush opposite, she crossed the road to pluck it, picking her way through the red dust, not without certain fierce little shivers of disgust and some feline circumlocution. And then she came suddenly upon Sandy!

Of course she uttered the little staccato cry of her sex. But when she had paid that tribute to her physical weakness she became overbold and halted for a moment—at least six feet from this prostrate monster—with her white skirts gathered in her hand, ready for flight. With one little foot she then overturned the satirical headboard, and muttered "Beasts!"—an epithet which probably, at the moment, conveniently classified in her mind the entire male population of Red Gulch.

For Miss Mary, being possessed of certain rigid notions of her own, had not perhaps properly appreciated the demonstrative gallantry for which the Californian had been so justly celebrated by his brother Californians, and had, as a newcomer, perhaps fairly earned the reputation of being "stuck up."

As she stood there she noticed also that the slant sunbeams were heating Sandy's head to what she judged to be an unhealthy temperature and that his hat was lying uselessly at his side. To pick it up and to place it over his face was a work requiring some courage, particularly as his eyes were open.

Yet she did it and made good her retreat. But she was somewhat concerned, on looking back, to see that the hat was removed and that Sandy was sitting up and saying something.

The truth was that in the calm depths of Sandy's mind he was satisfied that the rays of the sun were beneficial and healthful; that from childhood he had objected to lying down in a hat; that no people but condemned fools, past redemption, ever wore hats; and that his right to dispense with them when he pleased was inalienable. This was the statement of his inner consciousness. Unfortunately, its outward expression was vague, being limited to a repetition of the following formula: "Su'shine all ri'! Wasser maär, eh? Wass up, su'shine?"

Miss Mary stopped, and, taking fresh courage from her vantage of distance, asked him if there was anything that he wanted.

"Wass up? Wasser maär?" continued Sandy, in a very high key.

"Get up, you horrid man!" said Miss Mary, now thoroughly incensed; "get up and go home."

Sandy staggered to his feet. He was six feet high, and Miss Mary trembled. He started forward a few paces and then stopped.

"Wass I go home for?" he suddenly asked, with great gravity.

"Go and take a bath," replied Miss Mary, eyeing his grimy person with great disfavor.

To her infinite dismay, Sandy suddenly pulled off his coat and vest, threw them on the ground, kicked off his boots, and, plunging wildly forward, darted headlong over the hill in the direction of the river.

"Goodness heavens! the man will be drowned!" said Miss Mary; and then, with feminine inconsistency, she ran back to the schoolhouse and locked herself in.

That night, while seated at supper with her hostess, the blacksmith's wife, it came to Miss Mary to ask, demurely, if her husband ever got drunk. "Abner," responded Mrs. Stidger reflectively—"let's see! Abner hasn't been tight since last 'lection."

Miss Mary would have liked to ask if he preferred lying in
the sun on these occasions and if a cold bath would have hurt
him; but this would have involved an explanation which she
did not then care to give. So she contented herself with opening her gray eyes widely at the red-cheeked Mrs. Stidger—a
fine specimen of Southwestern efflorescence—and then dismissed the subject altogether.

The next day she wrote to her dearest friend in Boston: "I
think I find the intoxicated portion of the community the
least objectionable. I refer, my dear, to the men, of course. I
do not know anything that could make the women tolerable."

In less than a week Miss Mary had forgotten this episode
except that her afternoon walks took thereafter, almost unconsciously, another direction. She noticed, however, that
every morning a fresh cluster of azalea blossoms appeared
among the flowers on her desk. This was not strange, as her
little flock were aware of her fondness for flowers, and invariably kept her desk bright with anemones, syringas, and
lupines; but, on questioning them, they one and all professed
ignorance of the azaleas.

A few days later, Master Johnny Stidger, whose desk was
nearest to the window, was suddenly taken with spasms of
apparently gratuitous laughter that threatened the discipline
of the school. All that Miss Mary could get from him was that
someone had been "looking in the winder." Irate and indig-
nant, she sallied from her hive to do battle with the intruder.
As she turned the corner of the schoolhouse, she came plump
upon the quondam drunkard, now perfectly sober, and inex-
pressibly sheepish and guilty-looking.

These facts Miss Mary was not slow to take a feminine advantage of, in her present humor. But it was somewhat con-
fusing to observe also that the beast, despite some faint signs
of past dissipation, was amiable-looking—in fact, a kind of
blond Samson, whose corn-colored silken beard apparently had
never yet known the touch of barber's razor or Delilah's shears.
So that the cutting speech which quivered on her ready tongue
died upon her lips, and she contented herself with receiving

his stammering apology with supercilious eyelids and the gathered skirts of uncontamination.

When she re-entered the schoolroom, her eyes fell upon the azaleas with a new sense of revelation; and then she laughed, and the little people all laughed, and they were all unconsciously very happy.

It was a hot day, and not long after this, that two short-legged boys came to grief on the threshold of the school with a pail of water which they had laboriously brought from the spring, and that Miss Mary compassionately seized the pail and started for the spring herself. At the foot of the hill a shadow crossed her path and a blue-shirted arm dexterously but gently relieved her of her burden.

Miss Mary was both embarrassed and angry. "If you carried more of that for yourself," she said spitefully to the blue arm, without deigning to raise her lashes to its owner, "you'd do better."

In the submissive silence that followed, she regretted the speech and thanked him so sweetly at the door that he stumbled. Which caused the children to laugh again—a laugh in which Miss Mary joined, until the color came faintly into her pale cheek. The next day a barrel was mysteriously placed beside the door and as mysteriously filled with fresh spring water every morning.

Nor was this superior young person without other quiet attentions. "Profane Bill," driver of the Slumgullion Stage, widely known in the newspapers for his "gallantry" in invariably offering the box-seat to the fair sex, had excepted Miss Mary from this attention, on the ground that he had a habit of "cussin' on up grades," and gave her half the coach to herself. Jack Hamlin, a gambler, having once silently ridden with her in the same coach, afterward threw a decanter at the head of a confederate for mentioning her name in a bar-room. The overdressed mother of a pupil whose paternity was doubtful had often lingered near this astute Vestal's temple, never daring to enter its sacred precincts, but content to worship the priestess from afar.

With such unconscious intervals the monotonous procession of blue skies, glittering sunshine, brief twilights, and star-lit nights passed over Red Gulch. Miss Mary grew fond of walking in the sedate and proper woods. Perhaps she believed, with Mrs. Stidger, that the balsamic odors of the firs "did her chest good," for certainly her slight cough was less frequent and her step was firmer; perhaps she had learned the unending lesson which the patient pines are never weary of repeating to heedful or listless ears. And so one day she planned a picnic on Buckeye Hill and took the children with her.

Away from the dusty road, the straggling shanties, the yellow ditches, the clamor of restless engines, the cheap finery of shop-windows, the deeper glitter of paint and colored glass, and the thin veneering which barbarism takes upon itself in such localities—what infinite relief was theirs! The last heap of ragged rock and clay passed, the last unsightly chasm crossed—how the waiting woods opened their long files to receive them!

How the children—perhaps because they had not yet grown quite away from the breast of the bounteous Mother—threw themselves face downward on her brown bosom with uncouth caresses, filling the air with their laughter; and how Miss Mary herself—felinely fastidious and entrenched as she was in the purity of spotless skirts, collar, and cuffs—forgot all, and ran like a crested quail at the head of her brood, until, romping, laughing, and panting, with a loosened braid of brown hair, a hat hanging by a knotted ribbon from her throat, she came suddenly and violently, in the heart of the forest, upon the luckless Sandy!

The explanations, apologies, and not overwise conversation that ensued need not be indicated here. It would seem, however, that Miss Mary had already established some acquaintance with this ex-drunkard. Enough that he was soon accepted as one of the party; that the children, with that quick intelligence which Providence gives the helpless, recognized a friend, and played with his blond beard and long silken mustache, and took other liberties—as the helpless are apt to do. And when he had built a fire against a tree and had shown them other mysteries of woodcraft, their admiration knew no bounds.

At the close of two such foolish, idle, happy hours he found himself lying at the feet of the schoolmistress, gazing dreamily in her face as she sat upon the sloping hillside weaving wreaths of laurel and syringa, in very much the same attitude as he had lain when first they met. Nor was the similitude greatly forced. The weakness of an easy, sensuous nature, that had found a dreamy exaltation in liquor, it is to be feared was now finding an equal intoxication in love.

I think that Sandy was dimly conscious of this himself. I know that he longed to be doing something—slaying a grizzly, scalping a savage, or sacrificing himself in some way for the sake of this sallow-faced, gray-eyed schoolmistress. As I should like to present him in an heroic attitude, I stay my hand with great difficulty at this moment, being only withheld from introducing such an episode by a strong conviction that it does not usually occur at such times. And I trust that my fairest reader, who remembers that, in a real crisis, it is always some uninteresting stranger or unromantic policeman, and not Adolphus, who rescues, will forgive the omission.

So they sat there undisturbed—the woodpeckers chattering overhead and the voices of the children coming pleasantly from the hollow below. What they said matters little. What they thought—which might have been interesting—did not transpire. The woodpeckers only learned how Miss Mary was an orphan; how she left her uncle's house to come to California for the sake of health and independence; how Sandy was an orphan too; how he came to California for excitement; how he had lived a wild life, and how he was trying to reform; and other details, which, from a woodpecker's viewpoint, undoubtedly must have seemed stupid and a waste of time.

But even in such trifles was the afternoon spent; and when the children were again gathered, and Sandy, with a delicacy which the schoolmistress well understood, took leave of them quietly at the outskirts of the settlement, it had seemed the shortest day of her weary life.

As the long, dry summer withered to its roots, the school term of Red Gulch—to use a local euphuism—"dried up" also. In another day Miss Mary would be free, and for a season, at least, Red Gulch would know her no more. She was seated alone in the schoolhouse, her cheek resting on her hand, her eyes half-closed in one of those day-dreams in which Miss Mary, I fear, to the danger of school discipline, was lately in the habit of indulging. Her lap was full of mosses, ferns, and other woodland memories.

She was so preoccupied with these and her own thoughts that a gentle tapping at the door passed unheard or translated itself into a remembrance of far-off woodpeckers. When at last it asserted itself more distinctly, she started up with a flushed cheek and opened the door. On the threshold stood a woman, the self-assertion and audacity of whose dress were in singular contrast to her timid, irresolute bearing.

Miss Mary recognized at a glance the dubious mother of her anonymous pupil. Perhaps she was disappointed, perhaps she was only fastidious; but as she coldly invited her to enter, she half unconsciously settled her white cuffs and collar and gathered closer her own chaste skirts. It was perhaps for this reason that the embarrassed stranger, after a moment's hesitation, left her gorgeous parasol open and sticking in the dust beside the door, and then sat down at the farther end of a long bench. Her voice was husky as she began:

"I heerd tell that you were goin' down to the Bay tomorrow, and I couldn't let you go until I came to thank you for your kindness to my Tommy."

Tommy, Miss Mary said, was a good boy, and deserved more than the poor attention she could give him.

"Thank ye, miss; thank ye!" cried the stranger, brightening even through the color which Red Gulch knew facetiously as her "war paint," and striving, in her embarrassment, to drag the long bench nearer the schoolmistress. "I thank ye, miss, for that; and if I am his mother, thar ain't a sweeter, dearer, better boy lives than him. And if I ain't much as says it, thar ain't a sweeter, dearer, angeler teacher lives than he's got."

Miss Mary, sitting primly behind her desk, with a ruler over her shoulder, opened her gray eyes widely at this, but said nothing.

"It ain't for you to be complimented by the like of me, I know," she went on hurriedly. "It ain't for me to be comin' here, in broad day, to do it, either; but I come to ask a favor —not for me, miss—not for me, but for the darling boy."

Encouraged by a look in the young schoolmistress's eye, and putting her lilac-gloved hands together, the fingers downward, between her knees, she went on, in a low voice:

"You see, miss, there's no one the boy has any claim on but me, and I ain't the proper person to bring him up. I thought some, last year, of sending him away to Frisco to school, but when they talked of bringing a schoolma'am here, I waited till I saw you, and then I knew it was all right, and I could keep my boy a little longer. And, oh! miss, he loves you so much; and if you could hear him talk about you in his pretty way, and if he could ask you what I ask you now, you couldn't refuse him.

"It is natural," she went on rapidly, in a voice that trembled strangely between pride and humility—"it's natural that he should take to you, miss, for his father, when I first knew him, was a gentleman—and the boy must forget me, sooner or later—and so I ain't a-goin' to cry about that. For I come to ask you to take my Tommy—God bless him for the bestest, sweetest boy that lives—to—to—take him with you."

She had risen and caught the young girl's hand in her own and had fallen on her knees beside her.

"I've money plenty, and it's all yours and his. Put him in some good school, where you can go and see him and help him to—to—to forget his mother. Do with him what you like. The worst you can do will be kindness to what he will learn with me. Only take him out of this wicked life, this cruel place, this home of shame and sorrow. You will! I know you will—won't you? You will—you must not, you cannot say no! You will make him as pure, as gentle as yourself; and when he has grown up, you will tell him his father's name—the name that hasn't passed my lips for years—the name of Alexander Morton, whom they call here Sandy! Miss Mary!—do not take your hand away! Miss Mary, speak to me! You will take my boy? Do not put your face from me. I know it ought not to look on such as me. Miss Mary!—my God, be merciful—she is leaving me!"

Miss Mary had risen, and, in the gathering twilight, had felt her way to the open window. She stood there, leaning against the casement, her eyes fixed on the last rosy tints that were fading from the western sky. There was still some of its light on her pure young forehead, on her white collar, on her clasped white hands, but all fading slowly away. The suppliant had dragged herself, still on her knees, beside her.

"I know it takes time to consider. I will wait here all night; but I cannot go until you speak. Do not deny me now. You will!—I see it in your sweet face—such a face as I have seen in my dreams. I see it in your eyes, Miss Mary!—you will take my boy!"

The last red beam crept higher, suffused Miss Mary's eyes with something of its glory, flickered, and faded, and went out. The sun had set on Red Gulch. In the twilight and silence Miss Mary's voice sounded pleasantly.

The happy mother raised the hem of Miss Mary's skirts to her lips. She would have buried her hot face in its virgin folds, but she dared not. She rose to her feet.

"Does—this man—know of your intention?" asked Miss Mary suddenly.

"No, nor cares. He has never even seen the child to know it."

"Go to him at once—tonight—now! Tell him what you have done. Tell him I have taken his child, and tell him—he must never see—see—the child again. Wherever it may be, he must not come; wherever I may take it, he must not follow! There, go now, please—I'm weary, and—have much yet to do!"

They walked together to the door. On the threshold the woman turned.

"Good-night!"

She could have fallen at Miss Mary's feet. But at the same moment the young girl reached out her arms, caught the sinful woman to her own pure breast for one brief moment, and then closed and locked the door.

It was with a sudden sense of great responsibility that Profane Bill took the reins of the Slumgullion Stage the next morning, for the schoolmistress was one of his passengers. As he entered the highroad, in obedience to a pleasant voice from the "inside," he suddenly reined up his horses and respectfully waited, as Tommy hopped out at the command of Miss Mary.

"Not that bush, Tommy—the next."

Tommy whipped out his new pocket knife, and cutting a branch from a tall azalea bush, returned with it to Miss Mary.

"All right now?"

"All right!"

And the stage door closed on the Idyll of Red Gulch.

Mary E. Wilkins Freeman

1852-1930

from A NEW ENGLAND NUN AND OTHER STORIES

A VILLAGE SINGER

(1891)

The trees were in full leaf, a heavy south wind was blowing, and there was a loud murmur among the new leaves. The people noticed it, for it was the first time that year that the trees had so murmured in the wind. The spring had come with a rush during the last few days.

The murmur of the trees sounded loud in the village church, where the people sat waiting for the service to begin. The windows were open; it was a very warm Sunday for May.

The church was already filled with this soft sylvan music— the tender harmony of the leaves and the south wind, and the sweet, desultory whistles of birds—when the choir arose and began to sing.

In the centre of the row of women singers stood Alma Way. All the people stared at her, and turned their ears critically. She was the new leading soprano. Candace Whitcomb, the old one, who had sung in the choir for forty years, had lately been given her dismissal. The audience considered that her voice had grown too cracked and uncertain on the upper notes. There had been much complaint, and after long deliberation the church-officers had made known their decision as mildly as possible to the old singer. She had sung for the last time the Sunday before, and Alma Way had been engaged to take her place. With the exception of the organist, the leading soprano was the only paid musician in the large choir. The salary was very modest, still the village people considered it large for a young woman. Alma was from the adjoining village of East Derby; she had quite a local reputation as a singer.

Now she fixed her large solemn blue eyes; her long, delicate face, which had been pretty, turned paler; the blue flowers on her bonnet trembled; her little thin gloved hands, clutching the singing-book, shook perceptibly; but she sang out bravely. That most formidable mountain-height of the world, self-distrust and timidity, arose before her, but her nerves were braced for its ascent. In the midst of the hymn she had a solo; her voice rang out piercingly sweet; the people nodded admiringly at each other; but suddenly there was a stir; all the faces turned toward the windows on the south side of the church. Above the din of the wind and the birds, above Alma Way's sweetly straining tones, arose another female voice, singing another hymn to another tune.

"It's her," the women whispered to each other; they were half aghast, half smiling.

Candace Whitcomb's cottage stood close to the south side of the church. She was playing on her parlor organ, and singing, to drown out the voice of her rival.

Alma caught her breath; she almost stopped; the hymn-book waved like a fan; then she went on. But the long husky drone of the parlor organ and the shrill clamor of the other voice seemed louder than anything else.

When the hymn was finished, Alma sat down. She felt faint; the woman next her slipped a peppermint into her hand. "It ain't worth minding," she whispered, vigorously. Alma tried to smile; down in the audience a young man was watching her with a kind of fierce pity.

In the last hymn Alma had another solo. Again the parlor organ droned above the carefully delicate accompaniment of the church organ, and again Candace Whitcomb's voice clamored forth in another tune.

After the benediction, the other singers pressed around Alma. She did not say much in return for their expressions of indignation and sympathy. She wiped her eyes furtively once or twice, and tried to smile. William Emmons, the choir leader, elderly, stout, and smooth-faced, stood over her, and raised his voice. He was the old musical dignitary of the village, the leader of the choral club and the singing-schools. "A most outrageous proceeding," he said. People had coupled his name with Candace Whitcomb's. The old bachelor tenor and old maiden soprano had been wont to walk together to her home next door after the Saturday night rehearsals, and they had sung duets to the parlor organ. People had watched sharply her old face, on which the blushes of youth sat pitifully, when William Emmons entered the singing-seats. They wondered if he would ever ask her to marry him.

And now he said further to Alma Way that Candace Whitcomb's voice had failed utterly of late, that she sang shockingly, and ought to have had sense enough to know it.

When Alma went down into the audience-room, in the midst of the chattering singers, who seemed to have descended, like birds, from song flights to chirps, the minister approached her. He had been waiting to speak to her. He was a steady-faced, fleshy old man, who had preached from that one pulpit over forty years. He told Alma, in his slow way, how much he regretted the annoyance to which she had been subjected, and intimated that he would endeavor to prevent a recurrence of it. "Miss Whitcomb—must be—reasoned with," said he; he had a slight hesitation of speech, not an impediment. It was as if his thoughts did not slide readily into his words, although both were present. He walked down the aisle with Alma, and bade her good-morning when he saw Wilson Ford waiting for her in the doorway. Everybody knew that Wilson Ford and Alma were lovers; they had been for the last ten years.

Alma colored softly, and made a little imperceptible motion with her head; her silk dress and the lace on her mantle fluttered, but she did not speak. Neither did Wilson, although they had not met before that day. They did not look at each other's faces—they seemed to see each other without that—and they walked along side by side.

They reached the gate before Candace Whitcomb's little house. Wilson looked past the front yard, full of pink and white spikes on flowering bushes, at the lace-curtained windows; a thin white profile, stiffly inclined, apparently over a book, was visible at one of them. Wilson gave his head a shake. He was a stout man, with features so strong that they overcame his flesh. "I'm going up home with you, Alma," said he; "and then—I'm just coming back, to give Aunt Candace one blowing up."

"Oh, don't, Wilson."

"Yes, I shall. If you want to stand this kind of a thing you may; I sha'n't."

"There's no need of your talking to her. Mr. Pollard's going to."

"Did he say he was?"

"Yes. I think he's going in before the afternoon meeting, from what he said."

"Well, there's one thing about it, if she does that thing again this afternoon, I'll go in there and break that old organ up into kindling-wood." Wilson set his mouth hard, and shook his head again.

Alma gave little side glances up at him, her tone was deprecatory, but her face was full of soft smiles. "I suppose she does feel dreadfully about it," said she. "I can't help feeling kind of guilty, taking her place."

"I don't see how you're to blame. It's outrageous, her acting so."

"The choir gave her a photograph album last week, didn't they?"

"Yes. They went there last Thursday night, and gave her an album and a surprise-party. She ought to behave herself."

"Well, she's sung there so long, I suppose it must be dreadful hard for her to give it up."

Other people going home from church were very near Wilson and Alma. She spoke softly that they might not hear; he did not lower her voice in the least. Presently Alma stopped before a gate.

"What are you stopping here for?" asked Wilson.

"Minnie Lansing wanted me to come and stay with her this noon."

"You're going home with me."

"I'm afraid I'll put your mother out."

"Put mother out! I told her you were coming, this morning. She's got all ready for you. Come along; don't stand here."

He did not tell Alma of the pugnacious spirit with which his mother had received the announcement of her coming, and how she had stayed at home to prepare the dinner, and make a parade of her hard work and her injury.

Wilson's mother was the reason why he did not marry Alma. He would not take his wife home to live with her, and was unable to support separate establishments. Alma was willing enough to be married and put up with Wilson's mother, but she did not complain of his decision. Her delicate blond features grew sharper, and her blue eyes more hollow. She had had a certain fine prettiness, but now she was losing it, and beginning to look old, and there was a prim, angular, old maiden carriage about her narrow shoulders.

Wilson never noticed it, and never thought of Alma as not possessed of eternal youth, or capable of losing or regretting it.

"Come along, Alma," said he; and she followed meekly after him down the street.

Soon after they passed Candace Whitcomb's house, the minister went up the front walk and rang the bell. The pale profile at the window had never stirred as he opened the gate and came up the walk. However, the door was promptly opened, in response to his ring. "Good-morning, Miss Whitcomb," said the minister.

"Good-morning." Candace gave a sweeping toss of her head as she spoke. There was a fierce upward curl to her thin nostrils and her lips, as if she scented an adversary. Her black eyes had two tiny cold sparks of fury in them, like an enraged bird's. She did not ask the minister to enter, but he stepped lumberingly into the entry, and she retreated rather than led the way into her little parlor. He settled into the great rocking-chair and wiped his face. Candace sat down again in her old place by the window. She was a tall woman, but very slender and full of pliable motions, like a blade of grass.

"It's a—very pleasant day," said the minister.

Candace made no reply. She sat still, with her head drooping. The wind stirred the looped lace-curtains; a tall rose-tree outside the window waved; soft shadows floated through the room. Candace's parlor organ stood in front of an open window that faced the church; on the corner was a pitcher with a bunch of white lilacs. The whole room was scented with them. Presently the minister looked over at them and sniffed pleasantly.

"You have—some beautiful—lilacs there."

Candace did not speak. Every line of her slender figure looked flexible, but it was a flexibility more resistant than rigor.

The minister looked at her. He filled up the great rocking-chair; his arms in his shiny black coat-sleeves rested squarely and comfortably upon the hair-cloth arms of the chair.

"Well, Miss Whitcomb, I suppose I—may as well come to—the point. There was—a little—matter I wished to speak to you about. I don't suppose you were—at least I can't suppose you were—aware of it, but—this morning, during the singing by the choir, you played and—sung a little too—loud. That is, with—the windows open. It—disturbed us—a little. I hope you won't feel hurt—my dear Miss Candace, but I knew you would rather I would speak of it, for I knew—you would be more disturbed than anybody else at the idea of such a thing."

Candace did not raise her eyes; she looked as if his words might sway her through the window. "I ain't disturbed at it," said she. "I did it on purpose; I meant to."

The minister looked at her.

"You needn't look at me. I know jest what I'm about. I sung the way I did on purpose, an' I'm goin' to do it again, an' I'd like to see you stop me. I guess I've got a right to set down to my own organ, an' sing a psalm tune on a Sabbath day, 'f I want to; an' there ain't no amount of talkin' an' pala-verin' a-goin' to stop me. See there!" Candace swung aside her skirts a little. "Look at that!"

The minister looked. Candace's feet were resting on a large red-plush photograph album.

"Makes a nice footstool, don't it?" said she.

The minister looked at the album, then at her; there was a slowly gathering alarm in his face; he began to think she was losing her reason.

Candace had her eyes full upon him now, and her head up. She laughed, and her laugh was almost a snarl. "Yes; I thought it would make a beautiful footstool," said she. "I've been wantin' one for some time." Her tone was full of vicious irony.

"Why, miss—" began the minister; but she interrupted him:

"I know what you're a-goin' to say, Mr. Pollard, an' now I'm goin' to have my say; I'm a-goin' to speak. I want to know what you think of folks that pretend to be Christians treatin' anybody the way they've treated me? Here I've sung in those singin'-seats forty year. I ain't never missed a Sunday, except when I've been sick, an' I've gone an' sung a good many times when I'd better been in bed, an' now I'm turned out without a word of warnin'. My voice is jest as good as ever 'twas; there can't anybody say it ain't. It wa'n't ever quite so high-pitched as that Way girl's, mebbe; but she flats the whole durin' time. My voice is as good an' high to-day as it was twenty year ago; an' if it wa'n't, I'd like to know where the Christianity comes in. I'd like to know if it wouldn't be more to the credit of folks in a church to keep an old singer an' an old minister, if they didn't sing an' hold forth quite so smart as they used to, ruther than turn 'em off an' hurt their feelin's. I guess it would be full as much to the glory of God. S'pose the singin' an' the preachin' wa'n't quite so good, what difference would it make? Salvation don't hang on anybody's hittin' a high note, that I ever heard of. Folks are gettin' as high-steppin' an' fussy in a meetin'-house as they are in a tavern, nowadays. S'pose they should turn you off, Mr. Pollard, come an' give you a photograph album, an' tell you to clear out, how'd you like it? I ain't findin' any fault with your preachin'; it was always good enough to suit me; but it don't stand to reason folks'll be as took up with your sermons as when you was a young man. You can't expect it. S'pose they should turn you out in your old age, an' call in some young bob squirt, how'd you feel? There's William Emmons, too; he's three years older'n I am, if he does lead the choir an' run all the singin' in town. If my voice has gi'en out, it stan's to reason his has. It ain't, though. William Emmons sings jest as well as he ever did. Why don't they turn him out the way they have me, an' give him a photograph album? I dun know but it would be a good idea to send everybody, as soon as they get a little old an' gone by, an' young folks begin to push, onto some desert island, an' give 'em each a photograph album. Then they can sit down an' look at pictures the rest of their days. Mebbe government'll take it up.

"There they come here last week Thursday, all the choir, jest about eight o'clock in the evenin', an' pretended they'd come to give me a nice little surprise. Surprise! h'm! Brought cake an' oranges, an' was jest as nice as they could be, an' I was real tickled. I never had a surprise-party before in my life. Jenny Carr she played, an' they wanted me to sing alone, an' I never suspected a thing. I've been mad ever since to think what a fool I was, an' how they must have laughed in their sleeves.

"When they'd gone I found this photograph album on the table, all done up as nice as you please, an' directed to Miss Candace Whitcomb from her many friends, an' I opened it, an' there was the letter inside givin' me notice to quit.

"If they'd gone about it any decent way, told me right out honest that they'd got tired of me, an' wanted Alma Way to sing instead of me, I wouldn't minded so much; I should have been hurt 'nough, for I'd felt as if some that had pretended to be my friends wa'n't; but it wouldn't have been as bad as this. They said in the letter that they'd always set great value on my services, an' it wa'n't from any lack of appreciation that they turned me off, but they thought the duty was gettin' a little too arduous for me. H'm! I hadn't complained. If they'd turned me right out fair an' square, showed me the door, an' said, 'Here, you get out,' but to go an' spill molasses, as it were, all over the threshold, tryin' to make me think it's all nice an' sweet—

"I'd sent that photograph album back quick's I could pack it, but I didn't know who started it, so I've used it for a footstool. It's all it's good for, 'cordin' to my way of thinkin'. An' I ain't been particular to get the dust off my shoes before I used it neither."

Mr. Pollard, the minister, sat staring. He did not look at Candace; his eyes were fastened upon a point straight ahead. He had a look of helpless solidity, like a block of granite. This country minister, with his steady, even temperament, treading with heavy precision his one track for over forty years, having nothing new in his life except the new sameness of the seasons, and desiring nothing new, was incapable of understanding a woman like this, who had lived as quietly as he, and all the time held within herself the elements of revolution. He could not account for such violence, such extremes, except in a loss of reason. He had a conviction that Candace was getting beyond herself. He himself was not a typical New-Englander; the national elements of character were not pronounced in him. He was aghast and bewildered at this outbreak, which was tropical, and more than tropical, for a New England nature has a floodgate, and the power which it releases is an accumulation. Candace Whitcomb had been a quiet woman, so delicately resolute that the quality had been scarcely noticed in her, and her ambition had been unsuspected. Now the resolution and the ambition appeared raging over her whole self.

She began to talk again. "I've made up my mind that I'm goin' to sing Sundays the way I did this mornin', an' I don't care what folks say," said she. "I've made up my mind that I'm goin' to take matters into my own hands. I'm goin' to let folks see that I ain't trod down quite flat, that there's a little rise left in me. I ain't goin' to give up beat yet a while; an' I'd like to see anybody stop me. If I ain't got a right to play a psalm tune on my organ an' sing, I'd like to know. If you don't like it, you can move the meetin'-house."

Candace had had an inborn reverence for clergymen. She had always treated Mr. Pollard with the utmost deference. Indeed, her manner toward all men had been marked by a certain delicate stiffness and dignity. Now she was talking to the old minister with the homely freedom with which she might have addressed a female gossip over the back fence. He could not say much in return. He did not feel competent to make headway against any such tide of passion; all he could do was to let it beat against him. He made a few expostulations, which increased Candace's vehemence; he expressed his regret over the whole affair, and suggested that they should kneel and ask the guidance of the Lord in the matter, that she might be led to see it all in a different light.

Candace refused flatly. "I don't see any use prayin' about it," said she. "I don't think the Lord's got much to do with it, anyhow."

It was almost time for the afternoon service when the minister left. He had missed his comfortable noontide rest, through this encounter with his revolutionary parishioner. After the minister had gone, Candace sat by the window and waited. The bell rang, and she watched the people file past. When her nephew Wilson Ford with Alma appeared, she grunted to herself. "She's thin as a rail," said she; "guess there won't be much left of her by the time Wilson gets her. Little soft-spoken nippin' thing, she wouldn't make him no kind of a wife, anyway. Guess it's jest as well."

When the bell had stopped tolling, and all the people entered the church, Candace went over to her organ and seated herself. She arranged a singing-book before her, and sat still, waiting. Her thin, colorless neck and temples were full of beating pulses; her black eyes were bright and eager; she leaned stiffly over toward the music-rack, to hear better. When the church organ sounded out she straightened herself; her long skinny fingers pressed her own organ-keys with nervous energy. She worked the pedals with all her strength; all her slender body was in motion. When the first notes of Alma's solo began, Candace sang. She had really possessed a fine voice, and it was wonderful how little she had lost it. Straining her throat with jealous fury, her notes were still for the main part true. Her voice filled the whole room; she sang with wonderful fire and expression. That, at least, mild little Alma Way could never emulate. She was full of steadfastness and unquestioning constancy, but there were in her no smouldering fires of ambition and resolution. Music was not to her what it had been to her older rival. To this obscure woman, kept relentlessly by circumstances in a narrow track, singing in the village choir had been as much as Italy was to Napoleon— and now on her island of exile she was still showing fight.

After the church service was done, Candace left the organ and went over to her old chair by the window. Her knees felt weak, and shook under her. She sat down, and leaned back her head. There were red spots on her cheeks. Pretty soon she heard a quick slam of her gate, and an impetuous tread on the gravel-walk. She looked up, and there was her nephew Wilson Ford hurrying up to the door. She cringed a little, then she settled herself more firmly in her chair.

Wilson came into the room with a rush. He left the door open, and the wind slammed it to after him.

"Aunt Candace, where are you?" he called out, in a loud voice.

She made no reply. He looked around fiercely, and his eyes seemed to pounce upon her.

"Look here, Aunt Candace," said he, "are you crazy?" Candace said nothing. "Aunt Candace!" She did not seem to see him. "If you don't answer me," said Wilson, "I'll just go over there and pitch that old organ out of the window!"

"Wilson Ford!" said Candace, in a voice that was almost a scream.

"Well, what say! What have you got to say for yourself, acting the way you have? I tell you what 'tis, Aunt Candace, I won't stand it."

"I'd like to see you help yourself."

"I will help myself. I'll pitch that old organ out of the window, and then I'll board up the window on that side of your house. Then we'll see."

"It ain't your house, and it won't never be."

"Who said it was my house? You're my aunt, and I've got a little lookout for the credit of the family. Aunt Candace, what are you doing this way for?"

"It don't make no odds what I'm doin' so for. I ain't bound to give my reasons to a young fellar like you, if you do act so mighty toppin'. But I'll tell you one thing, Wilson Ford, after the way you've spoke to-day, you sha'n't never have one cent of my money, an' you can't never marry that Way girl if you don't have it. You can't never take her home to live with your mother, an' this house would have been mighty nice an' convenient for you some day. Now you won't get it. I'm goin' to make another will. I'd made it, if you did but know it. Now you won't get a cent of my money, you nor your mother neither. An' I ain't goin' to live a dreadful while longer, neither. Now I wish you'd go home; I want to lay down. I'm 'bout sick."

Wilson could not get another word from his aunt. His indignation had not in the least cooled. Her threat of disinheriting him did not cow him at all; he had too much rough independence, and indeed his aunt Candace's house had always been too much of an air-castle for him to contemplate seriously. Wilson, with his burly frame and his headlong common-sense, could have little to do with air-castles, had he been hard enough to build them over graves. Still, he had not admitted that he never could marry Alma. All his hopes were based upon a rise in his own fortunes, not by some sudden convulsion, but by his own long and steady labor. Some time, he thought, he should have saved enough for the two homes.

He went out of his aunt's house still storming. She arose after the door had shut behind him, and got out into the kitchen. She thought that she would start a fire and make a cup of tea. She had not eaten anything all day. She put some kindling-wood into the stove and touched a match to it; then she went back to the sitting-room, and settled down again into the chair by the window. The fire in the kitchen-stove roared, and the light wood was soon burned out. She thought no more about it. She had not put on the teakettle. Her head ached, and once in a while she shivered. She sat at the window while the afternoon waned and the dusk came on. At seven o'clock the meeting bell rang again, and the people flocked by. This time she did not stir. She had shut her parlor organ. She did not need to out-sing her rival this evening; there was only congregational singing at the Sunday-night prayer-meeting.

She sat still until it was nearly time for meeting to be done; her head ached harder and harder, and she shivered more. Finally she arose. "Guess I'll go to bed," she muttered. She went about the house, bent over and shaking, to lock the doors. She stood a minute in the back door, looking over the fields to the woods. There was a red light over there. "The woods are on fire," said Candace. She watched with a dull interest the flames roll up, withering and destroying the tender green spring foliage. The air was full of smoke, although the fire was half a mile away.

Candace locked the door and went in. The trees with their delicate garlands of new leaves, with the new nests of song birds, might fall, she was in the roar of an intenser fire; the growths of all her springs and the delicate wontedness of her whole life were going down in it. Candace went to bed in her little room off the parlor, but she could not sleep. She lay awake all night. In the morning she crawled to the door and hailed a little boy who was passing. She bade him go for the doctor as quickly as he could, then to Mrs. Ford's, and ask her to come over. She held on to the door while she was talking. The boy stood staring wonderingly at her. The spring wind fanned her face. She had drawn on a dress skirt and put her shawl over her shoulders, and her gray hair was blowing over her red cheeks.

She shut the door and went back to her bed. She never arose from it again. The doctor and Mrs. Ford came and looked after her, and she lived a week. Nobody but herself thought until the very last that she would die; the doctor called her illness merely a light run of fever; she had her senses fully.

But Candace gave up at the first. "It's my last sickness," she said to Mrs. Ford that morning when she first entered; and Mrs. Ford had laughed at the notion; but the sick woman held to it. She did not seem to suffer much physical pain; she only grew weaker and weaker, but she was distressed mentally. She did not talk much, but her eyes followed everybody with an agonized expression.

On Wednesday William Emmons came to inquire for her. Candace heard him out in the parlor. She tried to raise herself on one elbow that she might listen better to his voice.

"William Emmons come in to ask how you was," Mrs. Ford said, after he was gone.

"I—heard him," replied Candace. Presently she spoke again. "Nancy," said she, "where's that photograph album?"

"On the table," replied her sister, hesitatingly.

"Mebbe—you'd better—brush it up a little."

"Well."

Sunday morning Candace wished that the minister should be asked to come in at the noon intermission. She had refused to see him before. He came and prayed with her, and she asked his forgiveness for the way she had spoken the Sunday before. "I—hadn't ought to—spoke so," said she. "I was— dreadful wrought up."

"Perhaps it was your sickness coming on," said the minister, soothingly.

Candace shook her head. "No—it wa'n't. I hope the Lord will—forgive me."

After the minister had gone, Candace still appeared unhappy. Her pitiful eyes followed her sister everywhere with the mechanical persistency of a portrait.

"What is it you want, Candace?" Mrs. Ford said at last. She had nursed her sister faithfully, but once in a while her impatience showed itself.

"Nancy!"

"What say?"

"I wish—you'd go out when—meetin's done, an'—head off Alma an' Wilson, an'—ask 'em to come in. I feel as if—I'd like to—hear her sing."

Mrs. Ford stared. "Well," said she.

The meeting was now in session. The windows were all open, for it was another warm Sunday. Candace lay listening to the music when it began, and a look of peace came over her face. Her sister had smoothed her hair back, and put on a clean cap. The white curtain in the bedroom window waved in the wind like a white sail. Candace almost felt as if she were better, but the thought of death seemed easy.

Mrs. Ford at the parlor window watched for the meeting to be out. When the people appeared, she ran down the walk and waited for Alma and Wilson. When they came she told them what Candace wanted, and they all went in together.

"Here's Alma an' Wilson, Candace," said Mrs. Ford, leading them to the bedroom door.

Candace smiled. "Come in," she said, feebly. And Alma and Wilson entered and stood beside the bed. Candace continued to look at them, the smile straining her lips.

"Wilson!"

"What is it, Aunt Candace?"

"I ain't altered that—will. You an' Alma can—come here an'—live—when I'm—gone. Your mother won't mind livin' alone. Alma can have—all—my things."

"Don't, Aunt Candace." Tears were running over Wilson's cheeks, and Alma's delicate face was all of a quiver.

"I thought—maybe—Alma'd be willin' to—sing for me," said Candace.

"What do you want me to sing?" Alma asked, in a trembling voice.

" 'Jesus, lover of my soul.' "

Alma, standing there beside Wilson, began to sing. At first she could hardly control her voice, then she sang sweetly and clearly.

Candace lay and listened. Her face had a holy and radiant expression. When Alma stopped singing it did not disappear, but she looked up and spoke, and it was like a secondary glimpse of the old shape of a forest tree through the smoke and flame of the transfiguring fire the instant before it falls. "You flatted a little on—soul," said Candace.

Sarah Orne Jewett

1849-1909

from TALES OF NEW ENGLAND

MISS TEMPY'S WATCHERS
(1894)

The time of year was April; the place was a small farming town in New Hampshire, remote from any railroad. One by one the lights had been blown out in the scattered houses near Miss Tempy Dent's; but as her neighbors took a last look out-of-doors, their eyes turned with instinctive curiosity toward the old house, where a lamp burned steadily. They gave a little sigh. "Poor Miss Tempy!" said more than one bereft acquaintance; for the good woman lay dead in her north chamber, and the light was a watcher's light. The funeral was set for the next day, at one o'clock.

The watchers were two of the oldest friends, Mrs. Crowe and Sarah Ann Binson. They were sitting in the kitchen, because it seemed less awesome than the unused best room, and they beguiled the long hours by steady conversation. One would think that neither topics nor opinions would hold out, at that rate, all through the long spring night; but there was a certain degree of excitement just then, and the two women had risen to an unusual level of expressiveness and confidence. Each had already told the other more than one fact that she had determined to keep secret; they were again and again tempted into statements that either would have found impossible by daylight. Mrs. Crowe was knitting a blue yarn stocking for her husband; the foot was already so long that it seemed as if she must have forgotten to narrow it at the proper time. Mrs. Crowe knew exactly what she was about, however; she was of a much cooler disposition than Sister Binson, who made futile attempts at some sewing, only to drop her work into her lap whenever the talk was most engaging.

Their faces were interesting,—of the dry, shrewd, quick-witted New England type, with thin hair twisted neatly back out of the way. Mrs. Crowe could look vague and benignant, and Miss Binson was, to quote her neighbors, a little too sharp-set; but the world knew that she had need to be, with the load she must carry of supporting an inefficient widowed sister and six unpromising and unwilling nieces and nephews. The eldest boy was at last placed with a good man to learn the mason's trade. Sarah Ann Binson, for all her sharp, anxious aspect, never defended herself, when her sister whined and fretted. She was told every week of her life that the poor children never would have had to lift a finger if their father had lived, and yet she had kept her steadfast way with the little farm, and patiently taught the young people many useful things, for which, as everybody said, they would live to thank her. However pleasureless her life appeared to outward view, it was brimful of pleasure to herself.

Mrs. Crowe, on the contrary, was well to do, her husband being a rich farmer and an easy-going man. She was a stingy woman, but for all that she looked kindly; and when she gave away anything, or lifted a finger to help anybody, it was thought a great piece of beneficence, and a compliment, indeed, which the recipient accepted with twice as much gratitude as double the gift that came from a poorer and more generous acquaintance. Everybody liked to be on good terms with Mrs. Crowe. Socially she stood much higher than Sarah Ann Binson. They were both old schoolmates and friends of Temperance Dent, who had asked them, one day, not long before she died, if they would not come together and look after the house, and manage everything, when she was gone. She may have had some hope that they might become closer friends in this period of intimate partnership, and that the richer woman might better understand the burdens of the poorer. They had not kept the house the night before; they were too weary with the care of their old friend, whom they had not left until all was over.

There was a brook which ran down the hillside very near the house, and the sound of it was much louder than usual. When there was silence in the kitchen, the busy stream had a strange insistence in its wild voice, as if it tried to make the watchers understand something that related to the past.

"I declare, I can't begin to sorrow for Tempy yet. I am so glad to have her at rest," whispered Mrs. Crowe. "It is strange to set here without her, but I can't make it clear that she has gone. I feel as if she had got easy and dropped off to sleep, and I'm more scared about waking her up than knowing any other feeling."

"Yes," said Sarah Ann, "it's just like that, ain't it? But I tell you we are goin' to miss her worse than we expect. She's helped me through with many a trial, has Temperance. I ain't the only one who says the same, neither."

These words were spoken as if there were a third person listening; somebody beside Mrs. Crowe. The watchers could not rid their minds of the feeling that they were being watched themselves. The spring wind whistled in the window crack, now and then, and buffeted the little house in a gusty way that had a sort of companionable effect. Yet, on the whole, it was a very still night, and the watchers spoke in a half-whisper.

"She was the freest-handed woman that ever I knew," said

Mrs. Crowe, decidedly. "According to her means, she gave away more than anybody. I used to tell her 'twa'n't right. I used really to be afraid that she went without too much, for we have a duty to ourselves."

Sister Binson looked up in a half-amused, unconscious way, and then recollected herself.

Mrs. Crowe met her look with a serious face. "It ain't so easy for me to give as it is for some," she said simply, but with an effort which was made possible only by the occasion. "I should like to say, while Tempy is laying here yet in her own house, that she has been a constant lesson to me. Folks are too kind, and shame me with thanks for what I do. I ain't such a generous woman as poor Tempy was, for all she had nothin' to do with, as one may say."

Sarah Binson was much moved at this confession, and was even pained and touched by the unexpected humility. "You have a good many calls on you"—she began, and then left her kind little compliment half finished.

"Yes, yes, but I've got means enough. My disposition's more of a cross to me as I grow older, and I made up my mind this morning that Tempy's example should be my pattern henceforth." She began to knit faster than ever.

" 'T ain't no use to get morbid; that's what Tempy used to say herself," said Sarah Ann, after a minute's silence. "Ain't it strange to say 'used to say'?" and her own voice choked a little. "She never did like to hear folks git goin' about themselves."

" 'T was only because they're apt to do so as other folks will say 't wasn't so, an' praise 'em up," humbly replied Mrs. Crowe, "and that ain't my object. There wa'n't a child but what Tempy set herself to work to see what she could do to please it. One time my brother's folks had been stopping here in the summer, from Massachusetts. The children was all little, and they broke up a sight of toys, and left 'em when they were going away. Tempy come right up after they rode by, to see if she couldn't help me set the house to rights, and she caught me just as I was going to fling some of the clutter into the stove. I was kind of tired out, starting 'em off in season.

'Oh, give me them!' says she, real pleading; and she wropped 'em up and took 'em home with her when she went, and she mended 'em up and stuck 'em together, and made some young one or other happy with every blessed one. You'd thought I'd done her the biggest favor. 'No thanks to me. I should ha' burnt 'em, Tempy,' says I."

"Some of 'em came to our house, I know," said Miss Binson. "She'd take a lot o' trouble to please a child, 'stead o' shoving of it out o' the way, like the rest of us when we're drove."

"I can tell you the biggest thing she ever done, and I don't know's there's anybody left but me to tell it. I don't want it forgot," Sarah Binson went on, looking up at the clock to see how the night was going. "It was that pretty-looking Trevor girl, who taught the Corners school, and married so well afterwards, out in New York State. You remember her, I dare say?"

"Certain," said Mrs. Crowe, with an air of interest.

"She was a splendid scholar, folks said, and give the school a great start; but she'd overdone herself getting her education, and working to pay for it, and she all broke down one spring, and Tempy made her come and stop with her a while,—you remember that? Well, she had an uncle, her mother's brother, out in Chicago, who was well off and friendly, and used to write to Lizzie Trevor, and I dare say make her some presents; but he was a lively, driving man, and didn't take time to stop and think about his folks. He hadn't seen her since she was a little girl. Poor Lizzie was so pale and weakly that she just got through the term o' school. She looked as if she was just going straight off in a decline. Tempy, she cosseted her up a while, and then, next thing folks knew, she was tellin' round how Miss Trevor had gone to see her uncle, and meant to visit Niagary Falls on the way, and stop over night. Now I happened to know, in ways I won't dwell on to explain, that the poor girl was in debt for her schoolin' when she come here, and her last quarter's pay had just squared it off at last, and left her without a cent ahead, hardly; but it had fretted her thinking of it, so she paid it all; those might have dunned her that she owed it to. An' I taxed Tempy about the girl's goin' off on such a journey till she owned up, rather 'n have Lizzie blamed, that she'd given her sixty dollars, same's if she was rolling in riches, and sent her off to have a good rest and vacation."

"Sixty dollars!" exclaimed Mrs. Crowe. "Tempy only had ninety dollars a year that came in to her; rest of her livin' she got by helpin' about, with what she raised off this little piece o' ground, sand one side an' clay the other. An' how often I've heard her tell, years ago, that she'd rather see Niagary than any other sight in the world!"

The women looked at each other in silence; the magnitude of the generous sacrifice was almost too great for their comprehension.

"She was just poor enough to do that!" declared Mrs. Crowe at last, in an abandonment of feeling. "Say what you may, I feel humbled to the dust," and her companion ventured to say nothing. She never had given away sixty dollars at once, but it was simply because she never had it to give. It came to her very lips to say in explanation, "Tempy was so situated;" but she checked herself in time, for she would not betray her own loyal guarding of a dependent household.

"Folks say a great deal of generosity, and this one's being public-sperited, and that one free-handed about giving," said Mrs. Crowe, who was a little nervous in the silence. "I suppose we can't tell the sorrow it would be to some folks not to give, same's 't would be to me not to save. I seem kind of made for that, as if 't was what I'd got to do. I should feel sights better about it if I could make it evident what I was savin' for. If I had a child, now, Sarah Ann," and her voice was a little husky,—"if I had a child, I should think I was heapin' of it up because he was the one trained by the Lord to scatter it again for good. But here's Mr. Crowe and me, we can't do anything with money, and both of us like to keep things same's they've always been. Now Priscilla Dance was talking away like a mill-clapper, week before last. She'd think I would go right off and get one o' them new-fashioned gilt-and-white papers for the best room, and some new furniture, an' a marble-top table. And I looked at her, all struck up. 'Why,' says I, 'Priscilla, that nice old velvet paper ain't hurt a mite. I shouldn't feel 't was my best room without it. Dan'el says 't is the first thing he can remember rubbin' his little baby fingers on to it, and how splendid he thought them red roses was.' I maintain," continued Mrs. Crowe stoutly, "that folks wastes sights o' good money doin' just such foolish things. Tearin' out the insides o' meetin'-houses, and fixin' the pews different; 't was good enough as 't was with mendin'; then times come, an' they want to put it all back same's 't was before."

This touched upon an exciting subject to active members of that parish. Miss Binson and Mrs. Crowe belonged to opposite parties, and had at one time come as near hard feelings as they could, and yet escape them. Each hastened to speak of other things and to show her untouched friendliness.

"I do agree with you," said Sister Binson, "that few of us know what use to make of money, beyond every-day necessities. You've seen more o' the world than I have, and know what's expected. When it comes to taste and judgment about such things, I ought to defer to others;" and with this modest avowal the critical moment passed when there might have been an improper discussion.

In the silence that followed, the fact of their presence in a house of death grew more clear than before. There was something disturbing in the noise of a mouse gnawing at the dry boards of a closet wall near by. Both the watchers looked up anxiously at the clock; it was almost the middle of the night, and the whole world seemed to have left them alone with their solemn duty. Only the brook was awake.

"Perhaps we might give a look up-stairs now," whispered Mrs. Crowe, as if she hoped to hear some reason against their going just then to the chamber of death; but Sister Binson rose, with a serious and yet satisfied countenance, and lifted the small lamp from the table. She was much more used to watching than Mrs. Crowe, and much less affected by it. They opened the door into a small entry with a steep stairway; they climbed the creaking stairs, and entered the cold upper room on tiptoe. Mrs. Crowe's heart began to beat very fast as the lamp was put on a high bureau, and made long, fixed shadows about the walls. She went hesitatingly toward the solemn shape under its white drapery, and felt a sense of remonstrance as Sarah Ann gently, but in a business-like way, turned back the thin sheet.

"Seems to me she looks pleasanter and pleasanter," whispered Sarah Ann Binson impulsively, as they gazed at the white face with its wonderful smile. "To-morrow 't will all have faded out. I do believe they kind of wake up a day or two after they die, and it's then they go." She replaced the light covering, and they both turned quickly away; there was a chill in this upper room.

" 'T is a great thing for anybody to have got through, ain't it?" said Mrs. Crowe softly, as she began to go down the stairs on tiptoe. The warm air from the kitchen beneath met them with a sense of welcome and shelter.

"I don' know why it is, but I feel as near again to Tempy down here as I do up there," replied Sister Binson. "I feel as if the air was full of her, kind of. I can sense things, now and then, that she seems to say. Now I never was one to take up with no nonsense of sperits and such, but I declare I felt as if she told me just now to put some more wood into the stove."

Mrs. Crowe preserved a gloomy silence. She had suspected before this that her companion was of a weaker and more credulous disposition than herself. " 'T is a great thing to have got through," she repeated, ignoring definitely all that had last been said. "I suppose you know as well as I that Tempy was one that always feared death. Well, it's all put behind her now; she knows what 't is." Mrs. Crowe gave a little sigh, and Sister Binson's quick sympathies were stirred toward this other old friend, who also dreaded the great change.

"I'd never like to forgit almost those last words Tempy spoke plain to me," she said gently, like the comforter she truly was. "She looked up at me once or twice, that last afternoon after I come to set by her, and let Mis' Owen go home; and I says, 'Can I do anything to ease you, Tempy?' and the tears come into my eyes so I couldn't see what kind of a nod she give me. 'No, Sarah Ann, you can't, dear,' says she; and then she got her breath again, and says she, looking at me real meanin', 'I'm only a-gettin' sleepier and sleepier; that's all there is,' says she, and smiled up at me kind of wishful, and shut her eyes. I knew well enough all she meant. She'd been lookin' out for a chance to tell me, and I don' know's she ever said much afterwards."

Mrs. Crowe was not knitting; she had been listening too eagerly. "Yes, 't will be a comfort to think of that sometimes," she said, in acknowledgment.

"I know that old Dr. Prince said once, in evenin' meetin', that he'd watched by many a dyin' bed, as we well knew, and enough o' his sick folks had been scared o' dyin' their whole lives through; but when they come to the last, he'd never seen one but was willin', and most were glad, to go. ' 'T is as natural as bein' born or livin' on,' he said. I don't know what had moved him to speak that night. You know he wa'n't in the habit of it, and 't was the monthly concert of prayer for foreign missions anyways," said Sarah Ann; "but 't was a great stay to the mind to listen to his words of experience."

"There never was a better man," responded Mrs. Crowe, in a really cheerful tone. She had recovered from her feeling of nervous dread, the kitchen was so comfortable with lamplight and firelight; and just then the old clock began to tell the hour of twelve with leisurely whirring strokes.

Sister Binson laid aside her work, and rose quickly and went to the cupboard. "We'd better take a little to eat," she explained. "The night will go fast after this. I want to know if you went and made some o' your nice cupcake, while you was home to-day?" she asked, in a pleased tone; and Mrs. Crowe acknowledged such a gratifying piece of thoughtfulness for this humble friend who denied herself all luxuries. Sarah Ann brewed a generous cup of tea, and the watchers drew their chairs up to the table presently, and quelled their hunger with good country appetites. Sister Binson put a spoon into a small, old-fashioned glass of preserved quince, and passed it to her friend. She was most familiar with the house, and played the part of hostess. "Spread some o' this on your bread and butter," she said to Mrs. Crowe. "Tempy wanted me to use some three or four times, but I never felt to. I know she'd like to have us comfortable now, and would urge us to make a good supper, poor dear."

"What excellent preserves she did make!" mourned Mrs. Crowe. "None of us has got her light hand at doin' things tasty. She made the most o' everything, too. Now, she only had that one old quince-tree down in the far corner of the piece, but she'd go out in the spring and tend to it, and look at it so pleasant, and kind of expect the old thorny thing into bloomin'."

"She was just the same with folks," said Sarah Ann. "And she'd never git more 'n a little apernful o' quinces, but she'd have every mite o' goodness out o' those, and set the glasses up onto her best-room closet shelf, so pleased. 'T wa'n't but a week ago to-morrow mornin' I fetched her a little taste o' jelly in a teaspoon; and she says 'Thank ye,' and took it, an' the minute she tasted it she looked up at me as worried as could be. 'Oh, I don't want to eat that,' says she. 'I always keep that in case o' sickness.' 'You're goin' to have the good o' one tumbler yourself,' says I. 'I'd just like to know who's sick now, if you ain't!' An' she couldn't help laughin', I spoke up so smart. Oh, dear me, how I shall miss talkin' over things with her! She always sensed things, and got just the p'int you meant."

"She didn't begin to age until two or three years ago, did she?" asked Mrs. Crowe. "I never saw anybody keep her looks as Tempy did. She looked young long after I begun to feel like an old woman. The doctor used to say 't was her young heart, and I don't know but what he was right. How she did do for other folks! There was one spell she wasn't at home a day to a fortnight. She got most of her livin' so, and that made her own potatoes and things last her through. None o' the

young folks could get married without her, and all the old ones
was disappointed if she wa'n't round when they was down
with sickness and had to go. An' cleanin', or tailorin' for boys,
or rug-hookin',—there was nothin' but what she could do as
handy as most. 'I do love to work,'—ain't you heard her say
that twenty times a week?"

Sarah Ann Binson nodded, and began to clear away the
empty plates. "We may want a taste o' somethin' more towards mornin'," she said. "There's plenty in the closet here;
and in case some comes from a distance to the funeral, we'll
have a little table spread after we get back to the house."

"Yes, I was busy all the mornin'. I've cooked up a sight o'
things to bring over," said Mrs. Crowe. "I felt 't was the last
I could do for her."

They drew their chairs near the stove again, and took up
their work. Sister Binson's rocking-chair creaked as she rocked;
the brook sounded louder than ever. It was more lonely when
nobody spoke, and presently Mrs. Crowe returned to her
thoughts of growing old.

"Yes, Tempy aged all of a sudden. I remember I asked her
if she felt as well as common, one day, and she laughed at me
good. There, when Mr. Crowe begun to look old, I couldn't
help feeling as if somethin' ailed him, and like as not 't was
somethin' he was goin' to git right over, and I dosed him for
it stiddy, half of one summer."

"How many things we shall be wanting to ask Tempy!" exclaimed Sarah Ann Binson, after a long pause. "I can't make
up my mind to doin' without her. I wish folks could come
back just once, and tell us how 't is where they've gone.
Seems then we could do without 'em better."

The brook hurried on, the wind blew about the house now
and then; the house itself was a silent place, and the supper,
the warm fire, and an absence of any new topics for conversation made the watchers drowsy. Sister Binson closed her eyes
first, to rest them for a minute; and Mrs. Crowe glanced at
her compassionately, with a new sympathy for the hard-

worked little woman. She made up her mind to let Sarah Ann have a good rest, while she kept watch alone; but in a few minutes her own knitting was dropped, and she, too, fell asleep. Overhead, the pale shape of Tempy Dent, the outworn body of that generous, loving-hearted, simple soul, slept on also in its white raiment. Perhaps Tempy herself stood near, and saw her own life and its surroundings with new understanding. Perhaps she herself was the only watcher.

Later, by some hours, Sarah Ann Binson woke with a start. There was a pale light of dawn outside the small windows. Inside the kitchen, the lamp burned dim. Mrs. Crowe awoke, too.

"I think Tempy'd be the first to say 't was just as well we both had some rest," she said, not without a guilty feeling.

Her companion went to the outer door, and opened it wide. The fresh air was none too cold, and the brook's voice was not nearly so loud as it had been in the midnight darkness. She could see the shapes of the hills, and the great shadows that lay across the lower country. The east was fast growing bright.

"'T will be a beautiful day for the funeral," she said, and turned again, with a sigh, to follow Mrs. Crowe up the stairs.

Miss Tempy was Charitable

Kate Chopin

1851-1904

from BAYOU FOLK

DÉSIRÉE'S BABY

(1894)

As the day was pleasant, Madame Valmondé drove over to
L'Abri to see Désirée and the baby.

It made her laugh to think of Désirée with a baby. Why, it
seemed but yesterday that Désirée was little more than a baby
herself; when Monsieur in riding through the gateway of Valmondé had found her lying asleep in the shadow of the big
stone pillar.

The little one awoke in his arms and began to cry for
"Dada." That was as much as she could do or say. Some people
thought she might have strayed there of her own accord,
for she was of the toddling age. The prevailing belief was that
she had been purposely left by a party of Texans, whose can-
vas-covered wagon, late in the day, had crossed the ferry that
Coton Maïs kept, just below the plantation. In time Madame
Valmondé abandoned every speculation but the one that Désirée had been sent to her by a beneficent Providence to be
the child of her affection, seeing that she was without child of
the flesh. For the girl grew to be beautiful and gentle, affectionate and sincere,—the idol of Valmondé.

It was no wonder, when she stood one day against
the stone pillar in whose shadow she had lain asleep, eighteen
years before, that Armand Aubigny riding by and seeing her
there, had fallen in love with her. That was the way all the
Aubignys fell in love, as if struck by a pistol shot. The won-

der was that he had not loved her before; for he had known her since his father brought him home from Paris, a boy of eight, after his mother died there. The passion that awoke in him that day, when he saw her at the gate, swept along like an avalanche, or like a prairie fire, or like anything that drives headlong over all obstacles.

Monsieur Valmondé grew practical and wanted things well considered: that is, the girl's obscure origin. Armand looked into her eyes and did not care. He was reminded that she was nameless. What did it matter about a name when he could give her one of the oldest and proudest in Louisiana? He ordered the *corbeille* from Paris, and contained himself with what patience he could until it arrived; then they were married.

Madame Valmondé had not seen Désirée and the baby for four weeks. When she reached L'Abri she shuddered at the first sight of it, as she always did. It was a sad looking place, which for many years had not known the gentle presence of a mistress, old Monsieur Aubigny having married and buried his wife in France, and she having loved her own land too well ever to leave it. The roof came down steep and black like a cowl, reaching out beyond the wide galleries that encircled the yellow stuccoed house. Big, solemn oaks grew close to it, and their thick-leaved, far-reaching branches shadowed it like a pall. Young Aubigny's rule was a strict one, too, and under it his negroes had forgotten how to be gay, as they had been during the old master's easy-going and indulgent lifetime.

The young mother was recovering slowly, and lay full length, in her soft white muslins and laces, upon a couch. The baby was beside her, upon her arm, where he had fallen asleep, at her breast. The yellow nurse woman sat beside a window fanning herself.

Madame Valmondé bent her portly figure over Désirée and kissed her, holding her an instant tenderly in her arms. Then she turned to the child.

"This is not the baby!" she exclaimed, in startled tones. French was the language spoken at Valmondé in those days.

"I knew you would be astonished," laughed Désirée, "at the way he has grown. The little *cochon de lait!* Look at his legs, mamma, and his hands and fingernails,—real finger-nails. Zandrine had to cut them this morning. Isn't it true, Zandrine?"

The woman bowed her turbaned head majestically, "Mais si, Madame."

"And the way he cries," went on Désirée, "is deafening. Armand heard him the other day as far away as La Blanche's cabin."

Madame Valmondé had never removed her eyes from the child. She lifted it and walked with it over to the window that was lightest. She scanned the baby narrowly, then looked as searchingly at Zandrine, whose face was turned to gaze across the fields.

"Yes, the child has grown, has changed;" said Madame Valmondé, slowly, as she replaced it beside its mother. "What does Armand say?"

Désirée's face became suffused with a glow that was happiness itself.

"Oh, Armand is the proudest father in the parish, I believe, chiefly because it is a boy, to bear his name; though he says not,—that he would have loved a girl as well. But I know it isn't true. I know he says that to please me. And mamma," she added, drawing Madame Valmondé's head down to her, and speaking in a whisper, "he hasn't punished one of them —not one of them—since baby is born. Even Négrillon, who pretended to have burnt his leg that he might rest from work —he only laughed, and said Négrillon was a great scamp. Oh, mamma, I'm so happy; it frightens me."

What Désirée said was true. Marriage, and later the birth of his son, had softened Armand Aubigny's imperious and exacting nature greatly. This was what made the gentle Désirée so happy, for she loved him desperately. When he frowned she trembled, but loved him. When he smiled, she asked no greater blessing of God. But Armand's dark, handsome face had not often been disfigured by frowns since the day he fell in love with her.

When the baby was about three months old, Désirée awoke one day to the conviction that there was something in the air menacing her peace. It was at first too subtle to grasp. It had only been a disquieting suggestion; an air of mystery among the blacks; unexpected visits from far-off neighbors who could hardly account for their coming. Then a strange, an awful change in her husband's manner, which she dared not ask him to explain. When he spoke to her, it was with averted eyes, from which the old love-light seemed to have gone out. He absented himself from home; and when there, avoided her presence and that of her child, without excuse. And the very spirit of Satan seemed suddenly to take hold of him in his dealings with the slaves. Désirée was miserable enough to die.

She sat in her room, one hot afternoon, in her *peignoir*, listlessly drawing through her fingers the strands of her long, silky brown hair that hung about her shoulders. The baby, half naked, lay asleep upon her own great mahogany bed, that was like a sumptuous throne, with its satin-lined half-canopy. One of La Blanche's little quadroon boys—half naked too— stood fanning the child slowly with a fan of peacock feathers. Désirée's eyes had been fixed absently and sadly upon the baby, while she was striving to penetrate the threatening mist that she felt closing about her. She looked from her child to the boy who stood beside him, and back again; over and over. "Ah!" It was a cry that she could not help; which she was not conscious of having uttered. The blood turned like ice in her veins, and a clammy moisture gathered upon her face.

She tried to speak to the little quadroon boy; but no sound would come, at first. When he heard his name uttered, he looked up, and his mistress was pointing to the door. He laid aside the great, soft fan, and obediently stole away, over the polished floor, on his bare tiptoes.

She stayed motionless, with gaze riveted upon her child, and her face the picture of fright.

Presently her husband entered the room, and without noticing her, went to a table and began to search among some papers which covered it.

"Armand," she called to him, in a voice which must have stabbed him, if he was human. But he did not notice. "Armand," she said again. Then she rose and tottered towards him. "Armand," she panted once more, clutching his arm, "look at our child. What does it mean? tell me."

He coldly but gently loosened her fingers from about his arm and thrust the hand away from him. "Tell me what it means!" she cried despairingly.

"It means," he answered lightly, "that the child is not white; it means that you are not white."

A quick conception of all that this accusation meant for her nerved her with unwonted courage to deny it. "It is a lie; it is not true, I am white! Look at my hair, it is brown; and my eyes are gray, Armand, you know they are gray. And my skin is fair," seizing his wrist. "Look at my hand; whiter than yours, Armand," she laughed hysterically.

"As white as La Blanche's," he returned cruelly; and went away leaving her alone with their child.

When she could hold a pen in her hand, she sent a despairing letter to Madame Valmondé.

"My mother, they tell me I am not white. Armand has told me I am not white. For God's sake tell them it is not true. You must know it is not true. I shall die. I must die. I cannot be so unhappy, and live."

The answer that came was as brief:

"My own Désirée: Come home to Valmondé; back to your mother who loves you. Come with your child."

When the letter reached Désirée she went with it to her husband's study, and laid it open upon the desk before which he sat. She was like a stone image: silent, white, motionless after she placed it there.

In silence he ran his cold eyes over the written words. He said nothing. "Shall I go, Armand?" she asked in tones sharp with agonized suspense.

"Yes, go."

"Do you want me to go?"

"Yes, I want you to go."

He thought Almighty God had dealt cruelly and unjustly with him; and felt, somehow, that he was paying Him back in kind when he stabbed thus into his wife's soul. Moreover he no longer loved her, because of the unconscious injury she had brought upon his home and his name.

She turned away like one stunned by a blow, and walked slowly towards the door, hoping he would call her back.

"Good-by, Armand," she moaned.

He did not answer her. That was his last blow at fate.

Désirée went in search of her child. Zandrine was pacing the sombre gallery with it. She took the little one from the nurse's arms with no word of explanation, and descending the steps, walked away, under the live-oak branches.

It was an October afternoon; the sun was just sinking. Out in the still fields the negroes were picking cotton.

Désirée had not changed the thin white garment nor the slippers which she wore. Her hair was uncovered and the sun's rays brought a golden gleam from its brown meshes. She did not take the broad, beaten road which led to the far-off plantation of Valmondé. She walked across a deserted field, where the stubble bruised her tender feet, so delicately shod, and tore her thin gown to shreds.

She disappeared among the reeds and willows that grew thick along the banks of the deep, sluggish bayou; and she did not come back again.

Some weeks later there was a curious scene enacted at L'Abri. In the centre of the smoothly swept back yard was a great bonfire. Armand Aubigny sat in the wide hallway that commanded a view of the spectacle; and it was he who dealt out to a half dozen negroes the material which kept this fire ablaze.

A graceful cradle of willow, with all its dainty furbishings, was laid upon the pyre, which had already been fed with the richness of a priceless *layette*. Then there were silk gowns, and velvet and satin ones added to these; laces, too, and em-

taken by industrialism with its corollaries of wage slavery, mass immigration, slums, strikes, and an abysmal gulf between the very rich and the very poor. The frontier period ended with the census of 1890, and equalitarian and Jeffersonian ideals were seriously challenged. What had been primarily a North European and Protestant country until the 1840's acquired vast populations of other faiths and kinds. Amid this chaotic change and growth the disruptive and agnostic doctrines of an often-misunderstood Darwinism, as well as the multiplying discoveries of science and technology, stirred people's minds like great spoons. To represent a nation changing so fast, realism itself had to change. It began deep in the romanticism of the beginning of the nineteenth century; it ended, or was seriously modified, in the naturalism and symbolism of the beginning of the twentieth.

In its native manifestations, realism began as the hand-maiden of cultural assertiveness, and cultural assertiveness began before the literary were quite sure what they had to assert. Not until after the Civil War would it be commonly acknowledged that authentic native cultures had grown up quietly in several regions; yet earlier American writers, galvanized by British criticism and ambitious to add to the "few dim blinking lights" of American letters, had no recourse except to celebrations of democratic principles and native materials.

For a long time defense of things American was hardly to be separated from attack on things European, and no paean to new world innocence was likely without a comment on old world wickedness and an unhappy though buried conviction of old world cultural superiority. Barlow, Noah Webster, Cooper, Emerson, and Whitman fought the war of cultural emancipation; the people who would win it, the Lincolns, the Mark Twains, would grow up farther west, hardly knowing that a war was on.

The "colonial complex" had one salutary effect to compensate for the bombast it sponsored: it kept American eyes

a dream may have a staring vividness, but the dream's pattern
be distorted, dissociated, and ambiguous, so the details of a
story (say Poe's "A Descent into the Maelstrom") may be
vivid and its exposition persuasive, without our taking the
performance as anything but clever make-believe. Realism of
method is a tool of every sort of writer, especially the writer of
the fantastic. On the other hand, a Stephen Crane could handle
individual images and details with a most cavalier impressionism
and still make them serve a larger realism of intention. Inten-
tional realism makes a cardinal virtue not of cleverness or vividness, but of honesty—an honesty that is as apparent in the fussy
linguistic studies of some of the local colorists as in De Forest's
emetic pictures of field hospitals after a battle. Stephen Crane
called "The Open Boat" "a tale intended to be after the fact."
Howells demanded what was "simple, natural, and honest."
And since man himself is a part of observable nature, realism
must be extended to include the honest penetration of motives,
aberrations, states of consciousness, and thus give shelter to
"psychological realists" such as James and Crane. The term is
less applicable to the naturalists, the "realists on all fours," who
began to emerge around the turn of the century. It is possible
to feel that Norris and London almost totally abandoned realism by fraternizing with distortion, and by abandoning Howells'
criteria of "the simple, the natural, and the honest." Though
presumably based on "scientific" views of man, Norris's Mc-
Teague is compounded from a recipe not greatly different from
that for a golem; and the beast that lurks in Vandover would
not feel lost if he were transplanted to the Castle of Otranto.

Take the realistic movement, then, not as a coherent and
purposeful system but as a series of approximations whose
period of closest approximation in America was 1865 to 1890.
Unfortunately for historians, intellectual history is always improvised; as Constance Rourke remarks, a people does not plan
its tradition. And literary realism is chronologically entangled
with many other things. The nineteenth century saw America
grow up as a world power and partly grow up as a culture; after
the Civil War the agrarian and mercantilist nation was over-

almost the whole tribe did, realists implied a preference for the ordinary events, the observable characters, the real places, as against the heroic, the bizarre, the exotic, the spectacular. Experience they were likely to appraise by the consensus method, and even literary taste might seem to reside, as Howells and Garland and on occasion Twain saw it residing, in the "glance of the common eye," in the democratic mass. Nevertheless, none of the realists or half-realists we shall consider defended a photographic transcription of life. An artist might deal himself a hand from life, and arrange the cards in it, though he should not stack the deck.

Concentration upon the phrase "without distortion" will keep us close to the intentions, if not always the practice, of the realistic school: to Mark Twain's insistence on accuracy of observation, his invocation of the authority of personal experience, his hatred of the "Sir Walter disease"; to Eggleston's low-keyed sociological honesty; to Howells' championship of the commonplace and his belief that realism is "nothing more and nothing less than the truthful treatment of material"; and even (to dip down into subliterary levels where much American realism began and where some limited forms of it have remained) to the jingling advice of James Whitcomb Riley:

> Tell of the things just like they was, they don't need no excuse,
> Don't tech 'em as the poet does, till they're all too fine for use.

However unuseful that doctrine might have been to Henry James, its dialectal folksiness, its pragmatic tone, and its suspicion of the effete and "literary" are characteristic of a whole body of literature that just as surely as the works of James himself belongs under the loose title of realism.

A preliminary distinction should be made between what we may call realism of *method* and realism of *intention*. The first is a technique of persuasion whose end is verisimilitude, a shoehorn to ease us into the "temporary suspension of disbelief" that Coleridge called poetic faith. Howells lumped its tricks and tendencies under Valdés' term "effectism." Just as the images of

INTRODUCTION

A discussion of what is called realism should begin with a definition. But definition of a literary trend is complicated by the fact that, as Harry Levin has remarked of Flaubert, a writer may reconcile in practice things intractably contrary in theory. The so-called realists of post-Civil War America combine tendencies quite as incongruous as Flaubert's mixture of naturalism, impressionism, and symbolism—so many that one is half tempted to wonder if the embracing of incompatibilities is not almost a rule of creative nature; if, to paraphrase Henry Adams, chaos is not the law of writers, and order the dream of critics.

Moreover, defining realism implies defining the real, and defining the real can involve us with solipsistic theories that dissolve our terms. It may be that reality, like beauty, is in the eye of the beholder, that perception and its echo, memory, are the only truth. Nevertheless, James and Crane were the only nineteenth century realists much concerned with the person of the observer, and even their impressionism did not hinder them from admitting the existence of the external, objective, sensuously-perceptible world, and defining realism, essentially, as the literary method which proposed to present it without distortion.

"Without distortion," notice. All art presents the perceived world; it has nothing else to present. But realism set limitations upon the ways in which observed details might be *arranged*. It set high value upon scientific detachment and objectivity; it prohibited a writer from warping his materials to the service of a thesis or a sentiment. In admitting the tests of experience and verification, as Howells, Twain, De Forest, Eggleston, and

broideries; bonnets and gloves; for the *corbeille* had been of rare quality.

The last thing to go was a tiny bundle of letters; innocent little scribblings that Désirée had sent to him during the days of their espousal. There was the remnant of one back in the drawer from which he took them. But it was not Désirée's; it was part of an old letter from his mother to his father. He read it. She was thanking God for the blessing of her husband's love:—

"But, above all," she wrote, "night and day, I thank the good God for having so arranged our lives that our dear Armand will never know that his mother, who adores him, belongs to the race that is cursed with the brand of slavery."

Hamlin Garland

1860-1940

from MAIN-TRAVELLED ROADS

A DAY'S PLEASURE

(1899)

When Markham came in from shovelling his last wagon-load of corn into the crib he found that his wife had put the children to bed, and was kneading a batch of dough with the dogged action of a tired and sullen woman.

He slipped his soggy boots off his feet, and having laid a piece of wood on top of the stove, put his heels on it comfortably. His chair squeaked as he leaned back on its hinder legs, but he paid no attention; he was used to it, exactly as he was used to his wife's lameness and ceaseless toil.

"That closes up my corn," he said after a silence. "I guess I'll go to town to-morrow to git my horses shod."

"I guess I'll git ready and go along," said his wife, in a sorry attempt to be firm and confident of tone.

"What do you want to go to town fer?" he grumbled.

"What does anybody want to go to town fer?" she burst out, facing him. "I ain't been out o' this house fer six months, while you go an' go!"

"Oh, it ain't six months. You went down that day I got the mower."

"When was that? The tenth of July, and you know it."

"Well, mebbe 'twas. I didn't think it was so long ago. I ain't no objection to your goin', only I'm goin' to take a load of wheat."

"Well, jest leave off a sack, an' that'll balance me an' the baby," she said spiritedly.

"All right," he replied good-naturedly, seeing she was roused. "Only that wheat ought to be put up to-night if you're goin'. You won't have any time to hold sacks for me in the morning with them young ones to get off to school."

"Well, let's go do it then," she said, sullenly resolute.

"I hate to go out agin; but I s'pose we'd better."

He yawned dismally and began pulling his boots on again, stamping his swollen feet into them with grunts of pain. She put on his coat and one of the boy's caps, and they went out to the granary. The night was cold and clear.

"Don't look so much like snow as it did last night," said Sam. "It may turn warm."

Laying out the sacks in the light of the lantern, they sorted out those which were whole, and Sam climbed into the bin with a tin pail in his hand, and the work began.

He was a sturdy fellow, and he worked desperately fast; the shining tin pail dived deep into the cold wheat and dragged heavily on the woman's tired hands as it came to the mouth of the sack, and she trembled with fatigue, but held on and dragged the sacks away when filled, and brought others, till at last Sam climbed out, puffing and wheezing, to tie them up.

"I guess I'll load 'em in the morning," he said. "You needn't wait fer me. I'll tie 'em up alone."

"Oh, I don't mind," she replied, feeling a little touched by his unexpectedly easy acquiescence to her request. When they went back to the house the moon had risen.

It had scarcely set when they were wakened by the crowing roosters. The man rolled stiffly out of bed and began rattling at the stove in the dark, cold kitchen.

His wife arose lamer and stiffer than usual, and began twisting her thin hair into a knot.

Sam did not stop to wash, but went out to the barn. The woman, however, hastily soused her face into the hard lime-stone water at the sink, and put the kettle on. Then she called the children. She knew it was early, and they would need several callings. She pushed breakfast forward, running over in her mind the things she must have: two spools of thread, six yards of cotton flannel, a can of coffee, and mittens for Kitty. These she must have—there were oceans of things she needed.

The children soon came scudding down out of the darkness of the upstairs to dress tumultuously at the kitchen stove. They humped and shivered, holding up their bare feet from the cold floor, like chickens in new fallen snow. They were ir-ritable, and snarled and snapped and struck like cats and dogs. Mrs. Markham stood it for a while with mere commands to "hush up," but at last her patience gave out, and she charged down on the struggling mob and cuffed them right and left.

They ate their breakfast by lamplight, and when Sam went back to his work around the barnyard it was scarcely dawn. The children, left alone with their mother, began to tease her to let them go to town also.

"No, sir—nobody goes but baby. Your father's goin' to take a load of wheat."

She was weak with the worry of it all when she had sent the older children away to school and the kitchen work was fin-ished. She went into the cold bedroom off the little sitting room and put on her best dress. It had never been a good fit, and now she was getting so thin it hung in wrinkled folds everywhere about the shoulders and waist. She lay down on the bed a moment to ease that dull pain in her back. She had a moment's distaste for going out at all. The thought of sleep was more alluring. Then the thought of the long, long day, and the sickening sameness of her life, swept over her again, and she rose and prepared the baby for the journey.

It was but little after sunrise when Sam drove out into the road and started for Belleplain. His wife sat perched upon the wheat-sacks behind him, holding the baby in her lap, a cotton quilt under her, and a cotton horse-blanket over her knees.

Sam was disposed to be very good-natured, and he talked back at her occasionally, though she could only understand him when he turned his face toward her. The baby stared out at the passing fence-posts, and wiggled his hands out of his mittens at every opportunity. He was merry at least.

It grew warmer as they went on, and a strong south wind arose. The dust settled upon the woman's shawl and hat. Her hair loosened and blew unkemptly about her face. The road which led across the high, level prairie was quite smooth and dry, but still it jolted her, and the pain in her back increased. She had nothing to lean against, and the weight of the child grew greater, till she was forced to place him on the sacks beside her, though she could not loose her hold for a moment.

The town drew in sight—a cluster of small frame houses and stores on the dry prairie beside a railway station. There were no trees yet which could be called shade trees. The pitilessly severe light of the sun flooded everything. A few teams were hitched about, and in the lee of the stores a few men could be seen seated comfortably, their broad hat-rims flopping up and down, their faces brown as leather.

Markham put his wife out at one of the grocery-stores, and drove off down toward the elevators to sell his wheat.

The grocer greeted Mrs. Markham in a perfunctorily kind manner, and offered her a chair, which she took gratefully. She sat for a quarter of an hour almost without moving, leaning against the back of the high chair. At last the child began to get restless and troublesome, and she spent half an hour helping him amuse himself around the nail-kegs.

At length she rose and went out on the walk, carrying the baby. She went into the dry-goods store and took a seat on one of the little revolving stools. A woman was buying some woollen goods for a dress. It was worth twenty-seven cents a yard, the clerk said, but he would knock off two cents if she took ten yards. It looked warm, and Mrs. Markham wished she could afford it for Mary.

A pretty young girl came in and laughed and chatted with the clerk, and bought a pair of gloves. She was the daughter of the grocer. Her happiness made the wife and mother sad. When Sam came back she asked him for some money.

"What you want to do with it?" he asked.

"I want to spend it," she said.

She was not to be trifled with, so he gave her a dollar.

"I need a dollar more."

"Well, I've got to go take up that note at the bank."

"Well, the children's got to have some new underclo'es," she said.

He handed her a two-dollar bill and then went out to pay his note.

She bought her cotton flannel and mittens and thread, and then sat leaning against the counter. It was noon, and she was hungry. She went out to the wagon, got the lunch she had brought, and took it into the grocery to eat it—where she could get a drink of water.

The grocer gave the baby a stick of candy and handed the mother an apple.

"It'll kind o' go down with your doughnuts," he said.

After eating her lunch she got up and went out. She felt ashamed to sit there any longer. She entered another dry-goods store, but when the clerk came toward her saying, "Anything to-day, Mrs. ——?" she answered, "No, I guess not," and turned away with foolish face.

She walked up and down the street, desolately homeless. She did not know what to do with herself. She knew no one except the grocer. She grew bitter as she saw a couple of ladies pass, holding their demi-trains in the latest city fashion. Another woman went by pushing a baby carriage, in which sat a child just about as big as her own. It was bouncing itself up and down on the long slender springs, and laughing and shouting. Its clean round face glowed from its pretty fringed hood. She looked down at the dusty clothes and grimy face of her own little one, and walked on savagely.

She went into the drug store where the soda fountain was, but it made her thirsty to sit there and she went out on the street again. She heard Sam laugh, and saw him in a group of men over by the blacksmith shop. He was having a good time and had forgotten her.

Her back ached so intolerably that she concluded to go in and rest once more in the grocer's chair. The baby was growing cross and fretful. She bought five cents' worth of candy to take home to the children, and gave baby a little piece to keep him quiet. She wished Sam would come. It must be getting late. The grocer said it was not much after one. Time seemed terribly long. She felt that she ought to do something while she was in town. She ran over her purchases—yes, that was all she had planned to buy. She fell to figuring on the things she needed. It was terrible. It ran away up into twenty or thirty dollars at the least. Sam, as well as she, needed underwear for the cold winter, but they would have to wear the old ones, even if they were thin and ragged. She would not need a dress, she thought bitterly, because she never went anywhere. She rose and went out on the street once more, and wandered up and down, looking at everything in the hope of enjoying something.

A man from Boon Creek backed a load of apples up to the sidewalk, and as he stood waiting for the grocer he noticed Mrs. Markham and the baby, and gave the baby an apple. This was a pleasure. He had such a hearty way about him. He on his part saw an ordinary farmer's wife with dusty dress, unkempt hair, and tired face. He did not know exactly why she appealed to him, but he tried to cheer her up.

The grocer was familiar with these bedraggled and weary wives. He was accustomed to see them sit for hours in his big wooden chair, and nurse tired and fretful children. Their forlorn, aimless, pathetic wandering up and down the street was a daily occurrence, and had never possessed any special meaning to him.

II

In a cottage around the corner from the grocery store two men and a woman were finishing a dainty luncheon. The woman was dressed in cool, white garments, and she seemed to make the day one of perfect comfort.

The home of the Honorable Mr. Hall was by no means the costliest in the town, but his wife made it the most attractive. He was one of the leading lawyers of the county, and a man of culture and progressive views. He was entertaining a friend who had lectured the night before in the Congregational church.

They were by no means in serious discussion. The talk was rather frivolous. Hall had the ability to caricature men with a few gestures and attitudes, and was giving to his Eastern friend some descriptions of the old-fashioned Western lawyers he had met in his practice. He was very amusing, and his guest laughed heartily for a time.

But suddenly Hall became aware that Otis was not listening. Then he perceived that he was peering out of the window at some one, and that on his face a look of bitter sadness was falling.

Hall stopped. "What do you see, Otis?"

Otis replied, "I see a forlorn, weary woman."

Mrs. Hall rose and went to the window. Mrs. Markham was walking by the house, her baby in her arms. Savage anger and weeping were in her eyes and on her lips, and there was hopeless tragedy in her shambling walk and weak back.

In the silence Otis went on: "I saw the poor, dejected creature twice this morning. I couldn't forget her."

"Who is she?" asked Mrs. Hall, very softly.

"Her name is Markham; she's Sam Markham's wife," said Hall.

The young wife led the way into the sitting room, and the men took seats and lit their cigars. Hall was meditating a diversion when Otis resumed suddenly:

"That woman came to town to-day to get a change, to have a little play-spell, and she's wandering around like a starved and weary cat. I wonder if there is a woman in this town with sympathy enough and courage enough to go out and help that woman? The saloon-keepers, the politicians, and the grocers make it pleasant for the man—so pleasant that he forgets his wife. But the wife is left without a word."

Mrs. Hall's work dropped, and on her pretty face was a look of pain. The man's harsh words had wounded her—and wakened her. She took up her hat and hurried out on the walk. The men looked at each other, and then the husband said:

"It's going to be a little sultry for the men around these diggings. Suppose we go out for a walk."

Delia felt a hand on her arm as she stood at the corner.

"You look tired, Mrs. Markham; won't you come in a little while? I'm Mrs. Hall."

Mrs. Markham turned with a scowl on her face and a biting word on her tongue, but something in the sweet, round little face of the other woman silenced her, and her brow smoothed out.

"Thank you kindly, but it's most time to go home. I'm looking fer Mr. Markham now."

"Oh, come in a little while, the baby is cross and tired out; please do."

Mrs. Markham yielded to the friendly voice, and together the two women reached the gate just as two men hurriedly turned the other corner.

"Let me relieve you," said Mrs. Hall.

The mother hesitated: "He's so dusty."

"Oh, that won't matter. Oh, what a big fellow he is! I haven't any of my own," said Mrs. Hall, and a look passed like an electric spark between the two women, and Delia was her willing guest from that moment.

They went into the little sitting room, so dainty and lovely to the farmer's wife, and as she sank into an easy-chair she was faint and drowsy with the pleasure of it. She submitted to being brushed. She gave the baby into the hands of the Swedish girl, who washed its face and hands and sang it to sleep, while its mother sipped some tea. Through it all she lay back in her easy-chair, not speaking a word, while the ache passed out of her back, and her hot, swollen head ceased to throb.

But she saw everything—the piano, the pictures, the curtains, the wall-paper, the little tea-stand. They were almost as grateful to her as the food and fragrant tea. Such housekeeping as this she had never seen. Her mother had worn her kitchen floor thin as brown paper in keeping a speckless house, and she had been in houses that were larger and costlier, but something of the charm of her hostess was in the arrangement of vases, chairs, or pictures. It was tasteful.

Mrs. Hall did not ask about her affairs. She talked to her about the sturdy little baby, and about the things upon which Delia's eyes dwelt. If she seemed interested in a vase she was told what it was and where it was made. She was shown all the pictures and books. Mrs. Hall seemed to read her visitor's mind. She kept as far from the farm and her guest's affairs as possible, and at last she opened the piano and sang to her— not slow-moving hymns, but catchy love-songs full of sentiment, and then played some simple melodies, knowing that Mrs. Markham's eyes were studying her hands, her rings, and the flash of her fingers on the keys—seeing more than she heard—and through it all Mrs. Hall conveyed the impression that she, too, was having a good time.

The rattle of the wagon outside roused them both. Sam was at the gate for her. Mrs. Markham rose hastily. "Oh, it's almost sundown!" she gasped in astonishment as she looked out of the window.

"Oh, that won't kill anybody," replied her hostess. "Don't

hurry. Carrie, take the baby out to the wagon for Mrs. Markham while I help her with her things."

"Oh, I've had such a good time," Mrs. Markham said as they went down the little walk.

"So have I," replied Mrs. Hall. She took the baby a moment as her guest climbed in. "Oh, you big, fat fellow!" she cried as she gave him a squeeze. "You must bring your wife in oftener, Mr. Markham," she said, as she handed the baby up.

Sam was staring with amazement.

"Thank you, I will," he finally managed to say.

"Good-night," said Mrs. Markham.

"Good-night, dear," called Mrs. Hall, and the wagon began to rattle off.

The tenderness and sympathy in her voice brought the tears to Delia's eyes—not hot or bitter tears, but tears that cooled her eyes and cleared her mind.

The wind had gone down, and the red sunlight fell mistily over the world of corn and stubble. The crickets were still chirping and the feeding cattle were drifting toward the farmyards. The day had been made beautiful by human sympathy.

Mary Hallock Foote

1847-1938

HOW THE PUMP STOPPED
AT THE MORNING WATCH

Editor's Note: Mary Hallock Foote was both writer and illustrator, and the fact that her husband, Arthur Foote, was a mining engineer gave her unprecedented opportunities to observe at first hand the life of a series of mining camps in the West: New Almaden, in California; Leadville, in Colorado; Boise and Coeur d'Alene, in Idaho; and finally Grass Valley, in the Sierra Nevada. Her writings reflect all of them—the only serious writing after Bret Harte to deal with mining-camp society, and virtually the only serious fiction which has dealt with the camps from intimate knowledge.

The present story was published in *Century Magazine* in June, 1899, but I saw it first in a typed, hand-sewn, and hand-bound copy which Mrs. Foote had made as an intimate childhood gift for her granddaughter, Mrs. Tyler Micoleau of Grass Valley. It was written sometime between October, 1896, and its publication date in 1899, and is included in this collection partly because it is one of Mrs. Foote's better stories, and shorter than most; and partly because, in the Foote papers now in the Stanford University Library, there are three letters to Helena DeKay Gilder which indicate part of the process by which mining-camp fact was transmuted into fiction. The letters reveal Mrs. Foote's painstaking intention to get the facts right —to deal fairly with the real life of the mines—and also her concern to get behind the facts to what she called the "human element," the significance of facts for people, the meaning of events in human terms.

The first of the three letters, for which I am indebted to Mr. George McMurry, is dated from Grass Valley, October 16, 1896. It speaks of Mrs. Foote's difficulty in getting the "feel" of this new place, so "stern and concentrated," so different from the raw newness of Idaho, from which she had just come. Then it summarizes what would later become the central incident of "How the Pump Stopped":

There was a tragedy in the mine the other day. John Thomas, an Englishman, who had been pump-man at the North Star for many years, was killed in the shaft. The first I knew of it Clemmo, the gardener, came to the kitchen door asking for an umbrella: "Any old one will do." Then he explained that the pump-man had been hurt and he wanted the umbrella to hold over him as they were carrying him home. I made the useless enquiries that one makes, and the useless offers: then I saw them carrying the old man by the house, on a mattress, six men, and Clemmo holding the umbrella over the head. His arms were bare to the elbow and crossed on his breast, and white in the sun as bleached bones— His head was wrapped in something red, and his profile was majestic in its endurance and its pallor—and its *age*. The age of toil.

The North Star Mine Shaft is an incline shaft 2000 feet deep and more. There is a series of pumps worked by one pump rod and the pump-man has a most important trust—on the pumps depend the life of the mine. They think that this man, for some time, has not been quite right in his head. He used to come out above ground, the men say, "between shifts," and seemed dazed and not sure of where he was . . . No one spoke of this, for fear it might lose him his place; and they were not certain of his symptoms: but now it is thought that he did not know what he was doing when he came out into the hoisting shaft, and an empty car struck him going down, and dragged him a hundred feet.

We went to his funeral . . . Arthur and Captain Glewas (Capt. of the Mine) walked with the procession of miners. They followed him from his house to the church—hundreds of men— with the strong old country faces all Cornish or *English* (they make the distinction) pale from years underground. "You men who go down into the Mines, take Christ with you!" said the clergyman. "You do not know what day you may be going to your death— Take Christ with you!"

The singing was most thrilling. The men's voices, and the pure voices of the girls—very simple words—but a great volume of sound, and such sincerity. This, and two other Western funerals stand out in my mind . . . General Vinton's at Leadville—John Sherman's in Boise—though *mind* isn't the word for that—and this old man killed at his post—because his long years of service in the depths of the mine had strained his faculties . . .

The second letter, dated February 7, 1897, reports the second event on which the story would finally be built—the stopping of the pump. It did not occur in precisely the way the story has it occur, and in the difference may be observed something of how fiction, even realistic fiction, may legitimately warp history and fact to arrive at a human truth larger than the factual truth.

We have had a catastrophe at the North Star. The great spur wheel that drives the pump broke, three days ago, with a sound like the explosion of a magazine. The pump is old and the iron had crystalized. The pump rod is one half mile long! descending the incline Shaft (Main Shaft) and driving six or seven pumps at different stations, down to the 2000 foot level. All these pumps are stopped now, and the water is rising in the lower levels. Arthur is in San Francisco, attending to the casting of a new wheel . . .

The events of those two letters, recombined and given a relationship that in fact they did not have, gave Mrs. Foote the stuff of her story. The third letter makes it clear that the material continued to be recalcitrant, that shape and meaning were hard to come at, and that for all her attempts at understanding and sympathy she found the "Cousin Jacks" difficult people to like. It may have been this difficulty, which she ultimately ignored entirely in order to get the story written, which persuaded her not to publish it: she may have felt it a failure, down "in the same rut with all the other new Western and Mining stories." This third letter is dated January 3, 1898, close to two years after the first.

. . . I have to soak things in long and silently before I can make any fit use of them. There is material here, but it requires strong and original handling—else it will go into the same rut with all the other new Western and Mining stories . . . and there are enough of them.

I haven't got down to the human element here, yet. It is difficult to do so, for there is a different race, first, to comprehend. The Cornish are a peculiar people—and the second generation has taken a start and changed the type and made it still less to be taken for granted.

The worst is they are a false people—and to write of them one could hardly leave out their timidity and propensity to underhandedness, but one must deal with them largely, not on local or personal lines.

Get a big strong theme first, that will sweep along the personal and local elements and fuse them into a homogeneous talk that will not suggest Grass Valley, or anywhere—I haven't been long enough in Grass Valley to get outside of Grass Valley . . .

The main shaft of the Morning Watch is an incline, sunk on the vein to a depth below daylight of eighteen hundred feet; there are lower workings still, in the twenty-one hundred, for the mine is one of the patriarchs of the golden age in northern California and its famous vein, though small, has been richly persistent.

The shaft is a specimen of good early construction in deep mining; it has two compartments, answering to the two vital functions of pumping and hoisting. A man walking up the hoist may step into the pump shaft between timbers to avoid a car, but he must then be wary of the pump rod.

The pump rod at the Morning Watch is half a mile long; with a measured movement, mighty, conclusive, slow, it crawls a little way up the shaft, waits a breath, then plunges down, and you hear subterranean sobs and gulpings where the twelve pumps at their stations are sucking water from the mine. These are the water guard which is never relieved. Nights and Sundays, frost or flood or dry, the pumps never rest. Each lifts its load to the brother above him, sweating cold sweat and smeared with grease and slime, fighting the climbing waters. The stroke of the pump rod is the pulse of the mine. If the pulse should stop and the waters rise, the pumps as they go under are "drowned". In their bitter costliness, in the depths from which they rise, though born in sunlight, the waters of the "sump" might typify the encroaching power of evil in man's nature—a power that springs from good, that yet may be turned to good, but over which conscience, like the pumps, must keep unsleeping watch and ward.

Between the Cornish miner and the Cornish pump there is a constitutional affinity and an ancient hereditary understanding. Both are governed and driven by the power on top; both have held their own underground from generation to generation without change or visible improvement. They do their work by virtue of main strength and dogged constancy, and neither one can be hurried.

On this last head, the pump-man will answer for his pump— speaking of it as of an old comrade, in the masculine singular, if you ask how many beats of the great connecting rod are normal:—

" 'E 'ave been as 'igh as seven and a quarter; 'e 'ave been, but it do strain 'im. Seven, about seven, is what 'e can bear."

John Trenberth of Penzance, spoken of familiarly as "old John," was pump-man first and last at the Morning Watch. He was there when the first pump-station was put in and the rod was but four hundred feet long. He saw that mighty member grow, section by section, pump added to pump, as the shaft went down. Each new pump was as a child born to him; there was room in his pride always for one more. If one had a failing more than another, he made a study of its individual crankiness and learned to spare the fault he could not remedy nor hide. To the mining captain, to whom he was forced to go for supplies, he might confess that "No. 5, 'e do chaw up more packin' than all the pumps in the mine"; but in general it was like touching upon delicate family matters with old John to question the conduct of his pumps.

He was a just man, Trenberth, but not perfect; he had his temporal bonds. It went hard with him on the Lord's day to choose between the public duty of worship in the miners' church above ground and his private leaning towards his pumps below. Can a man do his work in this world too well? Excessive devotion to the interests of the mine was not a common fault with its employees. The boys at the Morning Watch made friendly sport of the old enthusiast, declaring that he took his pumps to bed with him and dreamed at night of their kicking and bucking. It is true that the thought of Sammy Trebilcox, and what he might be doing or not doing as his substitute underground, took the heart out of his Sabbath observances and made his day of rest, when he gave himself one, the longest of the seven. Wherefore his little wife—"a good bit older nor 'e"—and a woman of grave disposition saddened by the want of children—sat mournful in church without her man, and thought of his clean shirts folded in the drawer at home and of him in his week day livery of mud, earning unblessed wages underground. She knew it was not the extra day's pay that ensnared him; her prayer was that he be delivered from pride in carnal labors, and that he make not unto himself a graven image and an idol of "they pumps".

A pump-man has his regular shifts; but so well known was the quality of John's service that not a man about the mine, from the oldest tributer to the new superintendent, would have questioned his appearance above ground at any irregular hour of the day or night. He looked, when he came on top, like some old piece of mining machinery that has been soaked underground for half a century—plastered with pallid mud of the deepest levels, coated with grease and stained with rust from fondlings of his pumps,—the recognizably human parts of him, his unsunned face and hands, pitted and drawn with steam.

The day's pay men were lively in the stopes; the car-boys romped with the landing men, and chalked the names of one another's sweethearts on the sides of the refractory cars; every tributer in the old workings had his partner to help him hammer out a "crushin'"; the contractors tunneled and drifted and argued in gangs; but old John, in the bowels of the mine, with death within a foot of him on either side, kept his one man watch alone. In his work there was no variety, no change of surroundings or of seasons, no irrelevant object to rest his fixed attention; solitude, monotony, and ceaseless nagging vigilance, imprisoned in a tube of darkness between the crashing of the cars on the one hand and the squeeze of the rod on the other.

Iron will crystallize after years of such use, lose its elasticity and cohesive strength. Old John had ceased to find pleasure in society or sunlight. He chose the darkest paths going home through the woods, the old roads deep in pine needles undisturbed by passing feet. The sound of a boy's whoop or a man's hearty halloo drove him deeper into the shade. If spoken to, he had no answer ready but would whisper one to himself, later, with his eyes on the ground.

Once the night shift, going down, saw the old man bare

headed in the hoist-shaft, standing motionless on the track, his hand up as if listening. He appeared not to hear the noise of the car, or to have heard it from some imaginary direction. They waved, they roared to him, and he vanished in the pump-shaft. Afterward they remembered his stare of bewilderment as if he had come awake suddenly in a strange place, uncertain how he had got there. Sometimes he would pop up like a stage ghost in the hoisting works, haggard and panting, as if in urgent haste. Greeted with jocular questioning, he would gaze about him vaguely, turn, and plunge down again without a word.

The wife began to hear from relatives and neighbors disquieting comments on her husband's looks.

"It's more than a whole month 'e 'aven't 'ad a Sunday off," said the buxom wife of one of the shift bosses. "Whatever is the sense of 'im workin' so 'ard, and you only two in family? A rest is what 'e need."

"Rest, dear! 'Aven't I telled 'im so, scores and scores of times! An' 'e just like a fish out o' water when 'e's parted from they pumps. 'E talk of 'em the same as they were humans—made of the same piece wi' 'is own flesh and blood."

"Eh! It's a bad lookout when a man can't leave his work behind 'im when the day is done. We belongs to 'ave our rest sometime. Why don't 'e coax 'im out more? 'Twould do him good to see the folks."

" 'E never was one to be coaxed. What 'e think right, that 'e'll do; man nor woman can't make 'im do other," Mrs. Trenberth would boast, proud of a husband's will unbroken after forty years of marriage.

One morning there was a summons for the mistress at the kitchen door of the superintendent's house.

"Clem' want see you—kitch'," was the Chinese cook's sketchy way of transmitting the message.

Clemmo was there, the gardener and general utility man. The two do not go together unless the man is good natured, as Clemmo was. He stood, hat in hand, in his deferential way, perspiring and quite noticeably pale. There was a catch in his breath from running. He had come to borrow an umbrella.

The mistress looked at him in surprise. It was cloudless summer weather, the hot valley steaming up in the face of the foothills, dust on the cloaking pine woods, red dust inches deep on all the roads and trails, dust like a steamer's smoke in the wake of ore teams miles away. The shadows of the mine buildings were short and black where a group of men had gathered, though the twelve bell had not yet struck. A sun umbrella did he mean?

"Any kind, ma'am; any old one will do," Clemmo repeated apologetically. "It's just to hold over Mr. Trenberth when they're carryin' him home. Yes, Ma'am, he was hurt in the shaft just now—an hour ago. Oh, yes, the doctor's seen him. He's pretty bad. It was an empty car struck him; dragged him quite a ways before the shaft men heard him scream. They can't tell just how it happened; he hasn't spoken since they brought him up. Yes, Ma'am, one of the boys has gone to tell the wife. They've got an old mattress to carry him on; they have brandy. No, Ma'am, there ain't anything, thank you— only the umbrella. Any old one will do."

When the umbrella was brought and it proved to be a silk one, Clemmo took it reluctantly, protesting that "any old one—", but the mistress cut him short. He went off with it finally, assuring her over his shoulder that he would carry it himself and see that it "came right back."

The Chinaman looked on calmly. "I think he pletty ole—he die pletty soon," he remarked.

Three little children were frolicking in the swing under the pine trees. Their mother quieted them out of respect for what was soon to pass the house; but she could not moderate the morning's display of pink faced roses, nor suggest to the sun to go under a brief cloud. All was heartless radiance and peace as the forlorn little procession came down the road —the workers carrying him home whose work was done; three men on a side, and between their stout backs and faces red with exertion, a broken shape stretched out and a stark white profile crowned with a bloody cloth.

What had the old man been doing in the hoist? "Fixin' up the bell rope," the mining captain said; "but it didn't look like any of John's work," he added meaningly. "He wasn't all there when he rigged up that thing. He'd slipped a cog, somehow.— Yes sir, you bet! A man in a shaft he's got to keep his eye out. He can watch for forty years, and the minute he forgets himself, that minute he's gone."

About the turn of the night, when the old man was nearing his end, he gave a loud cry and sprang up in bed, where he had lain speechless and helpless three days. The startled watchers flew to his side.

"Take your 'ands off me, women!" he panted. "I must up. Th' pump 'e's stopped!"

"Don't 'ee, deary!" The wife trembled at the look in his pinched gray face. "Don't 'ee be thinkin' o' they pumps no more. 'Owever could 'ee hear 'em, two miles away? Hark, now! 'Tis all as still as still."

It was so still, that windless summer night, they could hear the clock tick across the passage, and the hoarse straining of the dying man's breath as they struggled to hold him down. His weakness, not their strength, prevailed. He fell back on his pillows, and a passive, awestruck stare succeeded the energy of horror and resistance. His eyes were fixed, as one who watches spellbound the oncoming of a great disaster. They touched his still face; it was damp and cold. His chest pumped hard and slow.

"Two thousan' gone under! Drowned, drowned!" he whispered.

"'Tis all nothin' but they pumps!" the old wife grieved distractedly. She knew his time was short. "Oh, dear Savior, don't mind it of 'im! 'E were a hard worker, and a good man to me."

At that same hour, the night of John's release, when he had given his loud cry, the watchman at the mine heard above the roar of forty stamp heads a sound like a cannon smothered within walls. He rushed across to the hoisting works. There lay the great crown wheel of the pump, in pieces on the floor. The pump rod, settled on its chocks, had stopped with its last stroke.

One little cog, worn out, had dropped from its place; then two cogs came together, tooth to tooth, and the ten-ton wheel burst with a groan that had arrested the passing soul of the pump-man, duty bound to the last.

An old mine, or an old man, that is nearly worked out may run for years at small expense if no essential part gives way; but the cost of heavy repairs is too great a strain upon halting faith and an exhausted treasury. Even so small a thing as the dropping out of one little cog, in a system worth thousands to rebuild, may decide the question whether to give up or keep on.

In that moment of ultimate consciousness, the mystery of which is with the dead, it may be that old John beheld the whole sequence of disaster that was to follow the breaking of the pump. If he did foresee it all, as his ghostly eyes seemed to say, he accepted it as well; and that look of awe-struck, appealing submission in the face of immeasurable calamity he carried to the grave. Perhaps he had seen beyond the work of this world to some place of larger recompense where the unpaid increment of such service as his is waiting on the books. Perhaps he heard already the Master's patient "Well done."

While they were preaching the funeral sermon, his old enemy, the water of the black deeps, was creeping up, regaining ground which he and the pumps had fought for and defended, inch by inch and year by year.

"Two thousan' gone under!" The lowest pump is lost. Leave it where it drowned, at its post. Now there is hurry and rush of tearing up tracks before the levels are flooded; the order to shut down has come late. Pull out the pumps; the fight is over! They have taken up the track in the main incline; the water has reached the nine hundred, like the chill creeping up the limbs of a dying man. The old tributers take down their muddy mine suits from the change house walls; families will live poorer this winter for all that water in the mine. They go trooping home, boots and bundles over shoulder, by the paths their own feet have made. They meet no night shift coming on. Another year and those paths of labor will be deep in hush-ing pine needles; shadows of morning and evening will be the only change of shifts. The payrolls are closed; the last crushing has gone to the mill. The grave of ten millions is for sale cheap, with a thousand feet of water in it.

III Soldiers and Civilians

There is as yet no biography or extended critical study of De Forest; the best discussions are those of Gordon S. Haight, in his introductions to *Miss Ravenel's Conversion from Secession to Loyalty* (Harper & Brothers, 1939, and Rinehart Editions, 1955), and in Spiller, *et al.*, *Literary History of the United States*, 1948, Chapter 54. Ambrose Bierce, on the other hand, has been extensively studied. See Carey McWilliams, *Ambrose Bierce: A Biography*, 1929; C. Hartley Grattan, *Bitter Bierce: A Mystery of American Letters*, 1929; Franklin Walker, *Ambrose Bierce, the Wickedest Man in San Francisco*, 1941; Paul Fatout, *Ambrose Bierce, the Devil's Lexicographer*, 1951; and Napier Wilt, "Ambrose Bierce and the Civil War," *Amer. Lit.* (1929), I, 260-285.

On Henry James the literature is enormous. Particularly useful are Pelham Edgar, *Henry James: Man and Author*, 1927; Leon Edel, *The Untried Years: 1843-1870*, 1953; R. P. Blackmur, ed., *The Art of the Novel*, 1934—a compilation of James's prefaces to the New York Edition of his works; Joseph Warren Beach, *The Method of Henry James*, 1918; and F. O. Matthiessen, *Henry James: the Major Phase*, 1944. F. W. Dupee's *Henry James*, 1956, in the American Men of Letters Series, is a good brief biographical and critical study.

The full-length studies of Stephen Crane all have certain lacks. Thomas Beer's *Stephen Crane: A Study in American Letters*, 1923, is charming and perceptive, but omits much important data; John Berryman's *Stephen Crane*, 1950, Maxwell Geismar's discussion in *Rebels and Ancestors*, 1953, and Robert W. Stallman's in *Stephen Crane, An Omnibus*, 1952, all suffer from their authors' addiction to what Harry Levin calls the "inadmissible" in the interpretation of symbolism.

Frank Norris' own critical ideas are contained in his *The Responsibilities of the Novelist*, 1903. The best biographical and critical summaries are Franklin Walker, *Frank Norris: A Biography*, 1932, and Ernest Marchand, *Frank Norris: A Study*, 1942. See also Charles C. Walcutt, "Frank Norris on Realism and Naturalism," *Amer. Lit.* (1941), XIII, 61-63.

John W. De Forest

1826-1906

THE FIRST TIME UNDER FIRE

(1864)

Editor's Note: The original of "The First Time Under Fire" was published in *Harper's New Monthly Magazine* in September, 1864. In the 1880's De Forest revised his war articles and letters and reordered them into a manuscript entitled *A Volunteer's Adventures,* which was among his papers when they were deposited in the Yale University library. This manuscript was edited by James H. Croushore and published by the Yale University Press in 1946. The present excerpt is reprinted from that edition by permission of Mr. Croushore and the Yale University Press.

We found the bridge in place, and the two sentinel howitzers barking at intervals, while an invisible Rebel battery responded with similar deliberation. Here we first came under fire, and here I first beheld a wounded man. In a country carriage, upheld by two Negroes, was a ghastly sufferer, his knee crushed by a shot, his torn trousers soaked with a dirty crimson, his eyes full of the agony of death. I did not want my men to see the dismaying spectacle and called their attention to something, I have forgotten what, on the other side of the bayou.

As we trotted down the inner slope of the levee a surprisingly loud, harsh scream passed over us, ending in a sharp explosion and a splashing in the muddy water. I was not alarmed, but rather relieved and gratified. If they can't aim better than that they are welcome to fire all day, I innocently thought. Then came another shell, striking close to the crowded bridge and spattering some of the men, but without deterring the thirsty ones from stopping to fill their canteens. It was very good practice, considering that the guns were behind the levee half a mile downstream, where the fellows who worked them could not see us. But I did not believe that they could hit me, and my chief anxiety was lest I should wet my feet in the sloppy bottom of the boat.

In general, the terror of battle is not an abiding impression, but comes and goes like throbs of pain; and this is especially the case with veterans who have learned to know when there is pressing danger and when not; the moment a peril has passed they are as tranquil as if it had never come near. On the present occasion I was not as yet conscious of any emotion which could be called fear. I was still ignorant of the great horrors of battle, and buoyed up by the excitement of a rapid advance. A regiment of well-drilled greenhorns, if neatly brought into action, can charge as brilliantly as veterans.

The moment we were up the western bank, on the same side of the bayou with Semmes, he lost sight of us behind a wood and ceased firing. Looking southerly, we noted the Eighth New Hampshire coming toward us in double column, ready to form square against cavalry. As we pushed on into the fields, marching tranquilly by the flank, an aide rode up with orders.

"Colonel, General Weitzel's compliments. He says the Eighth will be on your left; you will move more to the right and give it room to deploy. Then you will front southwards, throw out skirmishers, and follow them in line of battle. Beyond the wood is an open field. You will cross that and drive the enemy from his position."

Two companies successively filed to the left and deployed as skirmishers. The remaining six companies marched about five hundred yards from the bayou when they fronted into line of battle. Concealed by the wood, the Twelfth and Eighth now advanced toward Mouton's centre, while the two hostile batteries pounded away at each other, although neither could see the other's position. Emerging from a field of tall, rustling reeds, the Twelfth came to a strong post-and-rail fence, such as one often sees in Louisiana.

"Down with the fence!" shouted Lieutenant Colonel Colburn, our commander. "Throw it over!"

Some rushed against it and pushed it flat, while others climbed over it. Next came a scattered array of thorny thickets which embarrassed us wofully. We might have met bayonets in good order, but we were thrown into confusion by this host of briars. The lieutenant colonel yelled repeatedly, "Centre dress! Close up those gaps! Centre dress!" The company officers yelled also, repeating the same orders. In our inexperience we believed that everything was lost if the men did not march shoulder to shoulder; and all through the battle we labored to keep a straight line with a single-mindedness which greatly supported our courage.

"By the right of companies to the front," shouted Colburn when he saw that the thornbushes were breaking us. The regiment filed into six little parallel columns, moving by the flank, and threaded more easily the prickly labyrinth. When we reached clearer ground, it was, "Halt; front; right into line, wheel; forward, guide centre." And once more we advanced in line of battle, agreeably conscious of having drilled well under unfavorable circumstances, and wondering how soon the enemy would open on us.

As we reached the wood which hid us from Mouton our skirmishing companies dropped back upon us, and Roach, the senior captain, reported his discoveries. "Colonel, the Rebs are rather more than a quarter of a mile ahead of us. They are on the other side of a long open lot, behind a fence which lines a crossroad, and protected by a ditch in which they are lying."

"Oh!" roared one of my Irish soldiers. "They've got all the advantage of us."

"Hold your tongue, you blockhead," said I, fearing he would discourage his comrades. "Do you want all the advantages yourself?"

"No, Captain, I don't; but I want some kind of fair play; and I don't see the harrum of saying so."

As we approached the edge of the wood the hostile gunners caught sight of us, and a shell screamed over our heads, passing through the lower branches and sending down a shower of leaves. Nearly the whole regiment made a bow to it, though without halting or breaking. Stepping to the front, I turned to my men and said, "Excuse me for not bowing with you; I didn't think of it till it was too late." This was a bit of bravado suggested by fear that my raw soldiers were getting shaky and needed encouragement. Poor as the joke was it made them laugh, so slight as yet was their worry, if any.

The shells came fast now, most of them screeching over the colors, at which they were evidently aimed. Not only were the guns in front of us booming rapidly, but a battery across the bayou, half a mile below us, was pitching its iron about us at a venture. Meantime our two howitzers at the bridge, the only ones as yet brought into action by Weitzel, had ceased firing in order not to interfere with our advance. Of course this was absolutely necessary, but it dampened my confidence just a little. Even veterans like to hear a robust clamor from their own artillery.

The Southern shots flew lower and lower. I said to myself, "They will hurt somebody soon." I did not duck or dodge, for I reflected that a missile would hit me about the time that I should hear it; and moreover I believed that all my men were watching me, whereas they were probably staring at the enemy. It cost me no great effort to keep my head up and move onward in good parade style. I had no twitching or trembling; I was not aware of any quickening of the pulse; in short, I was not scared. The Rebel gunners might hit me, but somehow I hoped not and thought not. It seemed to me perfectly natural that others should be killed and that I should escape. I have suffered more worry in subsequent engagements than I did in this first time under fire.

Presently we came to a second stout fence of cypress posts and rails. "Now then, Twelfth!" yelled the lieutenant colonel.

"I told you to break that last fence down, and half of you climbed it. Down with this one! Go at it and flatten it. Forward, battalion, double-quick!"

With a rush we flung our breasts against the fence, laying many lengths of it prostrate. But the right company, floundering ankle-deep in bog, was obliged to climb it while the two left companies were balked by a thicket of thornbushes.

"By the right flank!" ordered the captains, and they filed around the obstacle; then, "By company into line!" and they came up into position on the run. These various manoeuvres caused a disorganizing crush towards the centre; and our commander feared that his regiment was going to pieces. "Halt!" he shouted; "guides on the line; centre dress."

The company guides sprang forward, faced toward the centre with rifle-butts aloft, and coolly aligned themselves as is usual in correcting the front of a regiment. But circumstances pressed, and very hurriedly came the next order, "Guides, posts; forward, battalion; guide centre."

We were just entering a large open field, dotted by a few trees and thornbushes, with a swampy forest on the right and the levee of the bayou on the left, when the Rebels gave us their musketry. It was not a volley but a file fire; it was a continuous rattle like that which a boy makes in running a stick along a picket fence, only vastly louder; and meantime the sharp *whit whit* of bullets chippered close to our ears. In the field before us puffs of dust jumped up here and there; on the other side of it a long roll of blue smoke curled upward; to the right of that the grey smoke of artillery rose in a thin cloud; but no other sign of an enemy was visible.

Now occurred a curious incident which might have brought disaster, had I not happened to be at the right of my company, near the color guard. We had two flags, the United States flag borne by a sergeant named Edwards and the Connecticut flag borne by a sergeant whom I forbear to name. This last man, on hearing the Rebel bullets, faced about and started rearward. I never saw anything done more naturally and promptly. He did not look wild with fright; he simply looked alarmed and resolved to get out of danger; it was the simplest and most persuaded expression of countenance imaginable. He was not a thorough coward, and never afterward turned tail that I know of; but he was confounded by the peril of the moment and thought of nothing but getting away from it.

It would have been lawful and right to pistol him, for he ran a risk of guiding the regiment rearward and bringing about defeat. In a great rage and with sabre uplifted, I pounced upon him as he was struggling through the color corporals, all of whom were pushing forward eagerly and gallantly. "Forward, or I'll split your head open," I shouted, catching him by the shoulder and facing him about. He obeyed in silence, with a curious dazed expression, and I pushed him into his place in the front rank of the color guard. We got two volleys after that; and at each one this man fell back a pace with a nervous start; but each time I howled "Forward!" in his ear and sent him on again.

There were plenty of other incidents, very interesting to raw soldiers. The first lieutenant of Company D saw with astonishment two of his men fall and roll over each other. To his mind they each seemed to be struggling to squirm undermost in order to escape the bullets. "Get into the ranks!" he ordered, hitting the uppermost with the flat of his sabre. One of them pointed to a bloody hole in his trousers and lay still; the other rose with a mazed air, picked up his rifle and ran after the company. A bullet had struck this man's gun barrel with such force as to knock him down, and then had glanced through the thigh of his rear-rank comrade, both falling in a heap.

The first lieutenant of Company G was pushing forward a laggard when the latter was struck in the breast by a fragment of shell and killed instantly. Private Judson of Company C flung up both hands with a scream and dropped dead with a ball through his heart. Private Atkins of my company had his rifle knocked off his shoulder by a bullet and hurled end over end behind him. Picking it up, he showed me the broken lock and asked what he should do.

"Fetch it along," I said. "We may have a chance to use the bayonet. We shall be up with them presently."

Bringing the gun to a right-shoulder-shift, he fell into his place and made the charge in that fashion.

At the second volley, hearing on my right a sharp crash of broken bone, followed by a loud "Oh" of pain and horror, I glanced that way and saw Color Sergeant Edwards fall slowly backward, with blood spirting from his mouth and a stare of woful amazement in his eyes. A bullet had shattered his front teeth and come out behind his left jaw. He clung to the colors as he dropped, but Corporals Dutton and Kelly dragged them out of his hands; and after a brief pully-hauly between the two they remained with Kelly, a veteran of the British army. He jumped to the front and strode onward, tranquilly chewing his tobacco and guiding his march by a tall tree in the centre of the Rebel position. I quickly saw that he was a thorough soldier, and turned to look after my own company.

All this time we were exposed to both cannon and musketry without being allowed to reply. "Oh dear! when shall we fire?" I heard one of the color corporals exclaim. I looked at the youngster; he was not a coward; his color was good. But to be boomed at and volleyed at without answering is one of the most serious trials of battle. There was a general feeling of relief, near akin to delight, when the lieutenant colonel's clear, metallic voice pealed out, "Halt! Fire by file! Commence firing!"

The men could not wait to fire by file, which is a graduated discharge running from right to left of each company; they leveled those five hundred rifles together and sent a grand, crashing volley into the hostile line of smoke which confronted them; for as yet we could see no other sign of an enemy. In the next second every one was loading his piece as if his life depended on the speed of the operation. Then of a sudden, to my utter amazement, the two centre companies fell on their faces. Turning upon the man nearest me, I threatened to kill him if he did not get up. "We were ordered to lie down," he explained, and my second lieutenant added, "That is so, Captain."

"It can't be," I replied. "The right of the regiment is advancing, and the colonel with it."

The men promptly rose, and firing had already recommenced, when I and others near me distinctly heard an order to lie down. Of course we obeyed, all the more smartly because just then a shell flew between the colors, screeching like a mad panther. I laughed at the haste of my plunge, and saw one of my soldiers laughing also, probably at his own undignified hurry. I never could learn positively who uttered that stentorian cry of "Lie down." One story was that it came from the Thirteenth Connecticut which was just then close in rear of us as a support. Afterwards, when I could think of it at leisure, it reminded me of those godlike voices which resounded in ancient battles, giving encouragement or spreading panic. It certainly was not uttered by our commander, for we presently heard him yelling, "Forward, Twelfth!"

In great haste we of the centre sprang up and recovered our place in line. It was the last stop or pause in our advance. We had been drilled long enough under fire, and we broke away from the lieutenant colonel. Once he tried his utmost to make us halt, dress the line and give a volley, as regulars are said to do in battle. But he might as well have ordered a regiment of screeching devils to halt. On we swept in the teeth of canister and musketry, every man loading and firing as fast as possible. There was such a pressure inward toward the colors that some of my lightweights were crowded out of their places, and we were three ranks deep instead of two. Little Sweeny, who belonged on the left of the company, fidgeted along the rear in search of a crack to poke his gun through until my second lieutenant dragged him back to his post and roared at him, "What in h—ll are you doing on the right?"

"Liftenant, I'm purtectin' thim colors," yelped Sweeny, and then sent a bullet over Mouton's rear guard.

The swearing mania was irrepressible. In the excitement of the charge it seemed as if every extremity of language was excusable, providing it would help towards victory. Did I think of the other world, which was so near? Not once. I was anxious for nothing but to keep a steady line, and to reach the enemy quickly. I did not exhort my soldiers to fight gallantly and fire coolly. They were fighting the best they knew how, and aiming as well as the quick-step would permit. Nearly all that I said might be summed up as repetitions of the two orders, "Close up" and "Guide right."

It was contrary to rules for me to remain in the front rank after the firing had commenced; but I had two lieutenants behind the line, and I thought it best to let my men see one of their officers. Marching where I did in the centre of the regiment, I noticed that it had forged slightly ahead of the flank companies, so that I could look easily in both directions. On our left the Eighth New Hampshire had been tangled up by a colonel who knew so little of drill that he tried to deploy from column into line by inversion, and kept bawling helplessly, "Deploy!" until scores of his men lost patience and hurried forward in squads, or singly, to skirmish with the enemy.

Weitzel, who was riding close at our heels, noted the disaster and hurried up the Thirteenth to replace the Eighth, which was sent back to meet a reported force of Rebel cavalry in our rear. Meantime we of the Twelfth tramped onward, keeping up our tumultuous fire and gradually straightening our line. Several times I thought impatiently, "Shall we ever get there?" I was angry because those Butternuts shot at us; and I wanted to make them quit it; wanted to whale them for it. I had sabre and revolver all ready, for of course I expected a severe hand-to-hand struggle; not having yet learned that bayonet fighting occurs mainly in newspapers and other works of fiction.

The field, as I have said, was some five hundred yards long. We had traversed more than half of it before I saw any Confederates; and their cannon I did not see at all, so well were they masked by shrubbery; I could only distinguish their position by the puffs of smoke which they shot forth. The first troops that we caught sight of came running down the cross-road from the forest on the west, as if they had been hastily summoned to re-enforce the line in front of us. I suppose that they were the Terre Bonne militiamen, about five hundred strong, mostly of French stock and not very zealous Rebels. Without forming or halting they opened a hasty sidelong fire, and then broke for the neighboring thickets, disappearing like young partridges.

Mouton's centre, the Crescents and the Eighteenth Louisiana, old soldiers and good ones, still remained firm. But ere we had got within a hundred yards of them, the guns on their right ceased firing; and a moment later swarms of men in grey uniforms sprang out of the ditch which had sheltered them, and fled at full speed; to my eyes they seemed to be jumping over each other like panic-stricken sheep. At this sight the Twelfth raised a scream of exultation and redoubled its uproar of musketry.

Just then a stunning volley, the voice of the Thirteenth coming into action, rang out on our left. It was given without orders from Colonel Birge, but the sight of the escaping enemy was an irresistible temptation. Forward trampled both regiments, smack up to the cypress fence, yelling with delight and blazing away at the woods, although the enemy had vanished like a dream. It was all that the officers could do to halt the excited men and put an end to their riotous shouting. I was amazed at the feebleness of the Southern resistance and could not imagine that we had already won the battle.

"Can't this firing be stopped?" I said to the lieutenant colonel. "Are we not wasting ammunition on a mere party of skirmishers?"

"Cease firing!" he ordered, riding down the line; and with no little difficulty quiet was restored.

"Can't the regiment push into the woods?" I now queried. "The enemy may reform there and drive us back."

The lieutenant colonel improved on my suggestion; he ordered out two companies to search the wood. Meantime the captains of the remaining companies reformed ranks, counted off their men and had the roll called. We had scarcely got into shape when we heard a cheer on our left and saw that Weitzel was making a speech to the Thirteenth. What he said to our comrades in victory I could not hear, but his address to us was an admirable bit of practical instruction.

"Twelfth Connecticut, you have done well. That is the way to do it. Never stop, and the enemy won't stay."

"That is the best speech I ever heard," commented one of my men.

Of course the regiment hurrahed vaingloriously for the general and for itself. Our lieutenant colonel now had a dialogue with us.

"Twelfth, you have done well," he declared. "But not so well as I had hoped."

A *Voice*. "What did you want, Colonel? We made them skedaddle."

Lieutenant Colonel. "Yes, I know that. That was all right. But I wanted you to do it more coolly. After the drilling that you have had I thought you would go through it like a parade. I tried to halt you in the middle of the field to dress the line and fire a volley. I shouted at you with all my might; but I couldn't get you to stop."

Voices. "We didn't hear a word of it, Colonel."

Lieutenant Colonel. "I suppose not. I don't see how you could hear when you were yelling so and keeping up such a fire. I never heard such a racket before. And now, color guard, why didn't you shake out those colors?"

Color Sergeant. "We rolled them up to go through the woods, Colonel."

Lieutenant Colonel. "That was all right. But next time, whenever you come to a clear spot, let them fly. Never mind the battle rents. They only make the old flag more glorious."

There was some grumbling at the unthankful tone of our commander's remarks. We thought that we had done our duty as well as could be expected, considering the difficulties of the ground and the fact that it was our first fight. Even now, after a respectable experience under fire, I declare that I never saw a more dexterous, vigorous and effective advance, and that it reflected great credit on the training which we had received from our critical commander.

We had scarcely routed Mouton's main force before his left wing, presumably the Second Louisiana cavalry, appeared in our rear and began skirmishing with our baggage guard. But when it stumbled upon the Eighth New Hampshire, and divined therefrom how the main battle had gone, it lost heart and hurried off by a circuitous route to Thibodeaux.

Meantime Perkins' cavalry, a section of artillery and the Thirteenth Connecticut followed up the Crescents and the Eighteenth Louisiana. For half an hour longer we could hear the guns booming farther and farther southward. On the ground and in the boggy woods a fieldpiece was captured and about two hundred prisoners. The Twelfth caught the color sergeant of the Crescents up to his waist in mire, but he had torn off and hidden the cloth of his flag, and we merely secured the stick.

The night was chilly, but my servant brought up my overcoat from the rear, and I suffered little. The prisoners, being uniformed for the most part in coarse cottonade, and some of them soaked with swamp water, were piteously uncomfortable and gladly appropriated the ragged blankets of their dead comrades. Our fellows would have been as badly off, but that their clothing was all woolen. Their knapsacks and overcoats were across the bayou, three miles or more to the rear, and did not reach us till morning. But after pickets had been thrown out, the rest of the men collected rails and built huge campfires, around which they passed the night, chewing hardtack, smoking, and bragging of their victory. The Thirteenth, by the way, had returned from its pursuit, and shared our comfortless but contented bivouac.

From the prisoners we learned the cause of their precipitate flight from the battlefield. There was a swamp in their rear, and only one narrow road through it in the direction of Thibodeaux, so that retreat was difficult in case of disaster. Their immediate commander, Colonel McPheeters of the Crescent regiment, had to take this matter into consideration. He watched the fight with the Eighth composedly, until the Twelfth and Thirteenth appeared on the field. Then he said, "We could have fought that first regiment all day; but those other fellows are coming sure."

Thereupon he ordered the Crescents and the Eighteenth to jump up and run. He himself stood gazing at us, while his men thronged by him, and so standing received a bullet through the head. When our men reached him he was lying on his back and facing us, his head supported by a thornbush, his handsome face grey with death, and one eye lying on his cheek. He seemed to be about thirty years old, a man of noble height and presence, with Grecian features.

The prisoners spoke of him regretfully and tenderly as a brave officer and a thorough gentleman. It was the first retreat, they said, that he had ever ordered, although he had been in eight engagements. A captain added that our advance was a startling thing to look at from his side of the field. "We expected," he explained, "to see you come on in the usual style,—halt to fire and then advance again—not fire and come on all together."

"Your firing didn't hurt us," said a soldier. "But your coming on and yelling scared us."

One of the first men whom I beheld in the morning was Color Sergeant Edwards whom I had seen fall with what I supposed to be a mortal wound. He complained that his mouth was very sore and that he could swallow nothing but soup. All the same, having heard that we were to have another battle, he had dodged the surgeon and come to demand the colors. Of course a man with a bullet hole through his head could not fight, and he was ordered back to hospital where he had a long illness in the way of fever. One of the most noticeable things in warfare is the heroism frequently shown by the wounded.

Although I have described the combat of Labadieville at great length, it cost our regiment but three killed and sixteen wounded while the whole brigade lost but ninety-seven men. The fight had been short; from the passage of the first shell over the Twelfth to our victorious halt at the final fence only eighty minutes had elapsed; and during our charge across the open lot we had spoiled the enemy's aim by blazing away as we advanced. Some of the prisoners told us that, what with the whistling of our bullets and the flying of cypress splinters, their ditch was a most disagreeable hole to be in.

It was obvious that our musketry had killed the enemy's, for out of our nineteen hurt only six were hit by bullets. Notwithstanding our lieutenant colonel's criticism, I think we did wisely to blaze away while advancing, for, besides deranging the aim of the Southerners, it kept up the spirits of our own fellows, who thought they were doing as much harm as they received, and so felt that they had a fair chance. Of course there was some danger to the front rank from the rifles of the rear rank; for instance, I had my neck slightly scorched by the fire of one of my own soldiers.

The battle was a scientific one, and its science is perfectly comprehensible. It was won by an unexpected concentration on Mouton's centre, and this was possible through the forethought which provided the rude but serviceable pontoon bridge. It was also a scientifically interesting battle as showing the value of minutes. If we had been slow in our advance and hesitating in our charge, we might have been attacked in the rear, thrown into confusion, and beaten.

Mouton's plan was an excellent one, so far as he knew the facts of the situation. He proposed to "amuse" our main column on the eastern side of the bayou, and to concentrate his own main force on the front and rear of the Eighth New Hampshire, which seemed to him completely isolated. There was but one flaw in his tactics; he knew nothing of our bridge until the fight began. Weitzel hurried two regiments across the bayou, and their swift charge won a swift victory with little loss.

Henry James

1843-1916

FOUR MEETINGS

(1877)

I saw her but four times, though I remember them vividly; she
made her impression on me. I thought her very pretty and very
interesting—a touching specimen of a type with which I had
had other and perhaps less charming associations. I'm sorry to
hear of her death, and yet when I think of it why *should* I be?
The last time I saw her she was certainly not—! But it will be
of interest to take our meetings in order.

I

The first was in the country, at a small tea-party, one snowy
night some seventeen years ago. My friend Latouche, going to
spend Christmas with his mother, had insisted on my company, and the good lady had given in our honour the entertainment of which I speak. To me it was really full of savour
—it had all the right marks: I had never been in the depths of
New England at that season. It had been snowing all day and
the drifts were knee-high. I wondered how the ladies had made
their way to the house; but I inferred that just those general
rigours rendered any assembly offering the attraction of two
gentlemen from New York worth a desperate effort.

Mrs. Latouche in the course of the evening asked me if I
"didn't want to" show the photographs to some of the young

"Four Meetings" is reprinted by permission of John Farquharson
Ltd., representing the Estate of Henry James.

ladies. The photographs were in a couple of great portfolios, and had been brought home by her son, who, like myself, was lately returned from Europe. I looked round and was struck with the fact that most of the young ladies were provided with an object of interest more absorbing than the most vivid sun-picture. But there was a person alone near the mantelshelf who looked round the room with a small vague smile, a discreet, a disguised yearning, which seemed somehow at odds with her isolation. I looked at her a moment and then chose. "I should like to show them to that young lady."

"Oh yes," said Mrs. Latouche, "she's just the person. She doesn't care for flirting—I'll speak to her." I replied that if she didn't care for flirting she wasn't perhaps just the person; but Mrs. Latouche had already, with a few steps, appealed to her participation. "She's delighted," my hostess came back to report; "and she's just the person—so quiet and so bright." And she told me the young lady was by name Miss Caroline Spencer—with which she introduced me.

Miss Caroline Spencer was not quite a beauty, but was none the less, in her small odd way, formed to please. Close upon thirty, by every presumption, she was made almost like a little girl and had the complexion of a child. She had also the prettiest head, on which her hair was arranged as nearly as possible like the hair of a Greek bust, though indeed it was to be doubted if she had ever seen a Greek bust. She was "artistic," I suspected, so far as the polar influences of North Verona could allow for such yearnings or could minister to them. Her eyes were perhaps just too round and too inveterately surprised, but her lips had a certain mild decision and her teeth, when she showed them, were charming. About her neck she wore what ladies call, I believe, a "ruche" fastened with a very small pin of pink coral, and in her hand she carried a fan made of plaited straw and adorned with pink ribbon. She wore a scanty black silk dress. She spoke with slow soft neatness, even without smiles showing the prettiness of her teeth, and she seemed extremely pleased, in fact quite fluttered, at the prospect of my demonstrations. These went forward very smoothly after I had moved the portfolios out of their corner and placed a couple of chairs near a lamp. The photographs were usually things I knew—large views of Switzerland, Italy and Spain, landscapes, reproductions of famous buildings, pictures and statues. I said what I could for them, and my companion, looking at them as I held them up, sat perfectly still, her straw fan raised to her under-lip and gently, yet, as I could feel, almost excitedly, rubbing it. Occasionally, as I laid one of the pictures down, she said without confidence, which would have been too much: "Have you seen that place?" I usually answered that I had seen it several times—I had been a great traveller, though I was somehow particularly admonished not to swagger—and then I felt her look at me askance for a moment with her pretty eyes. I had asked her at the outset whether she had been to Europe; to this she had answered "No, no, no"—almost as much below her breath as if the image of such an event scarce, for solemnity, brooked phrasing. But after that, though she never took her eyes off the pictures, she said so little that I feared she was at last bored. Accordingly when we had finished one portfolio I offered, if she desired it, to desist. I rather guessed the exhibition really held her, but her reticence puzzled me and I wanted to make her speak. I turned round to judge better and then saw a faint flush in each of her cheeks. She kept waving her little fan to and fro. Instead of looking at me she fixed her eyes on the remainder of the collection, which leaned, in its receptacle, against the table.

"Won't you show me that?" she quavered, drawing the long breath of a person launched and afloat but conscious of rocking a little.

"With pleasure," I answered, "if you're really not tired."

"Oh I'm not tired a bit. I'm just fascinated." With which as I took up the other portfolio she laid her hand on it, rubbing it softly. "And have you been here too?"

On my opening the portfolio it appeared I had indeed been there. One of the first photographs was a large view of the Castle of Chillon by the Lake of Geneva. "Here," I said, "I've

been many a time. Isn't it beautiful?" And I pointed to the
perfect reflexion of the rugged rocks and pointed towers in
the clear still water. She didn't say "Oh enchanting!" and push
it away to see the next picture. She looked a while and then
asked if it weren't where Bonnivard, about whom Byron wrote,
had been confined. I assented, trying to quote Byron's verses,
but not quite bringing it off.

She fanned herself a moment and then repeated the lines
correctly, in a soft flat voice but with charming conviction.
By the time she had finished, she was nevertheless blushing. I
complimented her and assured her she was perfectly equipped
for visiting Switzerland and Italy. She looked at me askance
again, to see if I might be serious, and I added that if
she wished to recognize Byron's descriptions she must go
abroad speedily—Europe was getting sadly dis-Byronised.
"How soon must I go?" she thereupon enquired.

"Oh I'll give you ten years."

"Well, I guess I can go in *that* time," she answered as if
measuring her words.

"Then you'll enjoy it immensely," I said; "you'll find it of
the highest interest." Just then I came upon a photograph
of some nook in a foreign city which I had been very fond of
and which recalled tender memories. I discoursed (as I suppose) with considerable spirit; my companion sat listening
breathless.

"Have you been *very* long over there?" she asked some time
after I had ceased.

"Well, it mounts up, put all the times together."

"And have you travelled everywhere?"

"I've travelled a good deal. I'm very fond of it and happily
have been able."

Again she turned on me her slow shy scrutiny. "Do you
know the foreign languages?"

"After a fashion."

"Is it hard to speak them?"

"I don't imagine you'd find it so," I gallantly answered.

"Oh I shouldn't want to speak—I should only want to listen." Then on a pause she added: "They say the French theatre's so beautiful."

"Ah the best in the world."

"Did you go there very often?"

"When I was first in Paris I went every night."

"Every night!" And she opened her clear eyes very wide. "That to me is"—and her expression hovered—"as if you tell me a fairy-tale." A few minutes later she put to me: "And which country do you prefer?"

"There's one I love beyond any. I think you'd do the same."

Her gaze rested as on a dim revelation and then she breathed "Italy?"

"Italy," I answered softly too; and for a moment we communed over it. She looked as pretty as if instead of showing her photographs I had been making love to her. To increase the resemblance she turned off blushing. It made a pause which she broke at last by saying: "That's the place which— in particular—I thought of going to."

"Oh that's the place—that's the place!" I laughed.

She looked at two or three more views in silence. "They say it's not very dear."

"As some other countries? Well, one gets back there one's money. That's not the least of the charms."

"But it's *all* very expensive, isn't it?"

"Europe, you mean?"

"Going there and travelling. That has been the trouble. I've very little money. I teach, you know," said Miss Caroline Spencer.

"Oh of course one must have money," I allowed; "but one can manage with a moderate amount judiciously spent."

"I think I should manage. I've saved and saved up, and I'm always adding a little to it. It's all for that." She paused a moment, and then went on with suppressed eagerness, as if telling me the story were a rare, but possibly an impure satisfaction. "You see it hasn't been only the money—it has been everything. Everything has acted against it. I've waited and waited. It has been my castle in the air. I'm almost afraid to talk about it. Two or three times it has come a little nearer, and then I've talked about it and it has melted away. I've talked about it too much," she said hypocritically—for I saw such talk was now a small tremulous ecstasy. "There's a lady who's a great friend of mine—she doesn't want to go, but I'm always at her about it. I think I must tire her dreadfully. She told me just the other day she didn't know what would become of me. She guessed I'd go crazy if I didn't sail, and yet certainly I'd go crazy if I did."

"Well," I laughed, "you haven't sailed up to now—so I suppose you *are* crazy."

She took everything with the same seriousness. "Well, I guess I must be. It seems as if I couldn't think of anything else—and I don't require photographs to work me up! I'm always right *on* it. It kills any interest in things nearer home—things I ought to attend to. That's a kind of craziness."

"Well then the cure for it's just to go," I smiled—"I mean the cure for this kind. Of course you may have the other kind worse," I added—"the kind you get over there."

"Well, I've a faith that I'll go *some* time all right!" she quite elatedly cried. "I've a relative right there on the spot," she went on, "and I guess he'll know how to control me." I expressed the hope that he would, and I forget whether we turned over more photographs; but when I asked her if she had always lived just where I found her, "Oh no sir," she quite eagerly replied; "I've spent twenty-two months and a half in Boston." I met it with the inevitable joke that in this case foreign lands might prove a disappointment to her, but I quite failed to alarm her. "I know more about them than you might think"—her earnestness resisted even that. "I mean by reading—for I've really read considerable. In fact I guess I've prepared my mind about as much as you *can*—in advance. I've not only read Byron—I've read histories and guide-books and articles and lots of things. I know I shall rave about everything."

" 'Everything' is saying much, but I understand your case," I returned. "You've the great American disease, and you've got it 'bad'—the appetite, morbid and monstrous, for colour and form, for the picturesque and the romantic at any price. I don't know whether we come into the world with it—with the germs implanted and antecedent to experience; rather perhaps we catch it early, almost before developed consciousness —we *feel*, as we look about, that we're going (to save our souls, or at least our senses) to be thrown back on it hard. We're like travellers in the desert—deprived of water and subject to the terrible mirage, the torment of illusion, of the thirst-fever. They hear the plash of fountains, they see green gardens and orchards that are hundreds of miles away. So we with *our* thirst—except that with us it's *more* wonderful: we have before us the beautiful old things we've never seen at all, and when we do at last see them—if we're lucky!—we simply recognize them. What experience does is merely to confirm and consecrate our confident dream."

She listened with her rounded eyes. "The way you express it's too lovely, and I'm sure it will be just like that. I've dreamt of everything—I'll know it all!"

"I'm afraid," I pretended for harmless comedy, "that you've wasted a great deal of time."

"Oh yes, that has been my great wickedness!" The people about us had begun to scatter; they were taking their leave. She got up and put out her hand to me, timidly, but as if quite shining and throbbing.

"I'm going back there—one *has* to," I said as I shook hands with her. "I shall look out for you."

Yes, she fairly glittered with her fever of excited faith. "Well, I'll tell you if I'm disappointed." And she left me, fluttering all expressively her little straw fan.

II

A few months after this I crossed the sea eastward again and some three years elapsed. I had been living in Paris and, toward the end of October, went from that city to the Havre, to meet a pair of relatives who had written me they were about to arrive there. On reaching the Havre I found the steamer al-

ready docked—I was two or three hours late. I repaired directly
to the hotel, where my travellers were duly established. My
sister had gone to bed, exhausted and disabled by her voyage;
she was the unsteadiest of sailors and her sufferings on this occasion had been extreme. She desired for the moment undisturbed rest and was able to see me but five minutes—long
enough for us to agree to stop over, restoratively, till the morrow. My brother-in-law, anxious about his wife, was unwilling
to leave her room; but she insisted on my taking him a walk
for aid to recovery of his spirits and his land-legs.

The early autumn day was warm and charming, and our
stroll through the bright-coloured busy streets of the old
French seaport beguiling enough. We walked along the sunny
noisy quays and then turned into a wide pleasant street
which lay half in sun and half in shade—a French provincial
street that resembled an old water-colour drawing: tall grey
steep-roofed red-gabled many-storied houses; green shutters on
windows and old scroll-work above them; flower-pots in
balconies and white-capped women in doorways. We walked
in the shade; all this stretched away on the sunny side of the
vista and made a picture. We looked at it as we passed along;
then suddenly my companion stopped—pressing my arm and
staring. I followed his gaze and saw that we had paused just
before reaching a café where, under an awning, several tables
and chairs were disposed upon the pavement. The windows
were open behind; half a dozen plants in tubs were ranged beside the door; the pavement was besprinkled with clean bran.
It was a dear little quiet old-world café; inside, in the comparative dusk, I saw a stout handsome woman, who had pink ribbons in her cap, perched up with a mirror behind her back and
smiling at some one placed out of sight. This, to be exact, I
noted afterwards; what I first observed was a lady seated alone,
outside, at one of the little marble-topped tables. My brother-
in-law had stopped to look at her. Something had been put
before her, but she only leaned back, motionless and with her
hands folded, looking down the street and away from us. I

saw her but in diminished profile; nevertheless I was sure I knew on the spot that we must already have met.

"The little lady of the steamer!" my companion cried.

"Was she on your steamer?" I asked with interest.

"From morning till night. She was never sick. She used to sit perpetually at the side of the vessel with her hands crossed that way, looking at the eastward horizon."

"And are you going to speak to her?"

"I don't know her. I never made acquaintance with her. I wasn't in form to make up to ladies. But I used to watch her and—I don't know why—to be interested in her. She's a dear little Yankee woman. I've an idea she's a school-mistress taking a holiday—for which her scholars have made up a purse."

She had now turned her face a little more into profile, looking at the steep grey house-fronts opposite. On this I decided. "I shall speak to her myself."

"I wouldn't—she's very shy," said my brother-in-law.

"My dear fellow, I know her. I once showed her photographs at a tea-party." With which I went up to her, making her, as she turned to look at me, leave me in no doubt of her identity. Miss Caroline Spencer had achieved her dream. But she was less quick to recognise me and showed a slight bewilderment. I pushed a chair to the table and sat down. "Well," I said, "I hope you're not disappointed!"

She stared, blushing a little—then gave a small jump and placed me. "It was you who showed me the photographs—at North Verona."

"Yes, it was I. This happens very charmingly, for isn't it quite proper for me to give you a formal reception here—the official welcome? I talked to you so much about Europe."

"You didn't say too much. I'm so intensely happy!" she declared.

Very happy indeed she looked. There was no sign of her being older; she was as gravely, decently, demurely pretty as before. If she had struck me then as a thin-stemmed, mild-hued flower of Puritanism it may be imagined whether in her present situation this clear bloom was less appealing. Beside her an old gentleman was drinking absinthe; behind her the *dame de comptoir* in the pink ribbons called "Alcibiade, Alcibiade!" to the long-aproned waiter. I explained to Miss Spencer that the gentleman with me had lately been her shipmate, and my brother-in-law came up and was introduced to her. But she looked at him as if she had never so much as seen him, and I remembered he had told me her eyes were always fixed on the eastward horizon. She had evidently not noticed him, and, still timidly smiling, made no attempt whatever to pretend the contrary. I stayed with her on the little terrace of the café while he went back to the hotel and to his wife. I remarked to my friend that this meeting of ours at the first hour of her landing partook, among all chances, of the miraculous, but that I was delighted to be there and receive her first impressions.

"Oh I can't tell you," she said—"I feel so much in a dream. I've been sitting here an hour and I don't want to move. Everything's so delicious and romantic. I don't know whether the coffee has gone to my head—it's *so* unlike the coffee of my dead past."

"Really," I made answer, "if you're so pleased with this poor prosaic Havre you'll have no admiration left for better things. Don't spend your appreciation all the first day—remember it's your intellectual letter of credit. Remember all the beautiful places and things that are waiting for you. Remember that lovely Italy we talked about."

"I'm not afraid of running short," she said gaily, still looking at the opposite houses. "I could sit here all day—just saying to myself that here I am at last. It's so dark and strange—so old and different."

"By the way then," I asked, "how come you to be encamped in this odd place? Haven't you gone to one of the inns?" For I was half-amused, half-alarmed at the good conscience with which this delicately pretty woman had stationed herself in conspicuous isolation on the edge of the sidewalk.

"My cousin brought me here and—a little while ago—left

me," she returned. "You know I told you I had a relation over here. He's still here—a real cousin. Well," she pursued with unclouded candour, "he met me at the steamer this morning."

It was absurd—and the case moreover none of my business; but I felt somehow disconcerted. "It was hardly worth his while to meet you if he was to desert you so soon."

"Oh he has only left me for half an hour," said Caroline Spencer. "He has gone to get my money."

I continued to wonder. "Where *is* your money?"

She appeared seldom to laugh, but she laughed for the joy of this. "It makes me feel very fine to tell you! It's in circular notes."

"And where are your circular notes?"

"In my cousin's pocket."

This statement was uttered with such clearness of candour that—I can hardly say why—it gave me a sensible chill. I couldn't at all at the moment have justified my lapse from ease, for I knew nothing of Miss Spencer's cousin. Since he stood in that relation to her—dear respectable little person —the presumption was in his favour. But I found myself wincing at the thought that half an hour after her landing her scanty funds should have passed into his hands. "Is he to travel with you?" I asked.

"Only as far as Paris. He's an art-student in Paris—I've always thought that so splendid. I wrote to him that I was coming, but I never expected him to come off to the ship. I supposed he'd only just meet me at the train in Paris. It's very kind of him. But he *is*," said Caroline Spencer, "very kind— and very bright."

I felt at once a strange eagerness to see this bright kind cousin who was an art-student. "He's gone to the banker's?" I enquired.

"Yes, to the banker's. He took me to an hotel—such a queer quaint cunning little place, with a court in the middle and a gallery all round, and a lovely landlady in such a beautifully fluted cap and such a perfectly fitting dress! After a while we came out to walk to the banker's, for I hadn't any French money. But I was very dizzy from the motion of the vessel and I thought I had better sit down. He found this place for me here—then he went off to the banker's himself. I'm to wait here till he comes back."

Her story was wholly lucid and my impression perfectly wanton, but it passed through my mind that the gentleman would never come back. I settled myself in a chair beside my friend and determined to await the event. She was lost in the vision and the imagination of everything near us and about us—she observed, she recognised and admired, with a touching intensity. She noticed everything that was brought before us by the movement of the street—the peculiarities of costume, the shapes of vehicles, the big Norman horses, the fat priests, the shaven poodles. We talked of these things, and there was something charming in her freshness of perception and the way her book-nourished fancy sallied forth for the revel.

"And when your cousin comes back what are you going to do?" I went on.

For this she had, a little oddly, to think. "We don't quite know."

"When do you go to Paris? If you go by the four o'clock train I may have the pleasure of making the journey with you."

"I don't think we shall do that." So far she was prepared. "My cousin thinks I had better stay here a few days."

"Oh!" said I—and for five minutes had nothing to add. I was wondering what our absentee was, in vulgar parlance, "up to." I looked up and down the street, but saw nothing that looked like a bright and kind American art-student. At last I took the liberty of observing that the Havre was hardly a place to choose as one of the æsthetic stations of a European tour. It was a place of convenience, nothing more; a place of transit, through which transit should be rapid. I recommended her to go to Paris by the afternoon train and meanwhile to amuse herself by driving to the ancient fortress at the mouth of the harbour—that remarkable circular structure which bore the

name of Francis the First and figured a sort of small Castle of
Saint Angelo. (I might really have foreknown that it was to be
demolished.)

She listened with much interest—then for a moment looked
grave. "My cousin told me that when he returned he should
have something particular to say to me, and that we could do
nothing or decide nothing till I should have heard it. But
I'll make him tell me right off, and then we'll go to the ancient
fortress. Francis the First, did you say? Why, that's lovely.
There's no hurry to get to Paris; there's plenty of time."

She smiled with her softly severe little lips as she spoke those
last words, yet, looking at her with a purpose, I made out in
her eyes, I thought, a tiny gleam of apprehension. "Don't
tell me," I said, "that this wretched man's going to give you
bad news!"

She coloured as if convicted of a hidden perversity, but she
was soaring too high to drop. "Well I guess it's a *little* bad, but
I don't believe it's *very* bad. At any rate I must listen to it."

I usurped an unscrupulous authority. "Look here; you
didn't come to Europe to listen—you came to *see!*" But now
I was sure her cousin would come back; since he had something disagreeable to say to her he'd infallibly turn up. We sat
a while longer and I asked her about her plans of travel. She
had them on her fingers' ends and told over the names as solemnly as a daughter of another faith might have told over the
beads of a rosary: from Paris to Dijon and to Avignon, from
Avignon to Marseilles and the Cornice road; thence to Genoa,
to Spezia, to Pisa, to Florence, to Rome. It apparently had
never occurred to her that there could be the least incommod-
ity in her travelling alone; and since she was unprovided with
a companion I of course civilly abstained from disturbing her
sense of security.

At last her cousin came back. I saw him turn toward us out
of a side-street, and from the moment my eyes rested on him
I knew he could but be the bright, if not the kind, American
art-student. He wore a slouch hat and a rusty black velvet
jacket, such as I had often encountered in the Rue Bonaparte.

His shirt-collar displayed a stretch of throat that at a distance wasn't strikingly statuesque. He was tall and lean, he had red hair and freckles. These items I had time to take in while he approached the café, staring at me with natural surprise from under his romantic brim. When he came up to us I immediately introduced myself as an old acquaintance of Miss Spencer's, a character she serenely permitted me to claim. He looked at me hard with a pair of small sharp eyes, then he gave me a solemn wave, in the "European" fashion, of his rather rusty sombrero.

"You weren't on the ship?" he asked.

"No, I wasn't on the ship. I've been in Europe these several years."

He bowed once more, portentously, and motioned me to be seated again. I sat down, but only for the purpose of observing him an instant—I saw it was time I should return to my sister. Miss Spencer's European protector was, by my measure, a very queer quantity. Nature hadn't shaped him for a Raphaelesque or Byronic attire, and his velvet doublet and exhibited though not columnar throat weren't in harmony with his facial attributes. His hair was cropped close to his head; his ears were large and ill-adjusted to the same. He had a lackadaisical carriage and a sentimental droop which were peculiarly at variance with his keen conscious strange-coloured eyes—of a brown that was almost red. Perhaps I was prejudiced, but I thought his eyes too shifty. He said nothing for some time; he leaned his hands on his stick and looked up and down the street. Then at last, slowly lifting the stick and pointing with it, "That's a very nice bit," he dropped with a certain flatness. He had his head to one side—he narrowed his ugly lids. I followed the direction of his stick; the object it indicated was a red cloth hung out of an old window. "Nice bit of colour," he continued; and without moving his head transferred his half-closed gaze to me. "Composes well. Fine old tone. Make a nice thing." He spoke in a charmless vulgar voice.

"I see you've a great deal of eye," I replied. "Your cousin tells me you're studying art." He looked at me in the same way, without answering, and I went on with deliberate urbanity: "I suppose you're at the studio of one of those great men." Still on this he continued to fix me, and then he named one of the greatest of that day; which led me to ask him if he liked his master.

"Do you understand French?" he returned.

"Some kinds."

He kept his little eyes on me; with which he remarked: "Je suis fou de la peinture!"

"Oh I understand that kind!" I replied. Our companion laid her hand on his arm with a small pleased and fluttered movement; it was delightful to be among people who were on such easy terms with foreign tongues. I got up to take leave and asked her where, in Paris, I might have the honour of waiting on her. To what hotel would she go?

She turned to her cousin enquiringly and he favoured me again with his little languid leer. "Do you know the Hôtel des Princes?"

"I know where it is."

"Well, that's the shop."

"I congratulate you," I said to Miss Spencer. "I believe it's the best inn in the world; but, in case I should still have a moment to call on you here, where are you lodged?"

"Oh it's such a pretty name," she returned gleefully. "À la Belle Normande."

"I guess I know my way round!" her kinsman threw in; and as I left them he gave me with his swaggering head-cover a great flourish that was like the wave of a banner over a conquered field.

III

My relative, as it proved, was not sufficiently restored to leave the place by the afternoon train; so that as the autumn dusk began to fall I found myself at liberty to call at the establishment named to me by my friends. I must confess that I had spent much of the interval in wondering what the disagreeable thing was that the less attractive of these had been telling the other. The *auberge* of the Belle Normande proved an hostelry in a shady by-street, where it gave me satisfaction to think Miss Spencer must have encountered local colour in abundance. There was a crooked little court, where much of the hospitality of the house was carried on; there was a staircase climbing to bedrooms on the outer side of the wall; there was a small trickling fountain with a stucco statuette set in the midst of it; there was a little boy in a white cap and apron cleaning copper vessels at a conspicuous kitchen door; there was a chattering landlady, neatly laced, arranging apricots and grapes into an artistic pyramid upon a pink plate. I looked about, and on a green bench outside of an open door labelled Salle-à-Manger, I distinguished Caroline Spencer. No sooner had I looked at her than I was sure something had happened since the morning. Supported by the back of her bench, with her hands clasped in her lap, she kept her eyes on the other side of the court, where the landlady manipulated the apricots.

But I saw that, poor dear, she wasn't thinking of apricots or even of landladies. She was staring absently, thoughtfully; on a nearer view I could have certified she had been crying. I had seated myself beside her before she was aware; then, when she had done so, she simply turned round without surprise and showed me her sad face. Something very bad indeed had happened; she was completely changed, and I immediately charged her with it. "Your cousin has been giving you bad news. You've had a horrid time."

For a moment she said nothing, and I supposed her afraid to speak lest her tears should again rise. Then it came to me that even in the few hours since my leaving her she had shed them all—which made her now intensely, stoically composed. "My poor cousin has been having one," she replied at last. "He has had great worries. His news was bad." Then after a dismally conscious wait: "He was in dreadful want of money."

"In want of yours, you mean?"

"Of any he could get—honourably of course. Mine *is* all—well, that's available."

Ah it was as if I had been sure from the first! "And he has taken it from you?"

Again she hung fire, but her face meanwhile was pleading. "I gave him what I had."

I recall the accent of those words as the most angelic human sound I had ever listened to—which is exactly why I jumped up almost with a sense of personal outrage. "Gracious goodness, madam, do you call that his getting it 'honourably'?"

I had gone too far—she coloured to her eyes. "We won't speak of it."

"We *must* speak of it," I declared as I dropped beside her again. "I'm your friend—upon my word I'm your protector; it seems to me you need one. What's the matter with this extraordinary person?"

She was perfectly able to say. "He's just badly in debt."

"No doubt he is! But what's the special propriety of your—in such tearing haste!—paying for that?"

"Well, he has told me all his story. I *feel* for him so much."

"So do I, if you come to that! But I hope," I roundly added, "he'll give you straight back your money."

As to this she was prompt. "Certainly he will—as soon as ever he can."

"And when the deuce will that be?"

Her lucidity maintained itself. "When he has finished his great picture."

It took me full in the face. "My dear young lady, damn his great picture! Where is this voracious man?"

It was as if she must let me feel a moment that I did push her!—though indeed, as appeared, he was just where he'd naturally be. "He's having his dinner."

I turned about and looked through the open door into the salle-à-manger. There, sure enough, alone at the end of a long table, was the object of my friend's compassion—the bright, the kind young art-student. He was dining too attentively to notice me at first, but in the act of setting down a well-emptied wineglass he caught sight of my air of observation. He paused in his repast and, with his head on one side and his meagre

jaws slowly moving, fixedly returned my gaze. Then the landlady came brushing lightly by with her pyramid of apricots.

"And that nice little plate of fruit is for him?" I wailed.

Miss Spencer glanced at it tenderly. "They seem to arrange
everything so nicely!" she simply sighed.

I felt helpless and irritated. "Come now, really," I said; "do
you think it right, do you think it decent, that that long strong
fellow should collar your funds?" She looked away from me—
I was evidently giving her pain. The case was hopeless; the
long strong fellow had "interested" her.

"Pardon me if I speak of him so unceremoniously," I said.
"But you're really too generous, and he hasn't, clearly, the
rudiments of delicacy. He made his debts himself—he ought
to pay them himself."

"He has been foolish," she obstinately said—"of course I
know that. He has told me everything. We had a long talk this
morning—the poor fellow threw himself on my charity. He has
signed notes to a large amount."

"The more fool he!"

"He's in real distress—and it's not only himself. It's his poor
young wife."

"Ah he has a poor young wife?"

"I didn't know—but he made a clean breast of it. He married two years since—secretly."

"Why secretly?"

My informant took precautions as if she feared listeners.
Then with low impressiveness: "She was a Countess!"

"Are you very sure of that?"

"She has written me the most beautiful letter."

"Asking you—whom she has never seen—for money?"

"Asking me for confidence and sympathy"—Miss Spencer
spoke now with spirit. "She has been cruelly treated by her
family—in consequence of what she has done for him. My
cousin has told me every particular, and she appeals to me in
her own lovely way in the letter, which I've here in my pocket.
It's such a wonderful old-world romance," said my prodigious
friend. "She was a beautiful young widow—her first husband

was a Count, tremendously high-born, but really most wicked, with whom she hadn't been happy and whose death had left her ruined after he had deceived her in all sorts of ways. My poor cousin, meeting her in that situation and perhaps a little too recklessly pitying her and charmed with her, found her, don't you see?"—Caroline's appeal on this head was amazing! —"but too ready to trust a better man after all she had been through. Only when her 'people,' as he says—and I do like the word!—understood she would have him, poor gifted young American art-student though he simply was, because she just adored him, her great-aunt, the old Marquise, from whom she had expectations of wealth which she could yet sacrifice for her love, utterly cast her off and wouldn't so much as speak to her, much less to him, in their dreadful haughtiness and pride. They can be haughty over here, it seems," she ineffably developed—"there's no mistake about that! It's like something in some famous old book. The family, my cousin's wife's," she by this time almost complacently wound up, "are of the oldest Provençal noblesse."

I listened half-bewildered. The poor woman positively found it so interesting to be swindled by a flower of that stock—if stock or flower or solitary grain of truth was really concerned in the matter—as practically to have lost the sense of what the forfeiture of her hoard meant for her. "My dear young lady," I groaned, "you don't want to be stripped of every dollar for such a rigmarole!"

She asserted, at this, her dignity—much as a small pink shorn lamb might have done. "It isn't a rigmarole, and I shan't be stripped. I shan't live any worse than I have lived, don't you see? And I'll come back before long to stay with them. The Countess—he still gives her, he says, her title, as they do to noble widows, that is to 'dowagers,' don't you know? in England—insists on a visit from me some time. So I guess for that I can start afresh—and meanwhile I'll have recovered my money."

It was all too heart-breaking. "You're going home then at once?"

I felt the faint tremor of voice she heroically tried to stifle. "I've nothing left for a tour."

"You gave it *all* up?"

"I've kept enough to take me back."

I uttered, I think, a positive howl, and at this juncture the hero of the situation, the happy proprietor of my little friend's sacred savings and of the infatuated *grande dame* just sketched for me, reappeared with the clear consciousness of a repast bravely earned and consistently enjoyed. He stood on the threshold an instant, extracting the stone from a plump apricot he had fondly retained; then he put the apricot into his mouth and, while he let it gratefully dissolve there, stood looking at us with his long legs apart and his hands thrust into the pockets of his velvet coat. My companion got up, giving him a thin glance that I caught in its passage and which expressed at once resignation and fascination—the last dregs of her sacrifice and with it an anguish of upliftedness. Ugly vulgar pretentious dishonest as I thought him, and destitute of every grace of plausibility, he had yet appealed successfully to her eager and tender imagination. I was deeply disgusted, but I had no warrant to interfere, and at any rate felt that it would be vain. He waved his hand meanwhile with a breadth of appreciation. "Nice old court. Nice mellow old place. Nice crooked old staircase. Several pretty things."

Decidedly I couldn't stand it, and without responding I gave my hand to my friend. She looked at me an instant with her little white face and rounded eyes and as she showed her pretty teeth I suppose she meant to smile. "Don't be sorry for me," she sublimely pleaded; "I'm very sure I shall see something of this dear old Europe yet."

I refused however to take literal leave of her—I should find a moment to come back next morning. Her awful kinsman, who had put on his sombrero again, flourished it off at me by way of a bow—on which I hurried away.

On the morrow early I did return, and in the court of the inn met the landlady, more loosely laced than in the evening.

On my asking for Miss Spencer, "*Partie*, monsieur," the good woman said. "She went away last night at ten o'clock, with her —her—not her husband, eh?—in fine her Monsieur. They went down to the American ship." I turned off—I felt the tears in my eyes. The poor girl had been some thirteen hours in Europe.

IV

I myself, more fortunate, continued to sacrifice to opportunity as I myself met it. During this period—of some five years —I lost my friend Latouche, who died of a malarious fever during a tour in the Levant. One of the first things I did on my return to America was to go up to North Verona on a consolatory visit to his poor mother. I found her in deep affliction and sat with her the whole of the morning that followed my arrival—I had come in late at night—listening to her tearful descant and singing the praises of my friend. We talked of nothing else, and our conversation ended only with the arrival of a quick little woman who drove herself up to the door in a "carry-all" and whom I saw toss the reins to the horse's back with the briskness of a startled sleeper throwing off the bed-clothes. She jumped out of the carry-all and she jumped into the room. She proved to be the minister's wife and the great town-gossip, and she had evidently, in the latter capacity, a choice morsel to communicate. I was as sure of this as I was that poor Mrs. Latouche was not absolutely too bereaved to listen to her. It seemed to me discreet to retire, and I described myself as anxious for a walk before dinner.

"And by the way," I added, "if you'll tell me where my old friend Miss Spencer lives, I think I'll call on her."

The minister's wife immediately responded. Miss Spencer lived in the fourth house beyond the Baptist church; the Baptist church was the one on the right, with that queer green thing over the door; they called it a portico, but it looked more like an old-fashioned bedstead swung in the air. "Yes, do look up poor Caroline," Mrs. Latouche further enjoined. "It will refresh her to see a strange face."

"I should think she had had enough of strange faces!" cried the minister's wife.

"To see, I mean, a charming visitor"—Mrs. Latouche amended her phrase.

"I should think she had had enough of charming visitors!" her companion returned. "But *you* don't mean to stay ten years," she added with significant eyes on me.

"Has she a visitor of that sort?" I asked in my ignorance.

"You'll make out the sort!" said the minister's wife. "She's easily seen; she generally sits in the front yard. Only take care what you say to her, and be very sure you're polite."

"Ah she's so sensitive?"

The minister's wife jumped up and dropped me a curtsey— a most sarcastic curtsey. "That's what she is, if you please. 'Madame la Comtesse!' "

And pronouncing these titular words with the most scathing accent, the little woman seemed fairly to laugh in the face of the lady they designated. I stood staring, wondering, remembering.

"Oh I shall be very polite!" I cried; and, grasping my hat and stick, I went on my way.

I found Miss Spencer's residence without difficulty. The Baptist church was easily identified, and the small dwelling near it, of a rusty white, with a large central chimney-stack and a Virginia creeper, seemed naturally and properly the abode of a withdrawn old maid with a taste for striking effects inexpensively obtained. As I approached I slackened my pace, for I had heard that some one was always sitting in the front yard, and I wished to reconnoitre. I looked cautiously over the low white fence that separated the small garden-space from the unpaved street, but I descried nothing in the shape of a Comtesse. A small straight path led up to the crooked door-step, on either side of which was a little grass-plot fringed with currant-bushes. In the middle of the grass, right and left, was a large quince-tree, full of antiquity and contortions, and beneath one of the quince-trees were placed a small table and a couple of light chairs. On the table lay a piece of unfinished embroidery and two or three books in bright-coloured paper covers. I went in at the gate and paused halfway along the path, scanning the place for some further token of its occupant, before whom—I could hardly have said why—I hesitated abruptly to present myself. Then I saw the poor little house to be of the shabbiest and felt a sudden doubt of my right to penetrate, since curiosity had been my motive and curiosity here failed of confidence. While I demurred a figure appeared in the open doorway and stood there looking at me. I immediately recognised Miss Spencer, but she faced me as if we had never met. Gently, but gravely and timidly, I advanced to the door-step, where I spoke with an attempt at friendly banter.

"I waited for you over there to come back, but you never came."

"Waited where, sir?" she quavered, her innocent eyes rounding themselves as of old. She was much older; she looked tired and wasted.

"Well," I said, "I waited at the old French port."

She stared harder, then recognised me, smiling, flushing, clasping her two hands together. "I remember you now—I remember that day." But she stood there, neither coming out nor asking me to come in. She was embarrassed.

I too felt a little awkward while I poked at the path with my stick. "I kept looking out for you year after year."

"You mean in Europe?" she ruefully breathed.

"In Europe of course! Here apparently you're easy enough to find."

She leaned her hand against the unpainted door-post and her head fell a little to one side. She looked at me thus without speaking, and I caught the expression visible in women's eyes when tears are rising. Suddenly she stepped out on the cracked slab of stone before her threshold and closed the door. Then her strained smile prevailed and I saw her teeth were as pretty as ever. But there had been tears too. "Have you been there ever since?" she lowered her voice to ask.

"Until three weeks ago. And you—you never came back?"

Still shining at me as she could, she put her hand behind her and reopened the door. "I'm not very polite," she said. "Won't you come in?"

"I'm afraid I incommode you."

"Oh no!"—she wouldn't hear of it now. And she pushed back the door with a sign that I should enter.

I followed her in. She led the way to a small room on the left of the narrow hall, which I supposed to be her parlour, though it was at the back of the house, and we passed the closed door of another apartment which apparently enjoyed a view of the quince-trees. This one looked out upon a small wood-shed and two clucking hens. But I thought it pretty until I saw its elegance to be of the most frugal kind; after which, presently, I thought it prettier still, for I had never seen faded chintz and old mezzotint engravings, framed in varnished autumn leaves, disposed with so touching a grace. Miss Spencer sat down on a very small section of the sofa, her hands tightly clasped in her lap. She looked ten years older, and I needn't now have felt called to insist on the facts of her person. But I still thought them interesting, and at any rate I was moved by them. She was peculiarly agitated. I tried to appear not to notice it; but suddenly, in the most inconsequent fashion—it was an irresistible echo of our concentrated passage in the old French port—I said to her: "I do incommode you. Again you're in distress."

She raised her two hands to her face and for a moment kept it buried in them. Then taking them away, "It's because you remind me," she said.

"I remind you, you mean, of that miserable day at the Havre?"

She wonderfully shook her head. "It wasn't miserable. It was delightful."

Ah was it? my manner of receiving this must have commented. "I never was so shocked as when, on going back to your inn the next morning, I found you had wretchedly retreated."

She waited an instant, after which she said: "Please let us not speak of that."

"Did you come straight back here?" I nevertheless went on.

"I was back here just thirty days after my first start."

"And here you've remained ever since?"

"Every minute of the time."

I took it in; I didn't know what to say, and what I presently said had almost the sound of mockery. "When then are you going to make that tour?" It might be practically aggressive; but there was something that irritated me in her depths of resignation, and I wished to extort from her some expression of impatience.

She attached her eyes a moment to a small sun-spot on the carpet; then she got up and lowered the windowblind a little to obliterate it. I waited, watching her with interest—as if she had still something more to give me. Well, presently, in answer to my last question, she gave it. "Never!"

"I hope at least your cousin repaid you that money," I said.

At this again she looked away from me. "I don't care for it now."

"You don't care for your money?"

"For ever going to Europe."

"Do you mean you wouldn't go if you could?"

"I can't—I can't," said Caroline Spencer. "It's all over. Everything's different. I never think of it."

"The scoundrel never repaid you then!" I cried.

"Please, please—!" she began.

But she had stopped—she was looking toward the door. There had been a rustle and a sound of steps in the hall.

I also looked toward the door, which was open and now admitted another person—a lady who paused just within the threshold. Behind her came a young man. The lady looked at me with a good deal of fixedness—long enough for me to rise to a vivid impression of herself. Then she turned to Caroline Spencer and, with a smile and a strong foreign accent, "Pardon, ma chère! I didn't know you had company," she said.

"The gentleman came in so quietly." With which she again gave me the benefit of her attention. She was very strange, yet I was at once sure I had seen her before. Afterwards I rather put it that I had only seen ladies remarkably like her. But I had seen them very far away from North Verona, and it was the oddest of all things to meet one of them in that frame. To what quite other scene did the sight of her transport me? To some dusky landing before a shabby Parisian *quatrième*—to an open door revealing a greasy ante-chamber and to Madame leaning over the banisters while she holds a faded wrapper together and bawls down to the portress to bring up her coffee. My friend's guest was a very large lady, of middle age, with a plump dead-white face and hair drawn back *à la chinoise*. She had a small penetrating eye and what is called in French *le sourire agrèable*. She wore an old pink cashmere dressing-gown covered with white embroideries, and, like the figure in my momentary vision, she confined it in front with a bare and rounded arm and a plump and deeply-dimpled hand.

"It's only to spick about my café," she said to her hostess with her *sourire agréable*. "I should like it served in the garden under the leetle tree."

The young man behind her had now stepped into the room, where he also stood revealed, though with rather less of a challenge. He was a gentleman of few inches but a vague importance, perhaps the leading man of the world of North Verona. He had a small pointed nose and a small pointed chin; also, as I observed, the most diminutive feet and a manner of no point at all. He looked at me foolishly and with his mouth open.

"You shall have your coffee," said Miss Spencer as if an army of cooks had been engaged in the preparation of it.

"C'est bien!" said her massive inmate. "Find your bouk"— and this personage turned to the gaping youth.

He gaped now at each quarter of the room. "My grammar, d' ye mean?"

The large lady however could but face her friend's visitor while persistently engaged with a certain laxity in the flow of her wrapper. "Find your bouk," she more absently repeated.

"My poetry, d' ye mean?" said the young man, who also couldn't take his eyes off me.

"Never mind your bouk"—his companion reconsidered. "To-day we'll just talk. We'll make some conversation. But we mustn't interrupt Mademoiselle's. Come, come"—and she moved off a step. "Under the leetle tree," she added for the benefit of Mademoiselle. After which she gave me a thin salutation, jerked a measured "Monsieur!" and swept away again with her swain following.

I looked at Miss Spencer, whose eyes never moved from the carpet, and I spoke, I fear, without grace. "Who in the world's that?"

"The Comtesse—that *was*: my *cousine* as they call it in French."

"And who's the young man?"

"The Countess's pupil, Mr. Mixter." This description of the tie uniting the two persons who had just quitted us must certainly have upset my gravity; for I recall the marked increase of my friend's own as she continued to explain. "She gives lessons in French and music, the simpler sorts—"

"The simpler sorts of French?" I fear I broke in.

But she was still impenetrable, and in fact had now an intonation that put me vulgarly in the wrong. "She has had the worst reverses—with no one to look to. She's prepared for any exertion—and she takes her misfortunes with gaiety."

"Ah well," I returned—no doubt a little ruefully, "that's all I myself am pretending to do. If she's determined to be a burden to nobody, nothing could be more right and proper."

My hostess looked vaguely, though I thought quite wearily enough, about: she met this proposition in no other way. "I must go and get the coffee," she simply said.

"Has the lady many pupils?" I none the less persisted.

"She has only Mr. Mixter. She gives him all her time." It might have set me off again, but something in my whole impression of my friend's sensibility urged me to keep strictly decent. "He pays very well," she at all events inscrutably went on. "He's not very bright—as a pupil; but he's very rich and he's very kind. He has a buggy—with a back, and he takes the Countess to drive."

"For good long spells I hope," I couldn't help interjecting—even at the cost of her so taking it that she had still to avoid my eyes. "Well, the country's beautiful for miles," I went on. And then as she was turning away: "You're going for the Countess's coffee?"

"If you'll excuse me a few moments."

"Is there no one else to do it?"

She seemed to wonder who there should be. "I keep no servants."

"Then can't I help?" After which, as she but looked at me, I bettered it. "Can't she wait on herself?"

Miss Spencer had a slow headshake—as if that too had been a strange idea. "She isn't used to *manual* labour."

The discrimination was a treat, but I cultivated decorum. "I see—and you *are*." But at the same time I couldn't abjure curiosity. "Before you go, at any rate, please tell me this: who *is* this wonderful lady?"

"I told you just who in France—that extraordinary day. She's the wife of my cousin, whom you saw there."

"The lady disowned by her family in consequence of her marriage?"

"Yes; they've never seen her again. They've completely broken with her."

"And where's her husband?"

"My poor cousin's dead."

I pulled up, but only a moment. "And where's your money?"

The poor thing flinched—I kept her on the rack. "I don't know," she woefully said.

I scarce know what it didn't prompt me to—but I went step by step. "On her husband's death this lady at once came to you?"

It was as if she had had too often to describe it. "Yes, she arrived one day."

"How long ago?"

"Two years and four months."

"And has been here ever since?"

"Ever since."

I took it all in. "And how does she like it?"

"Well, not *very* much," said Miss Spencer divinely.

That too I took in. "And how do *you*—?"

She laid her face in her two hands an instant as she had done ten minutes before. Then, quickly, she went to get the Countess's coffee.

Left alone in the little parlour I found myself divided between the perfection of my disgust and a contrary wish to see, to learn more. At the end of a few minutes the young man in attendance on the lady in question reappeared as for a fresh gape at me. He was inordinately grave—to be dressed in such parti-coloured flannels; and he produced with no great confidence on his own side the message with which he had been charged. "She wants to know if you won't come right out."

"Who wants to know?"

"The Countess. That French lady."

"She has asked you to bring me?"

"Yes sir," said the young man feebly—for I may claim to have surpassed him in stature and weight.

I went out with him, and we found his instructress seated under one of the small quince-trees in front of the house; where she was engaged in drawing a fine needle with a very fat hand through a piece of embroidery not remarkable for freshness. She pointed graciously to the chair beside her and I sat down. Mr. Mixter glanced about him and then accommodated himself on the grass at her feet; whence he gazed upward more gapingly than ever and as if convinced that between us something wonderful would now occur.

"I'm sure you spick French," said the Countess, whose eyes were singularly protuberant as she played over me her agreeable smile.

"I do, madam—*tant bien que mal*," I replied, I fear, more dryly.

"Ah voilà!" she cried as with delight. "I knew it as soon as I looked at you. You've been in my poor dear country."

"A considerable time."

"You love it then, *mon pays de France?*"

"Oh it's an old affection." But I wasn't exuberant.

"And you know Paris well?"

"Yes, *sans me vanter*, madam, I think I really do." And with a certain conscious purpose I let my eyes meet her own.

She presently, hereupon, moved her own and glanced down at Mr. Mixter. "What are we talking about?" she demanded of her attentive pupil.

He pulled his knees up, plucked at the grass, stared, blushed a little. "You're talking French," said Mr. Mixter.

"*La belle découverte!*" mocked the Countess. "It's going on ten months," she explained to me, "since I took him in hand. Don't put yourself out not to say he's *la bêtise même*," she added in fine style. "He won't in the least understand you."

A moment's consideration of Mr. Mixter, awkwardly sporting at our feet, quite assured me that he wouldn't. "I hope your other pupils do you more honour," I then remarked to my entertainer.

"I have no others. They don't know what French—or what anything else—is in this place; they don't want to know. You may therefore imagine the pleasure it is to me to meet a person who speaks it like yourself." I could but reply that my own pleasure wasn't less, and she continued to draw the stitches through her embroidery with an elegant curl of her little finger. Every few moments she put her eyes, near-sightedly, closer to her work—this as if for elegance too. She inspired me with no more confidence than her late husband, if husband he was, had done, years before, on the occasion with which this one so detestably matched: she was coarse, common, affected, dishonest—no more a Countess than I was a Caliph. She had an assurance—based clearly on experience; but this couldn't have been the experience of "race." Whatever it was indeed it did now, in a yearning fashion, flare out of her. "Talk to me of Paris, *mon beau Paris* that I'd give my eyes to see. The very name of it *me fait languir*. How long since you were there?"

"A couple of months ago."

"*Vous avez de la chance!* Tell me something about it. What were they doing? Oh for an hour of the Boulevard!"

"They were doing about what they're always doing—amusing themselves a good deal."

"At the theatres, *hein?*" sighed the Countess. "At the cafés-concerts? *sous ce beau ciel*—at the little tables before the doors? *Quelle existence!* You know I'm a Parisienne, monsieur," she added, "to my finger-tips."

"Miss Spencer was mistaken then," I ventured to return, "in telling me you're a Provençale."

She stared a moment, then put her nose to her embroidery, which struck me as having acquired even while we sat a dingier and more desultory air. "Ah I'm a Provençale by birth, but a Parisienne by—inclination." After which she pursued: "And by the saddest events of my life—as well as by some of the happiest, hélas!"

"In other words by a varied experience!" I now at last smiled.

She questioned me over it with her hard little salient eyes. "Oh experience!—I could talk of that, no doubt, if I wished. *On en a de toutes les sortes*—and I never dreamed that mine, for example, would ever have *this* in store for me." And she indicated with her large bare elbow and with a jerk of her head all surrounding objects; the little white house, the pair of quince-trees, the rickety paling, even the rapt Mr. Mixter.

I took them all bravely in. "Ah if you mean you're decidedly in exile—!"

"You may imagine what it is. These two years of my *épreuve* —*elles m'en ont données, des heures, des heures!* One gets used to things"—and she raised her shoulders to the highest shrug ever accomplished at North Verona; "so that I sometimes think I've got used to this. But there are some things that are always beginning again. For example my coffee."

I so far again lent myself. "Do you always have coffee at this hour?"

Her eyebrows went up as high as her shoulders had done

"At what hour would you propose to me to have it? I must have my little cup after breakfast."

"Ah you breakfast at this hour?"

"At mid-day—*comme cela se fait*. Here they breakfast at a quarter past seven. That 'quarter past' is charming!"

"But you were telling me about your coffee," I observed sympathetically.

"My *cousine* can't believe in it; she can't understand it. C'est une fille charmante, but that little cup of black coffee with a drop of '*fine*,' served at this hour—they exceed her comprehension. So I have to break the ice each day, and it takes the coffee the time you see to arrive. And when it does arrive, monsieur—! If I don't press it on *you*—though monsieur here sometimes joins me!—it's because you've drunk it on the Boulevard."

I resented extremely so critical a view of my poor friend's exertions, but I said nothing at all—the only way to be sure of my civility. I dropped my eyes on Mr. Mixter, who, sitting cross-legged and nursing his knees, watched my companion's foreign graces with an interest that familiarity had apparently done little to restrict. She became aware, naturally, of my mystified view of him and faced the question with all her boldness. "He adores me, you know," she murmured with her nose again in her tapestry—"he dreams of becoming *mon amoureux*. Yes, *il me fait une cour acharnée*—such as you see him. That's what we've come to. He has read some French novel—it took him six months. But ever since that he has thought himself a hero and me—such as I am, monsieur—*je ne sais quelle dévergondée!*"

Mr. Mixter may have inferred that he was to that extent the object of our reference; but of the manner in which he was handled he must have had small suspicion—preoccupied as he was, as to my companion, with the ecstasy of contemplation. Our hostess moreover at this moment came out of the house, bearing a coffee-pot and three cups on a neat little tray. I took from her eyes, as she approached us, a brief but intense appeal —the mute expression as I felt, conveyed in the hardest little look she had yet addressed me, of her longing to know what, as a man of the world in general and of the French world in particular, I thought of these allied forces now so encamped on the stricken field of her life. I could only "act" however, as they said at North Verona, quite impenetrably—only make no answering sign. I couldn't intimate, much less could I frankly utter, my inward sense of the Countess's probable past, with its measure of her virtue, value and accomplishments, and of the limits of the consideration to which she could properly pretend. I couldn't give my friend a hint of how I myself personally "saw" her interesting pensioner—whether as the runaway wife of a too-jealous hair-dresser or of a too-morose pastry-cook, say; whether as a very small bourgeoise, in fine, who had vitiated her case beyond patching up, or even as some character, of the nomadic sort, less edifying still. I couldn't let in, by the jog of a shutter, as it were, a hard informing ray and then, washing my hands of the business, turn my back for ever. I could on the contrary but save the situation, my own at least, for the moment, by pulling myself together with a master hand and appearing to ignore everything but that the dreadful person between us *was* a "grande dame." This effort was possible indeed but as a retreat in good order and with all the forms of courtesy. If I couldn't speak, still less could I stay, and I think I must, in spite of everything, have turned black with disgust to see Caroline Spencer stand there like a waiting-maid. I therefore won't answer for the shade of success that may have attended my saying to the Countess, on my feet and as to leave her: "You expect to remain some time in these *parages?*"

What passed between us, as from face to face, while she looked up at me, *that* at least our companion may have caught, that at least may have sown, for the aftertime, some seed of revelation. The Countess repeated her terrible shrug. "Who knows? I don't see my way—! It isn't an existence, but when one's in misery—! *Chère belle,*" she added as an appeal to Miss Spencer, "you've gone and forgotten the *'fine'!*"

I detained that lady as, after considering a moment in si-

lence the small array, she was about to turn off in quest of this
article. I held out my hand in silence—I had to go. Her wan
set little face, severely mild and with the question of a moment before now quite cold in it, spoke of extreme fatigue, but
also of something else strange and conceived—whether a desperate patience still, or at last some other desperation, being
more than I can say. What was clearest on the whole was
that she was glad I was going. Mr. Mixter had risen to his feet
and was pouring out the Countess's coffee. As I went back
past the Baptist church I could feel how right my poor friend
had been in her conviction at the other, the still intenser, the
now historic crisis, that she should still see something of that
dear old Europe.

Ambrose Bierce

1842-1914?

from TALES OF SOLDIERS AND CIVILIANS

THE COUP DE GRÂCE

(1891)

The fighting had been hard and continuous; that was attested
by all the senses. The very taste of battle was in the air. All
was now over; it remained only to succor the wounded and
bury the dead—to "tidy up a bit," as the humorist of a burial
squad put it. A good deal of "tidying up" was required. As far
as one could see through the forests, among the splintered trees,
lay wrecks of men and horses. Among them moved the
stretcher-bearers, gathering and carrying away the few who
showed signs of life. Most of the wounded had died of neglect
while the right to minister to their wants was in dispute. It is

an army regulation that the wounded must wait; the best way to care for them is to win the battle. It must be confessed that victory is a distinct advantage to a man requiring attention, but many do not live to avail themselves of it.

The dead were collected in groups of a dozen or a score and laid side by side in rows while the trenches were dug to receive them. Some, found at too great a distance from these rallying points, were buried where they lay. There was little attempt at identification, though in most cases, the burial parties being detailed to glean the same ground which they had assisted to reap, the names of the victorious dead were known and listed. The enemy's fallen had to be content with counting. But of that they got enough: many of them were counted several times, and the total, as given afterward in the official report of the victorious commander, denoted rather a hope than a result.

At some little distance from the spot where one of the burial parties had established its "bivouac of the dead," a man in the uniform of a Federal officer stood leaning against a tree. From his feet upward to his neck his attitude was that of weariness reposing; but he turned his head uneasily from side to side; his mind was apparently not at rest. He was perhaps uncertain in which direction to go; he was not likely to remain long where he was, for already the level rays of the setting sun straggled redly through the open spaces of the wood and the weary soldiers were quitting their task for the day. He would hardly make a night of it alone there among the dead. Nine men in ten whom you meet after a battle inquire the way to some fraction of the army—as if any one could know. Doubtless this officer was lost. After resting himself a moment he would presumably follow one of the retiring burial squads.

When all were gone he walked straight away into the forest toward the red west, its light staining his face like blood. The air of confidence with which he now strode along showed that he was on familiar ground; he had recovered his bearings. The dead on his right and on his left were unregarded as he passed. An occasional low moan from some sorely-stricken wretch whom the relief-parties had not reached, and who would have to pass a comfortless night beneath the stars with his thirst to keep him company, was equally unheeded. What, indeed, could the officer have done, being no surgeon and having no water?

At the head of a shallow ravine, a mere depression of the ground, lay a small group of bodies. He saw, and swerving suddenly from his course walked rapidly toward them. Scanning each one sharply as he passed, he stopped at last above one which lay at a slight remove from the others, near a clump of small trees. He looked at it narrowly. It seemed to stir. He stopped and laid his hand upon its face. It screamed.

The officer was Captain Downing Madwell, of a Massachusetts regiment of infantry, a daring and intelligent soldier, an honorable man.

In the regiment were two brothers named Halcrow—Caffal and Creede Halcrow. Caffal Halcrow was a sergeant in Captain Madwell's company, and these two men, the sergeant and the captain, were devoted friends. In so far as disparity of rank, difference in duties and considerations of military discipline would permit they were commonly together. They had, indeed, grown up together from childhood. A habit of the heart is not easily broken off. Caffal Halcrow had nothing military in his taste nor disposition, but the thought of separation from his friend was disagreeable; he enlisted in the company in which Madwell was second-lieutenant. Each had taken two steps upward in rank, but between the highest non-commissioned and the lowest commissioned officer the gulf is deep and wide and the old relation was maintained with difficulty and a difference.

Creede Halcrow, the brother of Caffal, was the major of the regiment—a cynical, saturnine man, between whom and Captain Madwell there was a natural antipathy which circumstances had nourished and strengthened to an active animosity. But for the restraining influence of their mutual relations to Caffal these two patriots would doubtless have endeavored to deprive their country of each other's services.

At the opening of the battle that morning the regiment was performing outpost duty a mile away from the main army. It was attacked and nearly surrounded in the forest, but stubbornly held its ground. During a lull in the fighting, Major Halcrow came to Captain Madwell. The two exchanged formal salutes, and the major said: "Captain, the colonel directs that you push your company to the head of this ravine and hold your place there until recalled. I need hardly apprise you of the dangerous character of the movement, but if you wish, you can, I suppose, turn over the command to your first-lieutenant. I was not, however, directed to authorize the substitution; it is merely a suggestion of my own, unofficially made."

To this deadly insult Captain Madwell coolly replied:

"Sir, I invite you to accompany the movement. A mounted officer would be a conspicuous mark, and I have long held the opinion that it would be better if you were dead."

The art of repartee was cultivated in military circles as early as 1862.

A half-hour later Captain Madwell's company was driven from its position at the head of the ravine, with a loss of one-third its number. Among the fallen was Sergeant Halcrow. The regiment was soon afterward forced back to the main line, and at the close of the battle was miles away. The captain was now standing at the side of his subordinate and friend.

Sergeant Halcrow was mortally hurt. His clothing was deranged; it seemed to have been violently torn apart, exposing the abdomen. Some of the buttons of his jacket had been pulled off and lay on the ground beside him and fragments of his other garments were strewn about. His leather belt was parted and had apparently been dragged from beneath him as he lay. There had been no great effusion of blood. The only visible wound was a wide, ragged opening in the abdomen. It was defiled with earth and dead leaves. Protruding from it was a loop of small intestine. In all his experience Captain Madwell had not seen a wound like this. He could neither conjecture how it was made nor explain the attendant circumstances—the strangely torn clothing, the parted belt, the be-smirching of the white skin. He knelt and made a closer examination. When he rose to his feet, he turned his eyes in different directions as if looking for an enemy. Fifty yards away, on the crest of a low, thinly wooded hill, he saw several dark objects moving about among the fallen men—a herd of swine. One stood with its back to him, its shoulders sharply elevated. Its forefeet were upon a human body, its head was depressed and invisible. The bristly ridge of its chine showed black against the red west. Captain Madwell drew away his eyes and fixed them again upon the thing which had been his friend.

The man who had suffered these monstrous mutilations was alive. At intervals he moved his limbs; he moaned at every breath. He stared blankly into the face of his friend and if touched screamed. In his giant agony he had torn up the ground on which he lay; his clenched hands were full of leaves and twigs and earth. Articulate speech was beyond his power; it was impossible to know if he were sensible to anything but pain. The expression of his face was an appeal; his eyes were full of prayer. For what?

There was no misreading that look; the captain had too frequently seen it in eyes of those whose lips had still the power to formulate it by an entreaty for death. Consciously or unconsciously, this writhing fragment of humanity, this type and example of acute sensation, this handiwork of man and beast, this humble, unheroic Prometheus, was imploring everything, all, the whole non-ego, for the boon of oblivion. To the earth and the sky alike, to the trees, to the man, to whatever took form in sense or consciousness, this incarnate suffering addressed that silent plea.

For what, indeed? For that which we accord to even the meanest creature without sense to demand it, denying it only to the wretched of our own race: for the blessed release, the rite of uttermost compassion, the *coup de grâce*.

Captain Madwell spoke the name of his friend. He repeated it over and over without effect until emotion choked his utterance. His tears plashed upon the livid face beneath his own and blinded himself. He saw nothing but a blurred and moving object, but the moans were more distinct than ever, interrupted at briefer intervals by sharper shrieks. He turned away, struck his hand upon his forehead, and strode from the spot. The swine, catching sight of him, threw up their crimson muzzles, regarding him suspiciously a second, and then with a gruff, concerted grunt, raced away out of sight. A horse, its foreleg splintered by a cannon-shot, lifted its head sidewise from the ground and neighed piteously. Madwell stepped forward, drew his revolver and shot the poor beast between the eyes, narrowly observing its death-struggle, which, contrary to his expectation, was violent and long; but at last it lay still. The tense muscles of its lips, which had uncovered the teeth in a horrible grin, relaxed; the sharp, clean-cut profile took on a look of profound peace and rest.

Along the distant, thinly wooded crest to westward the fringe of sunset fire had now nearly burned itself out. The light upon the trunks of the trees had faded to a tender gray; shadows were in their tops, like great dark birds aperch. Night was coming and there were miles of haunted forest between Captain Madwell and camp. Yet he stood there at the side of the dead animal, apparently lost to all sense of his surroundings. His eyes were bent upon the earth at his feet; his left hand hung loosely at his side, his right still held the pistol. Presently he lifted his face, turned it toward his dying friend and walked rapidly back to his side. He knelt upon one knee, cocked the weapon, placed the muzzle against the man's forehead, and turning away his eyes pulled the trigger. There was no report. He had used his last cartridge for the horse.

The sufferer moaned and his lips moved convulsively. The froth that ran from them had a tinge of blood.

Captain Madwell rose to his feet and drew his sword from the scabbard. He passed the fingers of his left hand along the edge from hilt to point. He held it out straight before him, as if to test his nerves. There was no visible tremor of the blade; the ray of bleak skylight that it reflected was steady and true. He stooped and with his left hand tore away the dying man's shirt, rose and placed the point of the sword just over the heart. This time he did not withdraw his eyes. Grasping the hilt with both hands, he thrust downward with all his strength and weight. The blade sank into the man's body—through his body into the earth; Captain Madwell came near falling forward upon his work. The dying man drew up his knees and at the same time threw his right arm across his breast and grasped the steel so tightly that the knuckles of the hand visibly whitened. By a violent but vain effort to withdraw the blade the wound was enlarged; a rill of blood escaped, running sinuously down into the deranged clothing. At that moment three men stepped silently forward from behind the clump of young trees which had concealed their approach. Two were hospital attendants and carried a stretcher.

The third was Major Creede Halcrow.

Stephen Crane

1871-1900

THE BLUE HOTEL

(1899)

I

The Palace Hotel at Fort Romper was painted a light blue, a shade that is on the legs of a kind of heron, causing the bird to declare its position against any background. The Palace Hotel, then, was always screaming and howling in a way that made the dazzling winter landscape of Nebraska seem only a gray swampish hush. It stood alone on the prairie, and when the snow was falling the town two hundred yards away was not visible. But when the traveller alighted at the railway station he was obliged to pass the Palace Hotel before he could come upon the company of low clapboard houses which composed

Fort Romper, and it was not to be thought that any traveller could pass the Palace Hotel without looking at it. Pat Scully, the proprietor, had proved himself a master of strategy when he chose his paints. It is true that on clear days, when the great transcontinental expresses, long lines of swaying Pullmans, swept through Fort Romper, passengers were overcome at the sight, and the cult that knows the brown-reds and the subdivisions of the dark greens of the East expressed shame, pity, horror, in a laugh. But to the citizens of this prairie town and to the people who would naturally stop there, Pat Scully had performed a feat. With this opulence and splendor, these creeds, classes, egotisms, that streamed through Romper on the rails day after day, they had no color in common.

As if the display delights of such a blue hotel were not sufficiently enticing, it was Scully's habit to go every morning and evening to meet the leisurely trains that stopped at Romper and work his seductions upon any man that he might see wavering, gripsack in hand.

One morning, when a snow-crusted engine dragged its long string of freight cars and its one passenger coach to the station, Scully performed the marvel of catching three men. One was a shaky and quick-eyed Swede, with a great shining cheap valise; one was a tall bronzed cowboy, who was on his way to a ranch near the Dakota line; one was a little silent man from the East, who didn't look it, and didn't announce it. Scully practically made them prisoners. He was so nimble and merry and kindly that each probably felt it would be the height of brutality to try to escape. They trudged off over the creaking board sidewalks in the wake of the eager little Irishman. He wore a heavy fur cap squeezed tightly down on his head. It caused his two red ears to stick out stiffly, as if they were made of tin.

At last, Scully, elaborately, with boisterous hospitality, conducted them through the portals of the blue hotel. The room which they entered was small. It seemed to be merely a proper temple for an enormous stove, which, in the center, was humming with godlike violence. At various points on its surface the iron had become luminous and glowed yellow from the heat. Beside the stove Scully's son Johnnie was playing High-Five with an old farmer who had whiskers both gray and sandy. They were quarrelling. Frequently the old farmer turned his face toward a box of sawdust—colored brown from tobacco juice—that was behind the stove, and spat with an air of great impatience and irritation. With a loud flourish of words Scully destroyed the game of cards, and bustled his son up-stairs with part of the baggage of the new guests. He himself conducted them to three basins of the coldest water in the world. The cowboy and the Easterner burnished themselves fiery red with this water, until it seemed to be some kind of metal polish. The Swede, however, merely dipped his fingers gingerly and with trepidation. It was notable that throughout this series of small ceremonies the three travellers were made to feel that Scully was very benevolent. He was conferring great favors upon them. He handed the towel from one to another with an air of philanthropic impulse.

Afterward they went to the first room, and, sitting about the stove, listened to Scully's officious clamor at his daughters, who were preparing the midday meal. They reflected in the silence of experienced men who tread carefully amid new people. Nevertheless, the old farmer, stationary, invincible in his chair near the warmest part of the stove, turned his face from the sawdust-box frequently and addressed a glowing commonplace to the strangers. Usually he was answered in short but adequate sentences by either the cowboy or the Easterner. The Swede said nothing. He seemed to be occupied in making furtive estimates of each man in the room. One might have thought that he had the sense of silly suspicion which comes to guilt. He resembled a badly frightened man.

Later, at dinner, he spoke a little, addressing his conversation entirely to Scully. He volunteered that he had come from New York, where for ten years he had worked as a tailor. These facts seemed to strike Scully as fascinating, and afterward he volunteered that he had lived at Romper for fourteen years. The Swede asked about the crops and the price of labor. He

seemed barely to listen to Scully's extended replies. His eyes
continued to rove from man to man.

Finally, with a laugh and a wink, he said that some of these
Western communities were very dangerous; and after his statement he straightened his legs under the table, tilted his head,
and laughed again, loudly. It was plain that the demonstration
had no meaning to the others. They looked at him wondering
and in silence.

II

As the men trooped heavily back into the front room, the two
little windows presented views of a turmoiling sea of snow.
The huge arms of the wind were making attempts—mighty,
circular, futile—to embrace the flakes as they sped. A gate-post
like a still man with a blanched face stood aghast amid this
profligate fury. In a hearty voice Scully announced the presence
of a blizzard. The guests of the blue hotel, lighting their pipes,
assented with grunts of lazy masculine contentment. No island
of the sea could be exempt in the degree of this little room
with its humming stove. Johnnie, son of Scully, in a tone
which defined his opinion of his ability as a card-player, challenged the old farmer of both gray and sandy whiskers to a
game of High-Five. The farmer agreed with a contemptuous
and bitter scoff. They sat close to the stove, and squared their
knees under a wide board. The cowboy and the Easterner
watched the game with interest. The Swede remained near the
window, aloof, but with a countenance that showed signs of
an inexplicable excitement.

The play of Johnnie and the gray-beard was suddenly ended
by another quarrel. The old man arose while casting a look of
heated scorn at his adversary. He slowly buttoned his coat, and
then stalked with fabulous dignity from the room. In the discreet silence of all the other men the Swede laughed. His
laughter rang somehow childish. Men by this time had begun
to look at him askance, as if they wished to inquire what ailed
him.

A new game was formed jocosely. The cowboy volunteered to become the partner of·Johnnie, and they all then turned to ask the Swede to throw in his lot with the little Easterner. He asked some questions about the game, and, learning that it wore many names, and that he had played it when it was under an alias, he accepted the invitation. He strode toward the men nervously, as if he expected to be assaulted. Finally, seated, he gazed from face to face and laughed shrilly. This laugh was so strange that the Easterner looked up quickly, the cowboy sat intent and with his mouth open, and Johnnie paused, holding the cards with still fingers.

Afterward there was a short silence. Then Johnnie said, "Well, let's get at it. Come on now!" They pulled their chairs forward until their knees were bunched under the board. They began to play, and their interest in the game caused the others to forget the manner of the Swede.

The cowboy was a board-whacker. Each time that he held superior cards he whanged them, one by one, with exceeding force, down upon the improvised table, and took the tricks with a glowing air of prowess and pride that sent thrills of indignation into the hearts of his opponents. A game with a board-whacker in it is sure to become intense. The countenances of the Easterner and the Swede were miserable whenever the cowboy thundered down his aces and kings, while Johnnie, his eyes gleaming with joy, chuckled and chuckled.

Because of the absorbing play none considered the strange ways of the Swede. They paid strict heed to the game. Finally, during a lull caused by a new deal, the Swede suddenly addressed Johnnie: "I suppose there have been a good many men killed in this room." The jaws of the others dropped and they looked at him.

"What in hell are you talking about?" said Johnnie.

The Swede laughed again his blatant laugh, full of a kind of false courage and defiance. "Oh, you know what I mean all right," he answered.

"I'm a liar if I do!" Johnnie protested. The card was halted, and the men stared at the Swede. Johnnie evidently felt that as the son of the proprietor he should make a direct inquiry. "Now, what might you be drivin' at, mister?" he asked. The Swede winked at him. It was a wink full of cunning. His fingers shook on the edge of the board. "Oh, maybe you think I have been to nowheres. Maybe you think I'm a tenderfoot?"

"I don't know nothin' about you," answered Johnnie, "and I don't give a damn where you've been. All I got to say is that I don't know what you're driving at. There hain't never been nobody killed in this room."

The cowboy, who had been steadily gazing at the Swede, then spoke: "What's wrong with you, mister?"

Apparently it seemed to the Swede that he was formidably menaced. He shivered and turned white near the corners of his mouth. He sent an appealing glance in the direction of the little Easterner. During these moments he did not forget to wear his air of advanced pot-valor. "They say they don't know what I mean," he remarked mockingly to the Easterner.

The latter answered after prolonged and cautious reflection. "I don't understand you," he said, impassively.

The Swede made a movement then which announced that he thought he had encountered treachery from the only quarter where he had expected sympathy, if not help. "Oh, I see you are all against me. I see—"

The cowboy was in a state of deep stupefaction. "Say," he cried, as he tumbled the deck violently down upon the board, "say, what are you gittin' at, hey?"

The Swede sprang up with the celerity of a man escaping from a snake on the floor. "I don't want to fight!" he shouted. "I don't want to fight!"

The cowboy stretched his long legs indolently and deliberately. His hands were in his pockets. He spat into the sawdust-box. "Well, who the hell thought you did?" he inquired.

The Swede backed rapidly toward a corner of the room. His hands were out protectingly in front of his chest, but he was making an obvious struggle to control his fright. "Gentlemen," he quavered, "I suppose I am going to be killed before I can leave this house! I suppose I am going to be killed before I can leave this house!" In his eyes was the dying-swan look. Through the windows could be seen the snow turning blue in the shadow of dusk. The wind tore at the house, and some loose thing beat regularly against the clapboards like a spirit tapping.

A door opened, and Scully himself entered. He paused in surprise as he noted the tragic attitude of the Swede. Then he said, "What's the matter here?"

The Swede answered him swiftly and eagerly: "These men are going to kill me."

"Kill you!" ejaculated Scully. "Kill you! What are you talkin'?"

The Swede made the gesture of a martyr.

Scully wheeled sternly upon his son. "What is this, Johnnie?"

The lad had grown sullen. "Damned if I know," he answered. "I can't make no sense to it." He began to shuffle the cards, fluttering them together with an angry snap. "He says a good many men have been killed in this room, or something like that. And he says he's goin' to be killed here too. I don't know what ails him. He's crazy, I shouldn't wonder."

Scully then looked for explanation to the cowboy, but the cowboy simply shrugged his shoulders.

"Kill you?" said Scully again to the Swede. "Kill you? Man, you're off your nut."

"Oh, I know," burst out the Swede. "I know what will happen. Yes, I'm crazy—yes. Yes, of course, I'm crazy—yes. But I know one thing—" There was a sort of sweat of misery and terror upon his face. "I know I won't get out of here alive."

The cowboy drew a deep breath, as if his mind was passing into the last stages of dissolution. "Well, I'm doggoned," he whispered to himself.

Scully wheeled suddenly and faced his son. "You've been troublin' this man!"

Johnnie's voice was loud with its burden of grievance. "Why, good Gawd, I ain't done nothin' to 'im."

The Swede broke in. "Gentlemen, do not disturb yourselves. I will leave this house. I will go away, because"—he accused them dramatically with his glance—"because I do not want to be killed."

Scully was furious with his son. "Will you tell me what is the matter, you young divil? What's the matter, anyhow? Speak out!"

"Blame it!" cried Johnnie in despair, "don't I tell you I don't know? He—he says we want to kill him, and that's all I know. I can't tell what ails him."

The Swede continued to repeat: "Never mind, Mr. Scully; never mind. I will leave this house. I will go away, because I do not wish to be killed. Yes, of course, I am crazy—yes. But I know one thing! I will go away. I will leave this house. Never mind, Mr. Scully; never mind. I will go away."

"You will not go 'way," said Scully. "You will not go 'way until I hear the reason of this business. If anybody has troubled you I will take care of him. This is my house. You are under my roof, and I will not allow any peaceable man to be troubled here." He cast a terrible eye upon Johnnie, the cowboy, and the Easterner.

"Never mind, Mr. Scully; never mind. I will go away. I do not wish to be killed." The Swede moved toward the door which opened upon the stairs. It was evidently his intention to go at once for his baggage.

"No, no," shouted Scully peremptorily; but the white-faced man slid by him and disappeared. "Now," said Scully severely, "what does this mane?"

Johnnie and the cowboy cried together: "Why, we didn't do nothin' to 'im!"

Scully's eyes were cold. "No," he said, "you didn't?"

Johnnie swore a deep oath. "Why, this is the wildest loon I ever see. We didn't do nothin' at all. We were jest sittin' here playin' cards, and he—"

The father suddenly spoke to the Easterner. "Mr. Blanc," he asked, "what has these boys been doin'?"

The Easterner reflected again. "I didn't see anything wrong at all," he said at last, slowly.

Scully began to howl. "But what does it mane?" He stared ferociously at his son. "I have a mind to lather you for this, my boy."

Johnnie was frantic. "Well, what have I done?" he bawled at his father.

III

"I think you are tongue-tied," said Scully finally to his son, the cowboy, and the Easterner; and at the end of this scornful sentence he left the room.

Upstairs the Swede was swiftly fastening the straps of his great valise. Once his back happened to be half turned toward the door, and, hearing a noise there, he wheeled and sprang up, uttering a loud cry. Scully's wrinkled visage showed grimly in the light of the small lamp he carried. This yellow effulgence, streaming upward, colored only his prominent features, and left his eyes, for instance, in mysterious shadow. He resembled a murderer.

"Man! man!" he exclaimed, "have you gone daffy?"

"Oh, no! Oh, no!" rejoined the other. "There are people in this world who know pretty nearly as much as you do—understand?"

For a moment they stood gazing at each other. Upon the Swede's deathly pale cheeks were two spots brightly crimson and sharply edged, as if they had been carefully painted. Scully placed the light on the table and sat himself on the edge of the bed. He spoke ruminatively. "By cracky, I never heard of such a thing in my life. It's a complete muddle. I can't, for the soul of me, think how you ever got this idea into your head." Presently he lifted his eyes and asked: "And did you sure think they were going to kill you?"

The Swede scanned the old man as if he wished to see into his mind. "I did," he said at last. He obviously suspected that this answer might precipitate an outbreak. As he pulled on a strap his whole arm shook, the elbow wavering like a bit of paper.

Scully banged his hand impressively on the footboard of

the bed. "Why, man, we're goin' to have a line of ilictric street-cars in this town next spring."

" 'A line of electric street-cars,' " repeated the Swede, stupidly.

"And," said Scully, "there's a new railroad goin' to be built down from Broken Arm to here. Not to mintion the four churches and the smashin' big brick schoolhouse. Then there's the big factory, too. Why, in two years Romper'll be a met-tro-*pol*-is."

Having finished the preparation of his baggage, the Swede straightened himself. "Mr. Scully," he said, with sudden hardi-hood, "how much do I owe you?"

"You don't owe me anythin'," said the old man, angrily.

"Yes, I do," retorted the Swede. He took seventy-five cents from his pocket and tendered it to Scully; but the latter snapped his fingers in disdainful refusal. However, it happened that they both stood gazing in a strange fashion at three silver pieces on the Swede's open palm.

"I'll not take your money," said Scully at last. "Not after what's been goin' on here." Then a plan seemed to strike him. "Here," he cried, picking up his lamp and moving toward the door. "Here! Come with me a minute."

"No," said the Swede, in overwhelming alarm.

"Yes," urged the old man. "Come on! I want you to come and see a picter—just across the hall—in my room."

The Swede must have concluded that his hour was come. His jaw dropped and his teeth showed like a dead man's. He ultimately followed Scully across the corridor, but he had the step of one hung in chains.

Scully flashed the light high on the wall of his own chamber. There was revealed a ridiculous photograph of a little girl. She was leaning against a balustrade of gorgeous decoration, and the formidable bang to her hair was prominent. The figure was as graceful as an upright sled-stake, and, withal, it was of the hue of lead. "There," said Scully, tenderly, "that's the picter of my little girl that died. Her name was Carrie. She had the purtiest hair you ever saw! I was that fond of her, she—"

Turning then, he saw that the Swede was not contemplating the picture at all, but, instead, was keeping keen watch on the gloom in the rear.

"Look, man!" cried Scully, heartily. "That's the picter of my little gal that died. Her name was Carrie. And then here's the picter of my oldest boy. Michael. He's a lawyer in Lincoln, an' doin' well. I gave that boy a grand eddication, and I'm glad for it now. He's a fine boy. Look at 'im now. Ain't he bold as blazes, him there in Lincoln, an honored an' respicted gintleman! An honored and respicted gintleman," concluded Scully with a flourish. And, so saying, he smote the Swede jovially on the back.

The Swede faintly smiled.

"Now," said the old man, "there's only one more thing." He dropped suddenly to the floor and thrust his head beneath the bed. The Swede could hear his muffled voice. "I'd keep it under me piller if it wasn't for that boy Johnnie. Then there's the old woman— Where is it now? I never put it twice in the same place. Ah, now come out with you!"

Presently he backed clumsily from under the bed, dragging with him an old coat rolled into a bundle. "I've fetched him," he muttered. Kneeling on the floor, he unrolled the coat and extracted from its heart a large yellow-brown whiskey-bottle.

His first manœuver was to hold the bottle up to the light. Reassured, apparently, that nobody had been tampering with it, he thrust it with a generous movement toward the Swede.

The weak-kneed Swede was about to eagerly clutch this element of strength, but he suddenly jerked his hand away and cast a look of horror upon Scully.

"Drink," said the old man affectionately. He had risen to his feet, and now stood facing the Swede.

There was a silence. Then again Scully said: "Drink!"

The Swede laughed wildly. He grabbed the bottle, put it to his mouth; and as his lips curled absurdly around the opening and his throat worked, he kept his glance, burning with hatred, upon the old man's face.

IV

After the departure of Scully the three men, with the cardboard still upon their knees, preserved for a long time an astounded silence. Then Johnnie said: "That's the doddangedest Swede I ever see."

"He ain't no Swede," said the cowboy, scornfully.

"Well, what is he then?" cried Johnnie. "What is he then?"

"It's my opinion," replied the cowboy deliberately, "he's some kind of a Dutchman." It was a venerable custom of the country to entitle as Swedes all light-haired men who spoke with a heavy tongue. In consequence the idea of the cowboy was not without its daring. "Yes, sir," he repeated. "It's my opinion this feller is some kind of a Dutchman."

"Well, he says he's a Swede, anyhow," muttered Johnnie, sulkily. He turned to the Easterner: "What do you think, Mr. Blanc?"

"Oh, I don't know," replied the Easterner.

"Well, what do you think makes him act that way?" asked the cowboy.

"Why, he's frightened." The Easterner knocked his pipe against a rim of the stove. "He's clear frightened out of his boots."

"What at?" cried Johnnie and the cowboy together.

The Easterner reflected over his answer.

"What at?" cried the others again.

"Oh, I don't know, but it seems to me this man has been reading dime novels, and he thinks he's right out in the middle of it—the shootin' and stabbin' and all."

"But," said the cowboy, deeply scandalized, "this ain't Wyoming, ner none of them places. This is Nebrasker."

"Yes," added Johnnie, "an' why don't he wait till he gits *out West*?"

The travelled Easterner laughed. "It isn't different there even—not in these days. But he thinks he's right in the middle of hell."

Johnnie and the cowboy mused long.

"It's awful funny," remarked Johnnie at last.

"Yes," said the cowboy. "This is a queer game. I hope we don't git snowed in, because then we'd have to stand this here man bein' around with us all the time. That wouldn't be no good."

"I wish pop would throw him out," said Johnnie.

Presently they heard a loud stamping on the stairs, accompanied by ringing jokes in the voice of old Scully, and laughter, evidently from the Swede. The men around the stove stared vacantly at each other. "Gosh!" said the cowboy. The door flew open, and old Scully, flushed and anecdotal, came into the room. He was jabbering at the Swede, who followed him, laughing bravely. It was the entry of two roisterers from a banquet hall.

"Come now," said Scully sharply to the three seated men, "move up and give us a chance at the stove." The cowboy and the Easterner obediently sidled their chairs to make room for the newcomers. Johnnie, however, simply arranged himself in a more indolent attitude, and then remained motionless.

"Come! Git over, there," said Scully.

"Plenty of room on the other side of the stove," said Johnnie.

"Do you think we want to sit in the draught?" roared the father.

But the Swede here interposed with a grandeur of confidence. "No, no. Let the boy sit where he likes," he cried in a bullying voice to the father.

"All right! All right!" said Scully, deferentially. The cowboy and the Easterner exchanged glances of wonder.

The five chairs were formed in a crescent about one side of the stove. The Swede began to talk; he talked arrogantly, profanely, angrily. Johnnie, the cowboy, and the Easterner maintained a morose silence, while old Scully appeared to be receptive and eager, breaking in constantly with sympathetic ejaculations.

Finally the Swede announced that he was thirsty. He moved in his chair, and said that he would go for a drink of water.

"I'll git it for you," cried Scully at once.

"No," said the Swede, contemptuously. "I'll get it for myself." He arose and stalked with the air of an owner off into the executive parts of the hotel.

As soon as the Swede was out of hearing Scully sprang to his feet and whispered intensely to the others: "Up-stairs he thought I was tryin' to poison 'im."

"Say," said Johnnie, "this makes me sick. Why don't you throw 'im out in the snow?"

"Why, he's all right now," declared Scully. "It was only that he was from the East, and he thought this was a tough place. That's all. He's all right now."

The cowboy looked with admiration upon the Easterner. "You were straight," he said. "You were on to that there Dutchman."

"Well," said Johnnie to his father, "he may be all right now, but I don't see it. Other time he was scared, but now he's too fresh."

Scully's speech was always a combination of Irish brogue and idiom, Western twang and idiom, and scraps of curiously formal diction taken from the story-books and newspapers. He now hurled a strange mass of language at the head of his son. "What do I keep? What do I keep? What do I keep?" he demanded, in a voice of thunder. He slapped his knee impressively, to indicate that he himself was going to make reply, and that all should heed. "I keep a hotel," he shouted. "A hotel, do you mind? A guest under my roof has sacred privileges. He is to be intimidated by none. Not one word shall he hear that would prijudice him in favor of goin' away. I'll not have it. There's no place in this here town where they can say they iver took in a guest of mine because he was afraid to stay here." He wheeled suddenly upon the cowboy and the Easterner. "Am I right?"

"Yes, Mr. Scully," said the cowboy, "I think you're right."

"Yes, Mr. Scully," said the Easterner, "I think you're right."

V

At six-o'clock supper, the Swede fizzed like a fire-wheel. He sometimes seemed on the point of bursting into riotous song, and in all his madness he was encouraged by old Scully. The Easterner was encased in reserve; the cowboy sat in wide-mouthed amazement, forgetting to eat, while Johnnie wrathily demolished great plates of food. The daughters of the house, when they were obliged to replenish the biscuits, approached as warily as Indians, and, having succeeded in their purpose, fled with ill-concealed trepidation. The Swede domineered the whole feast, and he gave it the appearance of a cruel bacchanal. He seemed to have grown suddenly taller; he gazed, brutally disdainful, into every face. His voice rang through the room. Once when he jabbed out harpoon-fashion with his fork to pinion a biscuit, the weapon nearly impaled the hand of the Easterner, which had been stretched quietly out for the same biscuit.

After supper, as the men filed toward the other room, the Swede smote Scully ruthlessly on the shoulder. "Well, old boy, that was a good, square meal." Johnnie looked hopefully at his father; he knew that shoulder was tender from an old fall; and, indeed, it appeared for a moment as if Scully was going to flame out over the matter, but in the end he smiled a sickly smile and remained silent. The others understood from his manner that he was admitting his responsibility for the Swede's new view-point.

Johnnie, however, addressed his parent in an aside. "Why don't you license somebody to kick you downstairs?" Scully scowled darkly by way of reply.

When they were gathered about the stove, the Swede insisted on another game of High-Five. Scully gently deprecated the plan at first, but the Swede turned a wolfish glare upon him. The old man subsided, and the Swede canvassed the others. In his tone there was always a great threat. The cowboy and the Easterner both remarked indifferently that they would play. Scully said that he would presently have to go to meet the 6.58 train, and so the Swede turned menacingly upon Johnnie. For a moment their glances crossed like blades, and then Johnnie smiled and said, "Yes, I'll play."

They formed a square, with the little board on their knees. The Easterner and the Swede were again partners. As the play went on, it was noticeable that the cowboy was not board-whacking as usual. Meanwhile, Scully, near the lamp, had put on his spectacles and, with an appearance curiously like an old priest, was reading a newspaper. In time he went out to meet the 6.58 train, and, despite his precautions, a gust of polar wind whirled into the room as he opened the door. Besides scattering the cards, it chilled the players to the marrow. The Swede cursed frightfully. When Scully returned, his entrance disturbed a cozy and friendly scene. The Swede again cursed. But presently they were once more intent, their heads bent forward and their hands moving swiftly. The Swede had adopted the fashion of board-whacking.

Scully took up his paper and for a long time remained immersed in matters which were extraordinarily remote from him. The lamp burned badly, and once he stopped to adjust the wick. The newspaper, as he turned from page to page, rustled with a slow and comfortable sound. Then suddenly he heard three terrible words: "You are cheatin'!"

Such scenes often prove that there can be little of dramatic import in environment. Any room can present a tragic front; any room can be comic. This little den was now hideous as a torture-chamber. The new faces of the men themselves had changed it upon the instant. The Swede held a huge fist in front of Johnnie's face, while the latter looked steadily over it into the blazing orbs of his accuser. The Easterner had grown pallid; the cowboy's jaw had dropped in that expression of bovine amazement which was one of his important mannerisms. After the three words, the first sound in the room was made by Scully's paper as it floated forgotten to his feet. His spectacles had also fallen from his nose, but by a clutch he had saved them in air. His hand, grasping the spectacles, now remained poised awkwardly and near his shoulder. He stared at the card-players.

Probably the silence was while a second elapsed. Then, if the floor had been suddenly twitched out from under the men they could not have moved quicker. The five had projected themselves headlong toward a common point. It happened that Johnnie, in rising to hurl himself upon the Swede, had stumbled slightly because of his curiously instinctive care for the cards and the board. The loss of the moment allowed time for the arrival of Scully, and also allowed the cowboy time to give the Swede a great push which sent him staggering back. The men found tongue together, and hoarse shouts of rage, appeal, or fear burst from every throat. The cowboy pushed and jostled feverishly at the Swede, and the Easterner and Scully clung wildly to Johnnie; but through the smoky air, above the swaying bodies of the peace-compellers, the eyes of the two warriors ever sought each other in glances of challenge that were at once hot and steely.

Of course the board had been overturned, and now the whole company of cards was scattered over the floor, where the boots of the men trampled the fat and painted kings and queens as they gazed with their silly eyes at the war that was waging above them.

Scully's voice was dominating the yells. "Stop now! Stop, I say! Stop, now—"

Johnnie, as he struggled to burst through the rank formed by Scully and the Easterner, was crying, "Well, he says I cheated! He says I cheated! I won't allow no man to say I cheated! If he says I cheated, he's a —— ——!"

The cowboy was telling the Swede, "Quit, now! Quit, d'ye hear—"

The screams of the Swede never ceased: "He did cheat! I saw him! I saw him—"

As for the Easterner, he was importuning in a voice that was not heeded: "Wait a moment, can't you? Oh, wait a moment.

What's the good of a fight over a game of cards? Wait a moment—"

In this tumult no complete sentences were clear. "Cheat"—"Quit"—"He says"—these fragments pierced the uproar and rang out sharply. It was remarkable that, whereas Scully undoubtedly made the most noise, he was the least heard of any of the riotous band.

Then suddenly there was a great cessation. It was as if each man had paused for breath; and although the room was still lighted with the anger of men, it could be seen that there was no danger of immediate conflict, and at once Johnnie, shouldering his way forward, almost succeeded in confronting the Swede. "What did you say I cheated for? What did you say I cheated for? I don't cheat, and I won't let no man say I do!"

The Swede said, "I saw you! I saw you!"

"Well," cried Johnnie, "I'll fight any man what says I cheat!"

"No, you won't," said the cowboy. "Not here."

"Ah, be still, can't you?" said Scully, coming between them.

The quiet was sufficient to allow the Easterner's voice to be heard. He was repeating, "Oh, wait a moment, can't you? What's the good of a fight over a game of cards? Wait a moment!"

Johnnie, his red face appearing above his father's shoulder, hailed the Swede again. "Did you say I cheated?"

The Swede showed his teeth. "Yes."

"Then," said Johnnie, "we must fight."

"Yes, fight," roared the Swede. He was like a demoniac. "Yes, fight! I'll show you what kind of a man I am! I'll show you who you want to fight! Maybe you think I can't fight! Maybe you think I can't! I'll show you, you skin, you cardsharp! Yes, you cheated! You cheated! You cheated!"

"Well, let's go at it, then, mister," said Johnnie, coolly.

The cowboy's brow was beaded with sweat from his efforts in intercepting all sorts of raids. He turned in despair to Scully. "What are you goin' to do now?"

A change had come over the Celtic visage of the old man. He now seemed all eagerness; his eyes glowed.

"We'll let them fight," he answered, stalwartly. "I can't put up with it any longer. I've stood this damned Swede till I'm sick. We'll let them fight."

VI

The men prepared to go out-of-doors. The Easterner was so nervous that he had great difficulty in getting his arms into the sleeves of his new leather coat. As the cowboy drew his fur cap down over his ears his hands trembled. In fact, Johnnie and old Scully were the only ones who displayed no agitation. These preliminaries were conducted without words.

Scully threw open the door. "Well, come on," he said. Instantly a terrific wind caused the flame of the lamp to struggle at its wick, while a puff of black smoke sprang from the chimney-top. The stove was in mid-current of the blast, and its voice swelled to equal the roar of the storm. Some of the scarred and bedabbled cards were caught up from the floor and dashed helplessly against the farther wall. The men lowered their heads and plunged into the tempest as into a sea.

No snow was falling, but great whirls and clouds of flakes, swept up from the ground by the frantic winds, were streaming southward with the speed of bullets. The covered land was blue with the sheen of an unearthly satin, and there was no other hue save where, at the low, black railway station—which seemed incredibly distant—one light gleamed like a tiny jewel. As the men floundered into a thigh-deep drift, it was known that the Swede was bawling out something. Scully went to him, put a hand on his shoulder, and projected an ear. "What's that you say?" he shouted.

"I say," bawled the Swede again, "I won't stand much show against this gang. I know you'll all pitch on me."

Scully smote him reproachfully on the arm. "Tut, man!" he yelled. The wind tore the words from Scully's lips and scattered them far alee.

"You are all a gang of—" boomed the Swede, but the storm also seized the remainder of this sentence.

Immediately turning their backs upon the wind, the men

had swung around a corner to the sheltered side of the hotel. It was the function of the little house to preserve here, amid this great devastation of snow, an irregular V-shape of heavily encrusted grass, which crackled beneath the feet. One could imagine the great drifts piled against the windward side. When the party reached the comparative peace of this spot it was found that the Swede was still bellowing.

"Oh, I know what kind of a thing this is! I know you'll all pitch on me. I can't lick you all!"

Scully turned upon him panther-fashion. "You'll not have to whip all of us. You'll have to whip my son Johnnie. An' the man what troubles you durin' that time will have me to dale with."

The arrangements were swiftly made. The two men faced each other, obedient to the harsh commands of Scully, whose face, in the subtly luminous gloom, could be seen set in the austere impersonal lines that are pictured on the countenances of the Roman veterans. The Easterner's teeth were chattering, and he was hopping up and down like a mechanical toy. The cowboy stood rock-like.

The contestants had not stripped off any clothing. Each was in his ordinary attire. Their fists were up, and they eyed each other in a calm that had the elements of leonine cruelty in it.

During this pause, the Easterner's mind, like a film, took lasting impressions of three men—the iron-nerved master of the ceremony; the Swede, pale, motionless, terrible; and Johnnie, serene yet ferocious, brutish yet heroic. The entire prelude had in it a tragedy greater than the tragedy of action, and this aspect was accentuated by the long, mellow cry of the blizzard, as it sped the tumbling and wailing flakes into the black abyss of the south.

"Now!" said Scully.

The two combatants leaped forward and crashed together like bullocks. There was heard the cushioned sound of blows, and of a curse squeezing out from between the tight teeth of one.

As for the spectators, the Easterner's pent-up breath exploded from him with a pop of relief, absolute relief from the tension of the preliminaries. The cowboy bounded into the air with a yowl. Scully was immovable as from supreme amazement and fear at the fury of the fight which he himself had permitted and arranged.

For a time the encounter in the darkness was such a perplexity of flying arms that it presented no more detail than would a swiftly revolving wheel. Occasionally a face, as if illumined by a flash of light, would shine out, ghastly and marked with pink spots. A moment later, the men might have been known as shadows, if it were not for the involuntary utterance of oaths that came from them in whispers.

Suddenly a holocaust of warlike desire caught the cowboy, and he bolted forward with the speed of a broncho. "Go it, Johnnie! go it! Kill him! Kill him!"

Scully confronted him. "Kape back," he said; and by his glance the cowboy could tell that this man was Johnnie's father.

To the Easterner there was a monotony of unchangeable fighting that was an abomination. This confused mingling was eternal to his sense, which was concentrated in a longing for the end, the priceless end. Once the fighters lurched near him, and as he scrambled hastily backward he heard them breathe like men on the rack.

"Kill him, Johnnie! Kill him! Kill him! Kill him!" The cowboy's face was contorted like one of those agony masks in museums.

"Keep still," said Scully, icily.

Then there was a sudden loud grunt, incomplete, cut short, and Johnnie's body swung away from the Swede and fell with sickening heaviness to the grass. The cowboy was barely in time to prevent the mad Swede from flinging himself upon his prone adversary. "No, you don't," said the cowboy, interposing an arm. "Wait a second."

Scully was at his son's side. "Johnnie! Johnnie, me boy!"

His voice had a quality of melancholy tenderness. "Johnnie! Can you go on with it?" He looked anxiously down into the bloody, pulpy face of his son.

There was a moment of silence, and then Johnnie answered in his ordinary voice, "Yes, I—it—yes."

Assisted by his father he struggled to his feet. "Wait a bit now till you git your wind," said the old man.

A few paces away the cowboy was lecturing the Swede. "No, you don't! Wait a second!"

The Easterner was plucking at Scully's sleeve. "Oh, this is enough," he pleaded. "This is enough! Let it go as it stands. This is enough!"

"Bill," said Scully, "git out of the road." The cowboy stepped aside. "Now." The combatants were actuated by a new caution as they advanced toward collision. They glared at each other, and then the Swede aimed a lightning blow that carried with it his entire weight. Johnnie was evidently half stupid from weakness, but he miraculously dodged, and his fist sent the over-balanced Swede sprawling.

The cowboy, Scully, and the Easterner burst into a cheer that was like a chorus of triumphant soldiery, but before its conclusion the Swede had scuffled agilely to his feet and come in berserk abandon at his foe. There was another perplexity of flying arms, and Johnnie's body again swung away and fell, even as a bundle might fall from a roof. The Swede instantly staggered to a little wind-waved tree and leaned upon it, breathing like an engine, while his savage and flame-lit eyes roamed from face to face as the men bent over Johnnie. There was a splendor of isolation in his situation at this time which the Easterner felt once when, lifting his eyes from the man on the ground, he beheld that mysterious and lonely figure, waiting.

"Are you any good yet, Johnnie?" asked Scully in a broken voice.

The son gasped and opened his eyes languidly. After a moment he answered, "No—I ain't—any good—any—more."

Then, from shame and bodily ill, he began to weep, the tears furrowing down through the blood-stains on his face. "He was too—too—too heavy for me."

Scully straightened and addressed the waiting figure. "Stranger," he said, evenly, "it's all up with our side." Then his voice changed into that vibrant huskiness which is commonly the tone of the most simple and deadly announcements. "Johnnie is whipped."

Without replying, the victor moved off on the route to the front door of the hotel.

The cowboy was formulating new and unspellable blasphemies. The Easterner was startled to find that they were out in a wind that seemed to come direct from the shadowed arctic floes. He heard again the wail of the snow as it was flung to its grave in the south. He knew now that all this time the cold had been sinking into him deeper and deeper, and he wondered that he had not perished. He felt indifferent to the condition of the vanquished man.

"Johnnie, can you walk?" asked Scully.

"Did I hurt—hurt him any?" asked the son.

"Can you walk, boy? Can you walk?"

Johnnie's voice was suddenly strong. There was a robust impatience in it. "I asked you whether I hurt him any!"

"Yes, yes, Johnnie," answered the cowboy, consolingly; "he's hurt a good deal."

They raised him from the ground, and as soon as he was on his feet he went tottering off, rebuffing all attempts at assistance. When the party rounded the corner they were fairly blinded by the pelting of the snow. It burned their faces like fire. The cowboy carried Johnnie through the drift to the door. As they entered, some cards again rose from the floor and beat against the wall.

The Easterner rushed to the stove. He was so profoundly chilled that he almost dared to embrace the glowing iron. The Swede was not in the room. Johnnie sank into a chair and, folding his arms on his knees, buried his face in them. Scully, warming one foot and then the other at a rim of the stove, muttered to himself with Celtic mournfulness. The cowboy had removed his fur cap, and with a dazed and rueful air he was running one hand through his tousled locks. From overhead they could hear the creaking of boards, as the Swede tramped here and there in his room.

The sad quiet was broken by the sudden flinging open of a door that led toward the kitchen. It was instantly followed by an inrush of women. They precipitated themselves upon Johnnie amid a chorus of lamentation. Before they carried their prey off to the kitchen, there to be bathed and harangued with that mixture of sympathy and abuse which is a feat of their sex, the mother straightened herself and fixed old Scully with an eye of stern reproach. "Shame be upon you, Patrick Scully!" she cried. "Your own son, too. Shame be upon you!"

"There, now! Be quiet, now!" said the old man, weakly.

"Shame be upon you, Patrick Scully!" The girls, rallying to this slogan, sniffed disdainfully in the direction of those trembling accomplices, the cowboy and the Easterner. Presently they bore Johnnie away, and left the three men to dismal reflection.

VII

"I'd like to fight this here Dutchman myself," said the cowboy, breaking a long silence.

Scully wagged his head sadly. "No, that wouldn't do. It wouldn't be right. It wouldn't be right."

"Well, why wouldn't it?" argued the cowboy. "I don't see no harm in it."

"No," answered Scully, with mournful heroism. "It wouldn't be right. It was Johnnie's fight, and now we mustn't whip the man just because he whipped Johnnie."

"Yes, that's true enough," said the cowboy; "but—he better not get fresh with me, because I couldn't stand no more of it."

"You'll not say a word to him," commanded Scully, and even then they heard the tread of the Swede on the stairs. His entrance was made theatric. He swept the door back with a bang and swaggered to the middle of the room. No one looked at him. "Well," he cried, insolently, at Scully, "I s'pose you'll tell me now how much I owe you?"

The old man remained stolid. "You don't owe me nothin'."

"Huh!" said the Swede, "huh! Don't owe 'im nothin'."

The cowboy addressed the Swede. "Stranger, I don't see how you come to be so gay around here."

Old Scully was instantly alert. "Stop!" he shouted, holding his hand forth, fingers upward. "Bill, you shut up!"

The cowboy spat carelessly into the sawdust-box. "I didn't say a word, did I?" he asked.

"Mr. Scully," called the Swede, "how much do I owe you?" It was seen that he was attired for departure, and that he had his valise in his hand.

"You don't owe me nothin'," repeated Scully in the same imperturbable way.

"Huh!" said the Swede. "I guess you're right. I guess if it was any way at all, you'd owe me somethin'. That's what I guess." He turned to the cowboy. " 'Kill him! Kill him! Kill him!' " he mimicked, and then guffawed victoriously. " 'Kill him!' " He was convulsed with ironical humor.

But he might have been jeering the dead. The three men were immovable and silent, staring with glassy eyes at the stove.

The Swede opened the door and passed into the storm, giving one derisive glance backward at the still group.

As soon as the door was closed, Scully and the cowboy leaped to their feet and began to curse. They trampled to and fro, waving their arms and smashing into the air with their fists. "Oh, but that was a hard minute!" wailed Scully. "That was a hard minute! Him there leerin' and scoffin'! One bang at his nose was worth forty dollars to me that minute! How did you stand it, Bill?"

"How did I stand it?" cried the cowboy in a quivering voice. "How did I stand it? Oh!"

The old man burst into sudden brogue. "I'd loike to take that Swade," he wailed, "and hould 'im down on a shtone flure and bate 'im to a jelly wid a shtick!"

The cowboy groaned in sympathy. "I'd like to git him by the neck and ha-ammer him"—he brought his hand down on a chair with a noise like a pistol-shot—"hammer that there Dutchman until he couldn't tell himself from a dead coyote!"

"I'd bate 'im until he—"

"I'd show *him* some things—"

And then together they raised a yearning, fanatic cry—"Oh-o-oh! if we only could—"

"Yes!"

"Yes!"

"And then I'd—"

"O-o-oh!"

VIII

The Swede, tightly gripping his valise, tacked across the face of the storm as if he carried sails. He was following a line of little naked, gasping trees which, he knew, must mark the way of the road. His face, fresh from the pounding of Johnnie's fists, felt more pleasure than pain in the wind and the driving snow. A number of square shapes loomed upon him finally, and he knew them as the houses of the main body of the town. He found a street and made travel along it, leaning heavily upon the wind whenever, at a corner, a terrific blast caught him.

He might have been in a deserted village. We picture the world as thick with conquering and elate humanity, but here, with the bugles of the tempest pealing, it was hard to imagine a peopled earth. One viewed the existence of man then as a marvel, and conceded a glamor of wonder to these lice which were caused to cling to a whirling, fire-smitten, ice-locked, disease-stricken, space-lost bulb. The conceit of man was explained by this storm to be the very engine of life. One was a coxcomb not to die in it. However, the Swede found a saloon.

In front of it an indomitable red light was burning, and the snowflakes were made blood-color as they flew through the circumscribed territory of the lamp's shining. The Swede pushed open the door of the saloon and entered. A sanded expanse was before him, and at the end of it four men sat about a table drinking. Down one side of the room extended a radiant bar, and its guardian was leaning upon his elbows listening to the talk of the men at the table. The Swede dropped his valise upon the floor and, smiling fraternally upon the barkeeper, said, "Gimme some whiskey, will you?" The man placed a bottle, a whiskey-glass, and a glass of ice-thick water upon the bar. The Swede poured himself an abnormal portion of whiskey and drank it in three gulps. "Pretty bad night," remarked the bartender, indifferently. He was making the pretension of blindness which is usually a distinction of his class; but it could have been seen that he was furtively studying the half-erased blood-stains on the face of the Swede. "Bad night," he said again.

"Oh, it's good enough for me," replied the Swede, hardily, as he poured himself some more whiskey. The barkeeper took his coin and manœvered it through its reception by the highly nickelled cash-machine. A bell rang; a card labelled "20 cts." had appeared.

"No," continued the Swede, "this isn't too bad weather. It's good enough for me."

"So?" murmured the barkeeper, languidly.

The copious drams made the Swede's eyes swim, and he breathed a trifle heavier. "Yes, I like this weather. I like it. It suits me." It was apparently his design to impart a deep significance to these words.

"So?" murmured the bartender again. He turned to gaze dreamily at the scroll-like birds and bird-like scrolls which had been drawn with soap upon the mirrors in back of the bar.

"Well, I guess I'll take another drink," said the Swede, presently. "Have something?"

"No, thanks; I'm not drinkin'," answered the bartender. Afterward he asked, "How did you hurt your face?"

The Swede immediately began to boast loudly. "Why, in a fight. I thumped the soul out of a man down here at Scully's hotel."

The interest of the four men at the table was at last aroused.

"Who was it?" said one.

"Johnnie Scully," blustered the Swede. "Son of the man what runs it. He will be pretty near dead for some weeks, I can tell you. I made a nice thing of him, I did. He couldn't get up. They carried him in the house. Have a drink?"

Instantly the men in some subtle way encased themselves in reserve. "No, thanks," said one. The group was of curious formation. Two were prominent local business men; one was the district attorney; and one was a professional gambler of the kind known as "square." But a scrutiny of the group would not have enabled an observer to pick the gambler from the men of more reputable pursuits. He was, in fact, a man so delicate in manner, when among people of fair class, and so judicious in his choice of victims, that in the strictly masculine part of the town's life he had come to be explicitly trusted and admired. People called him a thoroughbred. The fear and contempt with which his craft was regarded were undoubtedly the reason why his quiet dignity shone conspicuous above the quiet dignity of men who might be merely hatters, billiard-markers, or grocery-clerks. Beyond an occasional unwary traveller who came by rail, this gambler was supposed to prey solely upon reckless and senile farmers, who, when flush with good crops, drove into town in all the pride and confidence of an absolutely invulnerable stupidity. Hearing at times in circuitous fashion of the despoilment of such a farmer, the important men of Romper invariably laughed in contempt of the victim, and if they thought of the wolf at all, it was with a kind of pride at the knowledge that he would never dare think of attacking their wisdom and courage. Besides, it was popular that this gambler had a real wife and two real children in a neat cottage in a suburb, where he led an exemplary home life; and when any one even suggested a discrepancy in his character, the crowd immediately vociferated descriptions of this virtuous family circle. Then men who led exemplary home lives, and men who did not lead exemplary home lives, all subsided in a bunch, remarking that there was nothing more to be said.

However, when a restriction was placed upon him—as, for instance, when a strong clique of members of the new Polly-wog Club refused to permit him, even as a spectator, to appear in the rooms of the organization—the candor and gentleness with which he accepted the judgment disarmed many of his foes and made his friends more desperately partisan. He invariably distinguished between himself and a respectable Romper man so quickly and frankly that his manner actually appeared to be a continual broadcast compliment.

And one must not forget to declare the fundamental fact of his entire position in Romper. It is irrefutable that in all affairs outside his business, in all matters that occur eternally and commonly between man and man, this thieving card-player was so generous, so just, so moral, that, in a contest, he could have put to flight the consciences of nine tenths of the citizens of Romper.

And so it happened that he was seated in this saloon with the two prominent local merchants and the district attorney.

The Swede continued to drink raw whiskey, meanwhile babbling at the barkeeper and trying to induce him to indulge in potations. "Come on. Have a drink. Come on. What—no? Well, have a little one, then. By gawd, I've whipped a man to-night, and I want to celebrate. I whipped him good, too. Gentlemen," the Swede cried to the men at the table, "have a drink?"

"Ssh!" said the barkeeper.

The group at the table, although furtively attentive, had been pretending to be deep in talk, but now a man lifted his eyes toward the Swede and said, shortly, "Thanks. We don't want any more."

At this reply the Swede ruffled out his chest like a rooster. "Well," he exploded, "it seems I can't get anybody to drink with me in this town. Seems so, don't it? Well!"

"Ssh!" said the barkeeper.

"Say," snarled the Swede, "don't you try to shut me up. I won't have it. I'm a gentleman, and I want people to drink with me. And I want 'em to drink with me now. *Now*—do you understand?" He rapped the bar with his knuckles.

Years of experience had calloused the bartender. He merely grew sulky. "I hear you," he answered.

"Well," cried the Swede, "listen hard then. See those men over there? Well, they're going to drink with me, and don't you forget it. Now you watch."

"Hi!" yelled the barkeeper, "this won't do!"

"Why won't it?" demanded the Swede. He stalked over to the table, and by chance laid his hand upon the shoulder of the gambler. "How about this?" he asked wrathfully. "I asked you to drink with me."

The gambler simply twisted his head and spoke over his shoulder. "My friend, I don't know you."

"Oh, hell!" answered the Swede, "come and have a drink."

"Now, my boy," advised the gambler, kindly, "take your hand off my shoulder and go 'way and mind your own business." He was a little, slim man, and it seemed strange to hear him use this tone of heroic patronage to the burly Swede. The other men at the table said nothing.

"What! You won't drink with me, you little dude? I'll make you, then! I'll make you!" The Swede had grasped the gambler frenziedly at the throat, and was dragging him from his chair. The other men sprang up. The barkeeper dashed around the corner of his bar. There was a great tumult, and then was seen a long blade in the hand of the gambler. It shot forward, and a human body, this citadel of virtue, wisdom, power, was pierced as easily as if it had been a melon. The Swede fell with a cry of supreme astonishment.

The prominent merchants and the district attorney must have at once tumbled out of the place backward. The bartender found himself hanging limply to the arm of a chair and gazing into the eyes of a murderer.

"Henry," said the latter, as he wiped his knife on one of the towels that hung beneath the bar rail, "you tell 'em where to find me. I'll be home, waiting for 'em." Then he vanished. A moment afterward the barkeeper was in the street dinning through the storm for help and, moreover, companionship.

The corpse of the Swede, alone in the saloon, had its eyes fixed upon a dreadful legend that dwelt atop of the cash-machine: "This registers the amount of your purchase."

IX

Months later, the cowboy was frying pork over the stove of a little ranch near the Dakota line, when there was a quick thud of hoofs outside, and presently the Easterner entered with the letters and the papers.

"Well," said the Easterner at once, "the chap that killed the Swede has got three years. Wasn't much, was it?"

"He has? Three years?" The cowboy poised his pan of pork, while he ruminated upon the news. "Three years. That ain't much."

"No. It was a light sentence," replied the Easterner as he unbuckled his spurs. "Seems there was a good deal of sympathy for him in Romper."

"If the bartender had been any good," observed the cowboy, thoughtfully, "he would have gone in and cracked that there Dutchman on the head with a bottle in the beginnin' of it and stopped all this here murderin'."

"Yes, a thousand things might have happened," said the Easterner, tartly.

The cowboy returned his pan of pork to the fire, but his philosophy continued. "It's funny, ain't it? If he hadn't said Johnnie was cheatin' he'd be alive this minute. He was an awful fool. Game played for fun, too. Not for money. I believe he was crazy."

"I feel sorry for that gambler," said the Easterner.

"Oh, so do I," said the cowboy. "He don't deserve none of it for killin' who he did."

"The Swede might not have been killed if everything had been square."

"Might not have been killed?" exclaimed the cowboy. "Everythin' square? Why, when he said that Johnnie was cheatin' and acted like such a jackass? And then in the saloon he fairly walked up to git hurt?" With these arguments the cowboy browbeat the Easterner and reduced him to rage.

"You're a fool!" cried the Easterner, viciously. "You're a bigger jackass than the Swede by a million majority. Now let me tell you one thing. Let me tell you something. Listen! Johnnie *was* cheating!"

" 'Johnnie,' " said the cowboy, blankly. There was a minute of silence, and then he said, robustly, "Why, no. The game was only for fun."

"Fun or not," said the Easterner, "Johnnie was cheating. I saw him. I know it. I saw him. And I refused to stand up and be a man. I let the Swede fight it out alone. And you—you were simply puffing around the place and wanting to fight. And then old Scully himself! We are all in it! This poor gambler isn't even a noun. He is kind of an adverb. Every sin is the result of a collaboration. We, five of us, have collaborated in the murder of this Swede. Usually there are from a dozen to forty women really involved in every murder, but in this case it seems to be only five men—you, I, Johnnie, old Scully; and that fool of an unfortunate gambler came merely as a culmination, the apex of a human movement, and gets all the punishment."

The cowboy, injured and rebellious, cried out blindly into this fog of mysterious theory: "Well, I didn't do anythin', did I?"

Frank Norris

1870-1902

A DEAL IN WHEAT

(1902)

I. *The Bear—Wheat at Sixty-Two*

As Sam Lewiston backed the horse into the shafts of his buck-board and began hitching the tugs to the whiffletree, his wife came out from the kitchen door of the house and drew near, and stood for some time at the horse's head, her arms folded and her apron rolled around them. For a long moment neither spoke. They had talked over the situation so long and so com-prehensively the night before that there seemed to be nothing more to say.

The time was late in the summer, the place a ranch in south-western Kansas, and Lewiston and his wife were two of a vast population of farmers, wheat growers, who at that moment were passing through a crisis—a crisis that at any moment might culminate in tragedy. Wheat was down to sixty-six.

At length Emma Lewiston spoke.

"Well," she hazarded, looking vaguely out across the ranch toward the horizon, leagues distant; "well, Sam, there's always that offer of brother Joe's. We can quit—and go to Chicago—if the worst comes."

"And give up!" exclaimed Lewiston, running the lines through the torets. "Leave the ranch! Give up! After all these years!"

His wife made no reply for the moment. Lewiston climbed

into the buckboard and gathered up the lines. "Well, here goes for the last try, Emmie," he said. "Good-bye, girl. Maybe things will look better in town to-day."

"Maybe," she said gravely. She kissed her husband good-bye and stood for some time looking after the buckboard travelling toward the town in a moving pillar of dust.

"I don't know," she murmured at length; "I don't know just how we're going to make out."

When he reached town, Lewiston tied the horse to the iron railing in front of the Odd Fellows' Hall, the ground floor of which was occupied by the post-office, and went across the street and up the stairway of a building of brick and granite— quite the most pretentious structure of the town—and knocked at a door upon the first landing. The door was furnished with a pane of frosted glass, on which, in gold letters, was inscribed, "Bridges & Co., Grain Dealers."

Bridges himself, a middle-aged man who wore a velvet skull-cap and who was smoking a Pittsburgh stogie, met the farmer at the counter and the two exchanged perfunctory greetings.

"Well," said Lewiston, tentatively, after a while.

"Well, Lewiston," said the other, "I can't take that wheat of yours at any better than sixty-two."

"Sixty-*two!*"

"It's the Chicago price that does it, Lewiston. Truslow is bearing the stuff for all he's worth. It's Truslow and the bear clique that stick the knife into us. The price broke again this morning. We've just got a wire."

"Good heavens," murmured Lewiston, looking vaguely from side to side. "That—that ruins me. I *can't* carry my grain any longer—what with storage charges and—and—— Bridges, I don't see just how I'm going to make out. Sixty-two cents a bushel! Why, man, what with this and with that it's cost me nearly a dollar a bushel to raise that wheat, and now Trus-low——"

He turned away abruptly with a quick gesture of infinite discouragement.

He went down the stairs, and making his way to where his

buckboard was hitched, got in, and, with eyes vacant, the reins slipping and sliding in his limp, half-open hands, drove slowly back to the ranch. His wife had seen him coming, and met him as he drew up before the barn.

"Well?" she demanded.

"Emmie," he said as he got out of the buckboard, laying his arm across her shoulder, "Emmie, I guess we'll take up with Joe's offer. We'll go to Chicago. We're cleaned out!"

II. The Bull—Wheat at a Dollar-Ten

. . . ——*and said Party of the Second Part further covenants and agrees to merchandise such wheat in foreign ports, it being understood and agreed between the Party of the First Part and the Party of the Second Part that the wheat hereinbefore mentioned is released and sold to the Party of the Second Part for export purposes only, and not for consumption or distribution within the boundaries of the United States of America or of Canada.*

"Now, Mr. Gates, if you will sign for Mr. Truslow I guess that'll be all," remarked Hornung when he had finished reading.

Hornung affixed his signature to the two documents and passed them over to Gates, who signed for his principal and client, Truslow—or, as he had been called ever since he had gone into the fight against Hornung's corner—the Great Bear. Hornung's secretary was called in and witnessed the signatures, and Gates thrust the contract into his Gladstone bag and stood up, smoothing his hat.

"You will deliver the warehouse receipts for the grain," began Gates.

"I'll send a messenger to Truslow's office before noon," interrupted Hornung. "You can pay by certified check through the Illinois Trust people."

When the other had taken himself off, Hornung sat for some moments gazing abstractedly toward his office windows, thinking over the whole matter. He had just agreed to release to Truslow, at the rate of one dollar and ten cents per bushel, one hundred thousand out of the two million and odd bushels of wheat that he, Hornung, controlled, or actually owned. And for the moment he was wondering if, after all, he had done wisely in not goring the Great Bear to actual financial death. He had made him pay one hundred thousand dollars. Truslow was good for this amount. Would it not have been better to have put a prohibitive figure on the grain and forced the bear into bankruptcy? True, Hornung would then be without his enemy's money, but Truslow would have been eliminated from the situation, and that—so Hornung told himself—was always a consummation most devoutly, strenuously, and diligently to be striven for. Truslow once dead was dead, but the Bear was never more dangerous than when desperate.

"But so long as he can't get *wheat*," muttered Hornung at the end of his reflections, "he can't hurt me. And he can't get it. That I *know*."

For Hornung controlled the situation. So far back as the February of that year an "unknown bull" had been making his presence felt on the floor of the Board of Trade. By the middle of March the commercial reports of the daily press had begun to speak of "the powerful bull clique"; a few weeks later that legendary condition of affairs implied and epitomized in the magic words "Dollar Wheat" had been attained, and by the first of April, when the price had been boosted to one dollar and ten cents a bushel, Hornung had disclosed his hand, and in place of mere rumours, the definite and authoritative news that May wheat had been cornered in the Chicago pit went flashing around the world from Liverpool to Odessa and from Duluth to Buenos Ayres.

It was—so the veteran operators were persuaded—Truslow himself who had made Hornung's corner possible. The Great Bear had for once over-reached himself, and, believing himself all-powerful, had hammered the price just the fatal fraction too far down. Wheat had gone to sixty-two—for the time, and under the circumstances, an abnormal price. When the reaction came it was tremendous. Hornung saw his chance, seized it, and in a few months had turned the tables, had cornered the product, and virtually driven the bear clique out of the pit.

On the same day that the delivery of the hundred thousand bushels was made to Truslow, Hornung met his broker at his lunch club.

"Well," said the latter, "I see you let go that line of stuff to Truslow."

Hornung nodded; but the broker added:

"Remember, I was against it from the very beginning. I know we've cleared up over a hundred thou'. I would have fifty times preferred to have lost twice that and *smashed Truslow dead*. Bet you what you like he makes us pay for it somehow."

"Huh!" grunted his principal. "How about insurance, and warehouse charges, and carrying expenses on that lot? Guess we'd have had to pay those, too, if we'd held on."

But the other put up his chin, unwilling to be persuaded. "I won't sleep easy," he declared, "till Truslow is busted."

III. *The Pit*

Just as Going mounted the steps on the edge of the pit the great gong struck, a roar of a hundred voices developed with the swiftness of successive explosions, the rush of a hundred men surging downward to the centre of the pit filled the air with the stamp and grind of feet, a hundred hands in eager, strenuous gestures tossed upward from out the brown of the crowd, the official reporter in his cage on the margin of the pit leaned far forward with straining ear to catch the opening bid, and another day of battle was begun.

Since the sale of the hundred thousand bushels of wheat to Truslow the "Hornung crowd" had steadily shouldered the price higher until on this particular morning it stood at one dollar and a half. That was Hornung's price. No one else had any grain to sell.

But not ten minutes after the opening, Going was surprised out of all countenance to hear shouted from the other side of the pit these words:

"Sell May at one-fifty."

Going was for the moment touching elbows with Kimbark on one side and with Merriam on the other, all three belonging to the "Hornung crowd." Their answering challenge of "*Sold*" was as the voice of one man. They did not pause to reflect upon the strangeness of the circumstance. (That was for afterward.) Their response to the offer was as unconscious as reflex action and almost as rapid, and before the pit was well aware of what had happened the transaction of one thousand bushels was down upon Going's trading-card and fifteen hundred dollars had changed hands. But here was a marvel—the whole available supply of wheat cornered, Hornung master of the situation, invincible, unassailable; yet behold a man willing to sell, a bear bold enough to raise his head.

"That was Kennedy, wasn't it, who made that offer?" asked Kimbark, as Going noted down the trade—"Kennedy, that new man?"

"Yes; who do you suppose he's selling for; who's willing to go short at this stage of the game?"

"Maybe he ain't short."

"Short! Great heavens, man; where'd he get the stuff?"

"Blamed if I know. We can account for every handful of May. Steady! Oh, there he goes again."

"Sell a thousand May at one-fifty," vociferated the bear-broker, throwing out his hand, one finger raised to indicate the number of "contracts" offered. This time it was evident that he was attacking the Hornung crowd deliberately, for, ignoring the jam of traders that swept toward him, he looked across the pit to where Going and Kimbark were shouting "*Sold! Sold!*" and nodded his head.

A second time Going made memoranda of the trade, and either the Hornung holdings were increased by two thousand bushels of May wheat or the Hornung bank account swelled by at least three thousand dollars of some unknown short's money.

Of late—so sure was the bull crowd of its position—no one had even thought of glancing at the inspection sheet on the bulletin board. But now one of Going's messengers hurried up to him with the announcement that this sheet showed receipts at Chicago for that morning of twenty-five thousand bushels, and not credited to Hornung. Someone had got hold of a line of wheat overlooked by the "clique" and was dumping it upon them.

"Wire the Chief," said Going over his shoulder to Merriam. This one struggled out of the crowd, and on a telegraph blank scribbled:

"Strong bear movement—New man—Kennedy—Selling in lots of five contracts—Chicago receipts twenty-five thousand."

The message was despatched, and in a few moments the answer came back, laconic, of military terseness:

"Support the market."

And Going obeyed, Merriam and Kimbark following, the new broker fairly throwing the wheat at them in thousand-bushel lots.

"Sell May at 'fifty; sell May; sell May." A moment's indecision, an instant's hesitation, the first faint suggestion of weakness, and the market would have broken under them. But for the better part of four hours they stood their ground, taking all that was offered, in constant communication with the Chief, and from time to time stimulated and steadied by his brief, unvarying command:

"Support the market."

At the close of the session they had bought in the twenty-five thousand bushels of May. Hornung's position was as stable as a rock, and the price closed even with the opening figure—one dollar and a half.

But the morning's work was the talk of all La Salle Street. Who was back of the raid? What was the meaning of this unexpected selling? For weeks the pit trading had been merely nominal. Truslow, the Great Bear, from whom the most serious attack might have been expected, had gone to his country seat at Geneva Lake, in Wisconsin, declaring himself to be out of the market entirely. He went bass-fishing every day.

IV. *The Belt Line*

On a certain day toward the middle of the month, at a time when the mysterious Bear had unloaded some eighty thousand bushels upon Hornung, a conference was held in the library of Hornung's home. His broker attended it, and also a clean faced, bright-eyed individual whose name of Cyrus Ryder might have been found upon the pay-roll of a rather well-known detective agency. For upward of half an hour after the conference began the detective spoke, the other two listening attentively, gravely.

"Then, last of all," concluded Ryder, "I made out I was a hobo, and began stealing rides on the Belt Line Railroad. Know the road? It just circles Chicago. Truslow owns it. Yes? Well, then I began to catch on. I noticed that cars of certain numbers—thirty-one nought thirty-four, thirty-two one ninety —well, the numbers don't matter, but anyhow, these cars were always switched onto the sidings by Mr. Truslow's main elevator D soon as they came in. The wheat was shunted in, and they were pulled out again. Well, I spotted one car and stole a ride on her. Say, look here, *that car went right around the city on the Belt, and came back to D again, and the same wheat in her all the time.* The grain was reinspected—it was raw, I tell you—and the warehouse receipts made out just as though the stuff had come in from Kansas or Iowa."

"The same wheat all the time!" interrupted Hornung.

"The same wheat—your wheat, that you sold to Truslow."

"Great snakes!" ejaculated Hornung's broker. "Truslow never took it abroad at all."

"Took it abroad! Say, he's just been running it around Chicago, like the supers in 'Shenandoah,' round an' round, so you'd think it was a new lot, an' selling it back to you again."

"No wonder we couldn't account for so much wheat."

"Bought it from us at one-ten, and made us buy it back—our own wheat—at one-fifty."

Hornung and his broker looked at each other in silence for a moment. Then all at once Hornung struck the arm of his chair with his fist and exploded in a roar of laughter. The broker stared for one bewildered moment, then followed his example.

"Sold! Sold!" shouted Hornung almost gleefully. "Upon my soul it's as good as a Gilbert and Sullivan show. And we—— Oh, Lord! Billy, shake on it, and hats off to my distinguished friend, Truslow. He'll be President some day. Hey! What? Prosecute him? Not I."

"He's done us out of a neat hatful of dollars for all that," observed the broker, suddenly grave.

"Billy, it's worth the price."

"We've got to make it up somehow."

"Well, tell you what. We were going to boost the price to one seventy-five next week, and make that our settlement figure."

"Can't do it now. Can't afford it."

"No. Here; we'll let out a big link; we'll put wheat at two dollars, and let it go at that."

"Two it is, then," said the broker.

V. The Bread Line

The street was very dark and absolutely deserted. It was a district on the "South Side," not far from the Chicago River, given up largely to wholesale stores, and after nightfall was empty of all life. The echoes slept but lightly hereabouts, and the slightest footfall, the faintest noise, woke them upon the instant and sent them clamouring up and down the length of the pavement between the iron-shuttered fronts. The only light visible came from the side door of a certain "Vienna" bakery, where at one o'clock in the morning loaves of bread were given away to any who should ask. Every evening about nine o'clock the outcasts began to gather about the side door. The stragglers came in rapidly, and the line—the "bread line," as it was called—began to form. By midnight it was usually some hundred yards in length, stretching almost the entire length of the block.

Toward ten in the evening, his coat collar turned up against the fine drizzle that pervaded the air, his hands in his pockets, his elbows gripping his sides, Sam Lewiston came up and silently took his place at the end of the line.

Unable to conduct his farm upon a paying basis at the time when Truslow, the "Great Bear," had sent the price of grain down to sixty-two cents a bushel, Lewiston had turned over his entire property to his creditors, and, leaving Kansas for good, had abandoned farming, and had left his wife at her sister's boarding-house in Topeka with the understanding that she was to join him in Chicago as soon as he had found a steady job. Then he had come to Chicago and had turned workman. His brother Joe conducted a small hat factory on Archer Avenue, and for a time he found there a meagre employment. But difficulties had occurred, times were bad, the hat factory was involved in debts, the repealing of a certain import duty on manufactured felt overcrowded the home market with cheap Belgian and French products, and in the end his brother had assigned and gone to Milwaukee.

Thrown out of work, Lewiston drifted aimlessly about Chicago, from pillar to post, working a little, earning here a dollar, there a dime, but always sinking, sinking, till at last the ooze of the lowest bottom dragged at his feet and the rush of the great ebb went over him and engulfed him and shut him out from the light, and a park bench became his home and the "bread line" his chief makeshift of subsistence.

He stood now in the enfolding drizzle, sodden, stupefied with fatigue. Before and behind stretched the line. There was no talking. There was no sound. The street was empty. It was so still that the passing of a cable-car in the adjoining thoroughfare grated like prolonged rolling explosions, beginning and ending at immeasurable distances. The drizzle descended incessantly. After a long time midnight struck.

There was something ominous and gravely impressive in

this interminable line of dark figures, close-pressed, soundless; a crowd, yet absolutely still; a close-packed, silent file, waiting, waiting in the vast deserted night-ridden street; waiting without a word, without a movement, there under the night and under the slow-moving mists of rain.

Few in the crowd were professional beggars. Most of them were workmen, long since out of work, forced into idleness by long-continued "hard times," by ill luck, by sickness. To them the "bread line" was a godsend. At least they could not starve. Between jobs here in the end was something to hold them up —a small platform, as it were, above the sweep of black water, where for a moment they might pause and take breath before the plunge.

The period of waiting on this night of rain seemed endless to those silent, hungry men; but at length there was a stir. The line moved. The side door opened. Ah, at last! They were going to hand out the bread.

But instead of the usual white-aproned undercook with his crowded hampers there now appeared in the doorway a new man—a young fellow who looked like a bookkeeper's assistant. He bore in his hand a placard, which he tacked to the outside of the door. Then he disappeared within the bakery, locking the door after him.

A shudder of poignant despair, an unformed, inarticulate sense of calamity, seemed to run from end to end of the line. What had happened? Those in the rear, unable to read the placard, surged forward, a sense of bitter disappointment clutching at their hearts.

The line broke up, disintegrated into a shapeless throng—a throng that crowded forward and collected in front of the shut door whereon the placard was affixed. Lewiston, with the others, pushed forward. On the placard he read these words:

"Owing to the fact that the price of grain has been increased to two dollars a bushel, there will be no distribution of bread from this bakery until further notice."

Lewiston turned away, dumb, bewildered. Till morning he walked the streets, going on without purpose, without direction. But now at last his luck had turned. Overnight the wheel of his fortunes had creaked and swung upon its axis, and before noon he had found a job in the street-cleaning brigade. In the course of time he rose to be first shift-boss, then deputy inspector, then inspector, promoted to the dignity of driving in a red wagon with rubber tires and drawing a salary instead of mere wages. The wife was sent for and a new start made.

But Lewiston never forgot. Dimly he began to see the significance of things. Caught once in the cogs and wheels of a great and terrible engine, he had seen—none better—its workings. Of all the men who had vainly stood in the "bread line" on that rainy night in early summer, he, perhaps, had been the only one who had struggled up to the surface again. How many others had gone down in the great ebb? Grim question; he dared not think how many.

He had seen the two ends of a great wheat operation—a battle between Bear and Bull. The stories (subsequently published in the city's press) of Truslow's countermove in selling Hornung his own wheat, supplied the unseen section. The farmer—he who raised the wheat—was ruined upon one hand; the working-man—he who consumed it—was ruined upon the other. But between the two, the great operators, who never saw the wheat they traded in, bought and sold the world's food, gambled in the nourishment of entire nations, practised their tricks, their chicanery and oblique shifty "deals," were reconciled in their differences, and went on through their appointed way, jovial, contented, enthroned, and unassailable.

William Dean Howells

1837-1920

EDITHA

(1907)

The air was thick with the war feeling, like the electricity of a storm which has not yet burst. Editha sat looking out into the hot spring afternoon, with her lips parted, and panting with the intensity of the question whether she could let him go. She had decided that she could not let him stay, when she saw him at the end of the still leafless avenue, making slowly up towards the house, with his head down and his figure relaxed. She ran impatiently out on the veranda, to the edge of the steps, and imperatively demanded greater haste of him with her will before she called aloud to him: "George!"

He had quickened his pace in mystical response to her mystical urgence, before he could have heard her; now he looked up and answered, "Well?"

"Oh, how united we are!" she exulted, and then she swooped down the steps to him. "What is it?" she cried.

"It's war," he said, and he pulled her up to him and kissed her.

She kissed him back intensely, but irrelevantly, as to their passion, and uttered from deep in her throat, "How glorious!"

"It's war," he repeated, without consenting to her sense of it; and she did not know just what to think at first. She never knew what to think of him; that made his mystery, his charm. All through their courtship, which was contemporaneous with the growth of the war feeling, she had been puzzled by his

From *Between the Dark and the Daylight* (1907). Reprinted by permission of W. W. Howells, literary executor for William Dean Howells Estate.

want of seriousness about it. He seemed to despise it even more than he abhorred it. She could have understood his abhorring any sort of bloodshed; that would have been a survival of his old life when he thought he would be a minister, and before he changed and took up the law. But making light of a cause so high and noble seemed to show a want of earnestness at the core of his being. Not but that she felt herself able to cope with a congenital defect of that sort, and make his love for her save him from himself. Now perhaps the miracle was already wrought in him. In the presence of the tremendous fact that he announced, all triviality seemed to have gone out of him; she began to feel that. He sank down on the top step, and wiped his forehead with his handkerchief, while she poured out upon him her question of the origin and authenticity of his news.

All the while, in her duplex emotioning, she was aware that now at the very beginning she must put a guard upon herself against urging him, by any word or act, to take the part that her whole soul willed him to take, for the completion of her ideal of him. He was very nearly perfect as he was, and he must be allowed to perfect himself. But he was peculiar, and he might very well be reasoned out of his peculiarity. Before her reasoning went her emotioning: her nature pulling upon his nature, her womanhood upon his manhood, without her knowing the means she was using to the end she was willing. She had always supposed that the man who won her would have done something to win her; she did not know what, but something. George Gearson had simply asked her for her love, on the way home from a concert, and she gave her love to him, without, as it were, thinking. But now, it flashed upon her, if he could do something worthy to *have* won her—be a hero, *her* hero—it would be even better than if he had done it before asking her; it would be grander. Besides, she had believed in the war from the beginning.

"But don't you see, dearest," she said, "that it wouldn't have come to this if it hadn't been in the order of Providence? And I call any war glorious that is for the liberation of people who have been struggling for years against the cruelest oppression. Don't you think so, too?"

"I suppose so," he returned, languidly. "But war! Is it glorious to break the peace of the world?"

"That ignoble peace! It was no peace at all, with that crime and shame at our very gates." She was conscious of parroting the current phrases of the newspapers, but it was no time to pick and choose her words. She must sacrifice anything to the high ideal she had for him, and after a good deal of rapid argument she ended with the climax: "But now it doesn't matter about the how or why. Since the war has come, all that is gone. There are no two sides any more. There is nothing now but our country."

He sat with his eyes closed and his head leant back against the veranda, and he remarked, with a vague smile, as if musing aloud, "Our country—right or wrong."

"Yes, right or wrong!" she returned, fervidly. "I'll go and get you some lemonade." She rose rustling, and whisked away; when she came back with two tall glasses of clouded liquid on a tray, and the ice clucking in them, he still sat as she had left him, and she said, as if there had been no interruption: "But there is no question of wrong in this case. I call it a sacred war. A war for liberty and humanity, if ever there was one. And I know you will see it just as I do, yet."

He took half the lemonade at a gulp, and he answered as he set the glass down: "I know you always have the highest ideal. When I differ from you I ought to doubt myself."

A generous sob rose in Editha's throat for the humility of a man, so very nearly perfect, who was willing to put himself below her.

Besides, she felt, more subliminally, that he was never so near slipping through her fingers as when he took that meek way.

"You shall not say that! Only, for once I happen to be right." She seized his hand in her two hands, and poured her soul from her eyes into his. "Don't you think so?" she entreated him.

He released his hand and drank the rest of his lemonade, and she added, "Have mine, too," but he shook his head in answering, "I've no business to think so, unless I act so, too."

Her heart stopped a beat before it pulsed on with leaps that she felt in her neck. She had noticed that strange thing in men: they seemed to feel bound to do what they believed, and not think a thing was finished when they said it, as girls did. She knew what was in his mind, but she pretended not, and she said, "Oh, I am not sure," and then faltered.

He went on as if to himself, without apparently heeding her: "There's only one way of proving one's faith in a thing like this."

She could not say that she understood, but she did understand.

He went on again. "If I believed—if I felt as you do about this war— Do you wish me to feel as you do?"

Now she was really not sure; so she said: "George, I don't know what you mean."

He seemed to muse away from her as before. "There is a sort of fascination in it. I suppose that at the bottom of his heart every man would like at times to have his courage tested, to see how he would act."

"How can you talk in that ghastly way?"

"It *is* rather morbid. Still, that's what it comes to, unless you're swept away by ambition or driven by conviction. I haven't the conviction or the ambition, and the other thing is what it comes to with me. I ought to have been a preacher, after all; then I couldn't have asked it of myself, as I must, now I'm a lawyer. And you believe it's a holy war, Editha?" he suddenly addressed her. "Oh, I know you do! But you wish me to believe so, too?"

She hardly knew whether he was mocking or not, in the ironical way he always had with her plainer mind. But the only thing was to be outspoken with him.

"George, I wish you to believe whatever you think is true, at any and every cost. If I've tried to talk you into anything, I take it all back."

"Oh, I know that, Editha. I know how sincere you are, and how— I wish I had your undoubting spirit! I'll think it over; I'd like to believe as you do. But I don't, now; I don't, indeed. It isn't this war alone; though this seems peculiarly wanton and needless; but it's every war—so stupid; it makes me sick. Why shouldn't this thing have been settled reasonably?"

"Because," she said, very throatily again, "God meant it to be war."

"You think it was God? Yes, I suppose that is what people will say."

"Do you suppose it would have been war if God hadn't meant it?"

"I don t know. Sometimes it seems as if God had put this world into men's keeping to work it as they pleased."

"Now, George, that is blasphemy."

"Well, I won't blaspheme. I'll try to believe in your pocket Providence," he said, and then he rose to go.

"Why don t you stay to dinner?" Dinner at Balcom's Works was at one o'clock.

"I'll come back to supper, if you'll let me. Perhaps I shall bring you a convert."

"Well, you may come back, on that condition."

"All right. If I don't come, you'll understand."

He went away without kissing her, and she felt it a suspension of their engagement. It all interested her intensely; she was undergoing a tremendous experience, and she was being equal to it. While she stood looking after him, her mother came out through one of the long windows onto the veranda, with a catlike softness and vagueness.

"Why didn't he stay to dinner?"

"Because—because—war has been declared," Editha pronounced, without turning.

Her mother said, "Oh, my!" and then said nothing more until she had sat down in one of the large Shaker chairs and rocked herself for some time. Then she closed whatever tacit passage of thought there had been in her mind with the spoken words: "Well, I hope *he* won't go."

"And *I* hope he *will*," the girl said, and confronted her mother with a stormy exaltation that would have frightened any creature less unimpressionable than a cat.

Her mother rocked herself again for an interval of cogitation. What she arrived at in speech was: "Well, I guess you've done a wicked thing, Editha Balcom."

The girl said, as she passed indoors through the same window her mother had come out by: "I haven't done anything—yet."

In her room, she put together all her letters and gifts from Gearson, down to the withered petals of the first flower he had offered, with that timidity of his veiled in that irony of his. In the heart of the packet she enshrined her engagement ring which she had restored to the pretty box he had brought it her in. Then she sat down, if not calmly yet strongly, and wrote:

"GEORGE:—I understood when you left me. But I think we had better emphasize your meaning that if we cannot be one in everything we had better be one in nothing. So I am sending these things for your keeping till you have made up your mind.

"I shall always love you, and therefore I shall never marry any one else. But the man I marry must love his country first of all, and be able to say to me,

"   'I could not love thee, dear, so much,
        Loved I not honor more.'

"There is no honor above America with me. In this great hour there is no other honor.

"Your heart will make my words clear to you. I had never expected to say so much, but it has come upon me that I must say the utmost.

EDITHA."

She thought she had worded her letter well, worded it in a way that could not be bettered; all had been implied and nothing expressed.

She had it ready to send with the packet she had tied with red, white, and blue ribbon, when it occurred to her that she was not just to him, that she was not giving him a fair chance. He had said he would go and think it over, and she was not waiting. She was pushing, threatening, compelling. That was not a woman's part. She must leave him free, free, free. She could not accept for her country or herself a forced sacrifice.

In writing her letter she had satisfied the impulse from which it sprang; she could well afford to wait till he had thought it over. She put the packet and the letter by, and rested serene in the consciouness of having done what was laid upon her by her love itself to do, and yet used patience, mercy, justice.

She had her reward. Gearson did not come to tea, but she had given him till morning, when, late at night there came up from the village the sound of a fife and drum, with a tumult of voices, in shouting, singing, and laughing. The noise drew nearer and nearer; it reached the street end of the avenue; there it silenced itself, and one voice, the voice she knew best, rose over the silence. It fell; the air was filled with cheers; the fife and drum struck up, with the shouting, singing, and laughing again, but now retreating; and a single figure came hurrying up the avenue.

She ran down to meet her lover and clung to him. He was very gay, and he put his arm round her with a boisterous laugh. "Well, you must call me Captain now; or Cap, if you prefer; that's what the boys call me. Yes, we've had a meeting at the town-hall, and everybody has volunteered; and they selected me for captain, and I'm going to the war, the big war, the glorious war, the holy war ordained by the pocket Providence that blesses butchery. Come along; let's tell the whole family about it. Call them from their downy beds, father, mother, Aunt Hitty, and all the folks!"

But when they mounted the veranda steps he did not wait for a larger audience; he poured the story out upon Editha alone.

"There was a lot of speaking, and then some of the fools set up a shout for me. It was all going one way, and I thought it would be a good joke to sprinkle a little cold water on them. But you can't do that with a crowd that adores you. The first thing I knew I was sprinkling hell-fire on them. 'Cry havoc, and let slip the dogs of war.' That was the style. Now that it had come to the fight, there were no two parties; there was one country, and the thing was to fight to a finish as quick as possible. I suggested volunteering then and there, and I wrote my name first of all on the roster. Then they elected me—that's all. I wish I had some ice-water."

She left him walking up and down the veranda, while she ran for the ice-pitcher and a goblet, and when she came back he was still walking up and down, shouting the story he had told her to her father and mother, who had come out more sketchily dressed than they commonly were by day. He drank goblet after goblet of the ice-water without noticing who was giving it, and kept on talking, and laughing through his talk wildly. "It's astonishing," he said, "how well the worse reason looks when you try to make it appear the better. Why, I believe I was the first convert to the war in that crowd to-night! I never thought I should like to kill a man; but now I shouldn't care; and the smokeless powder lets you see the man drop that you kill. It's all for the country! What a thing it is to have a country that *can't* be wrong, but if it is, is right, anyway!"

Editha had a great, vital thought, an inspiration. She set down the ice-pitcher on the veranda floor, and ran up-stairs and got the letter she had written him. When at last he noisily bade her father and mother, "Well, good-night. I forgot I woke you up; I sha'n't want any sleep myself," she followed him down the avenue to the gate. There, after the whirling words that seemed to fly away from her thoughts and refuse to serve them, she made a last effort to solemnize the moment that seemed so crazy, and pressed the letter she had written upon him.

"What's this?" he said. "Want me to mail it?"

"No, no. It's for you. I wrote it after you went this morning. Keep it—keep it—and read it sometime—" She thought, and then her inspiration came: "Read it if ever you doubt what you've done, or fear that I regret your having done it. Read it after you've started."

They strained each other in embraces that seemed as ineffective as their words, and he kissed her face with quick, hot breaths that were so unlike him, that made her feel as if she had lost her old lover and found a stranger in his place. The stranger said: "What a gorgeous flower you are, with your red hair, and your blue eyes that look black now, and your face with the color painted out by the white moonshine! Let me hold you under the chin, to see whether I love blood, you tiger-lily!" Then he laughed Gearson's laugh, and released her, scared and giddy. Within her wilfulness she had been frightened by a sense of subtler force in him, and mystically mastered as she had never been before.

She ran all the way back to the house, and mounted the steps panting. Her mother and father were talking of the great affair. Her mother said: "Wa'n't Mr. Gearson in rather of an excited state of mind? Didn't you think he acted curious?"

"Well, not for a man who'd just been elected captain and had set 'em up for the whole of Company A," her father chuckled back.

"What in the world do you mean, Mr. Balcom? Oh! There's Editha!" She offered to follow the girl indoors.

"Don't come, mother!" Editha called, vanishing.

Mrs. Balcom remained to reproach her husband. "I don't see much of anything to laugh at."

"Well, it's catching. Caught it from Gearson. I guess it won't be much of a war, and I guess Gearson don't think so, either. The other fellows will back down as soon as they see we mean it. I wouldn't lose any sleep over it. I'm going back to bed, myself."

Gearson came again next afternoon, looking pale and rather sick, but quite himself, even to his languid irony. "I guess I'd better tell you, Editha, that I consecrated myself to your god

of battles last night by pouring too many libations to him
down my own throat. But I'm all right now. One has to carry
off the excitement, somehow."

"Promise me," she commanded, "that you'll never touch it
again!"

"What! Not let the cannikin clink? Not let the soldier drink?
Well, I promise."

"You don't belong to yourself now; you don't even belong
to *me*. You belong to your country, and you have a sacred
charge to keep yourself strong and well for your country's sake.
I have been thinking, thinking all night and all day long."

"You look as if you had been crying a little, too," he said,
with his queer smile.

"That's all past. I've been thinking, and worshipping *you*.
Don't you suppose I know all that you've been through, to
come to this? I've followed you every step from your old
theories and opinions."

"Well, you've had a long row to hoe."

"And I know you've done this from the highest motives—"

"Oh, there won't be much pettifogging to do till this cruel
war is—"

"And you haven't simply done it for my sake. I couldn't respect you if you had."

"Well, then we'll say I haven't. A man that hasn't got his
own respect intact wants the respect of all the other people he
can corner. But we won't go into that. I'm in for the thing
now, and we've got to face our future. My idea is that this
isn't going to be a very protracted struggle; we shall just scare
the enemy to death before it comes to a fight at all. But we
must provide for contingencies, Editha. If anything happens
to me—"

"Oh, George!" She clung to him, sobbing.

"I don't want you to feel foolishly bound to my memory. I
should hate that, wherever I happened to be."

"I am yours, for time and eternity—time and eternity."
She liked the words; they satisfied her famine for phrases.

"Well, say eternity; that's all right; but time's another thing; and I'm talking about time. But there is something! My mother! If anything happens—"

She winced, and he laughed. "You're not the bold soldier-girl of yesterday!" Then he sobered. "If anything happens, I want you to help my mother out. She won't like my doing this thing. She brought me up to think war a fool thing as well as a bad thing. My father was in the Civil War; all through it; lost his arm in it." She thrilled with the sense of the arm round her; what if that should be lost? He laughed as if divining her: "Oh, it doesn't run in the family, as far as I know!" Then he added, gravely: "He came home with misgivings about war, and they grew on him. I guess he and mother agreed between them that I was to be brought up in his final mind about it; but that was before my time. I only knew him from my mother's report of him and his opinions; I don't know whether they were hers first; but they were hers last. This will be a blow to her. I shall have to write and tell her—"

He stopped, and she asked: "Would you like me to write, too, George?"

"I don't believe that would do. No, I'll do the writing. She'll understand a little if I say that I thought the way to minimize it was to make war on the largest possible scale at once—that I felt I must have been helping on the war somehow if I hadn't helped keep it from coming, and I knew I hadn't; when it came, I had no right to stay out of it."

Whether his sophistries satisfied him or not, they satisfied her. She clung to his breast, and whispered, with closed eyes and quivering lips: "Yes, yes, yes!"

"But if anything should happen, you might go to her and see what you could do for her. You know? It's rather far off; she can't leave her chair—"

"Oh, I'll go, if it's the ends of the earth! But nothing will happen! Nothing *can!* I—"

She felt herself lifted with his rising, and Gearson was saying, with his arm still round her, to her father: "Well, we're off at once, Mr. Balcom. We're to be formally accepted at the capital, and then bunched up with the rest somehow, and sent into camp somewhere, and got to the front as soon as possible. We all want to be in the van, of course; we're the first company to report to the Governor. I came to tell Editha, but I hadn't got round to it."

She saw him again for a moment at the capital, in the station, just before the train started southward with his regiment. He looked well, in his uniform, and very soldierly, but somehow girlish, too, with his clean-shaven face and slim figure. The manly eyes and the strong voice satisfied her, and his preoccupation with some unexpected details of duty flattered her. Other girls were weeping and bemoaning themselves, but she felt a sort of noble distinction in the abstraction, the almost unconsciousness, with which they parted. Only at the last moment he said: "Don't forget my mother. It mayn't be such a walk-over as I supposed," and he laughed at the notion.

He waved his hand to her as the train moved off—she knew it among a score of hands that were waved to other girls from the platform of the car, for it held a letter which she knew was hers. Then he went inside the car to read it, doubtless, and she did not see him again. But she felt safe for him through the strength of what she called her love. What she called her God, always speaking the name in a deep voice and with the implication of a mutual understanding, would watch over him and keep him and bring him back to her. If with an empty sleeve, then he should have three arms instead of two, for both of hers should be his for life. She did not see, though, why she should always be thinking of the arm his father had lost.

There were not many letters from him, but they were such as she could have wished, and she put her whole strength into making hers such as she imagined he could have wished, glorifying and supporting him. She wrote to his mother glorifying him as their hero, but the brief answer she got was merely to the effect that Mrs. Gearson was not well enough to write herself, and thanking her for her letter by the hand of some one who called herself "Yrs truly, Mrs. W. J. Andrews."

Editha determined not to be hurt, but to write again quite as if the answer had been all she expected. Before it seemed as if she could have written, there came news of the first skirmish, and in the list of the killed, which was telegraphed as a trifling loss on our side, was Gearson's name. There was a frantic time of trying to make out that it might be, must be, some other Gearson; but the name and the company and the regiment and the State were too definitely given.

Then there was a lapse into depths out of which it seemed as if she never could rise again; then a lift into clouds far above all grief, black clouds, that blotted out the sun, but where she soared with him, with George—George! She had the fever that she expected of herself, but she did not die in it; she was not even delirious, and it did not last long. When she was well enough to leave her bed, her one thought was of George's mother, of his strangely worded wish that she should go to her and see what she could do for her. In the exaltation of the duty laid upon her—it buoyed her up instead of burdening her—she rapidly recovered.

Her father went with her on the long railroad journey from northern New York to western Iowa; he had business out at Davenport, and he said he could just as well go then as any other time; and he went with her to the little country town where George's mother lived in a little house on the edge of the illimitable cornfields, under trees pushed to a top of the rolling prairie. George's father had settled there after the Civil War, as so many other old soldiers had done; but they were Eastern people, and Editha fancied touches of the East in the June rose overhanging the front door, and the garden with early summer flowers stretching from the gate of the paling fence.

It was very low inside the house, and so dim, with the closed blinds, that they could scarcely see one another: Editha tall and black in her crapes which filled the air with the smell of their dyes; her father standing decorously apart with his hat on his forearm, as at funerals; a woman rested in a deep arm-chair, and the woman who had let the strangers in stood behind the chair.

The seated woman turned her head round and up, and asked the woman behind her chair: "Who did you say?"

Editha, if she had done what she expected of herself, would have gone down on her knees at the feet of the seated figure and said, "I am George's Editha," for answer.

But instead of her own voice she heard that other woman's voice, saying: "Well, I don't know as I did get the name just right. I guess I'll have to make a little more light in here," and she went and pushed two of the shutters ajar.

Then Editha's father said, in his public will-now-address-a-few-remarks tone: "My name is Balcom, ma'am—Junius H. Balcom, of Balcom's Works, New York; my daughter—"

"Oh!" the seated woman broke in, with a powerful voice, the voice that always surprised Editha from Gearson's slender frame. "Let me see you. Stand round where the light can strike on your face," and Editha dumbly obeyed. "So, you're Editha Balcom," she sighed.

"Yes," Editha said, more like a culprit than a comforter.

"What did you come for?" Mrs. Gearson asked.

Editha's face quivered and her knees shook. "I came—because—because George—" She could go no further.

"Yes," the mother said, "he told me he had asked you to come if he got killed. You didn't expect that, I suppose, when you sent him."

"I would rather have died myself than done it!" Editha said, with more truth in her deep voice than she ordinarily found in it. "I tried to leave him free—"

"Yes, that letter of yours, that came back with his other things, left him free."

Editha saw now where George's irony came from.

"It was not to be read before—unless—until—I told him so," she faltered.

"Of course, he wouldn't read a letter of yours, under the circumstances, till he thought you wanted him to. Been sick?" the woman abruptly demanded.

"Very sick," Editha said, with self-pity.

"Daughter's life," her father interposed, "was almost despaired of, at one time."

Mrs. Gearson gave him no heed. "I suppose you would have been glad to die, such a brave person as you! I don't believe *he* was glad to die. He was always a timid boy, that way; he was afraid of a good many things; but if he was afraid he did what he made up his mind to. I suppose he made up his mind to go, but I knew what it cost him by what it cost me when I heard of it. I had been through *one* war before. When you sent him you didn't expect he would get killed."

The voice seemed to compassionate Editha, and it was time. "No," she huskily murmured.

"No, girls don't; women don't, when they give their men up to their country. They think they'll come marching back, somehow, just as gay as they went, or if it's an empty sleeve, or even an empty pantaloon, it's all the more glory, and they're so much the prouder of them, poor things!"

The tears began to run down Editha's face; she had not wept till then; but it was now such a relief to be understood that the tears came.

"No, you didn't expect him to get killed," Mrs. Gearson repeated, in a voice which was startlingly like George's again. "You just expected him to kill some one else, some of those foreigners, that weren't there because they had any say about it, but because they had to be there, poor wretches—conscripts, or whatever they call 'em. You thought it would be all right for my George, *your* George, to kill the sons of those miserable mothers and the husbands of those girls that you would never see the faces of." The woman lifted her powerful voice in a psalmlike note. "I thank my God he didn't live to do it! I thank my God they killed him first, and that he ain't livin' with their blood on his hands!" She dropped her eyes, which she had raised with her voice, and glared at Editha. "What you got that black on for?" She lifted herself by her powerful arms so high that her helpless body seemed to hang limp its full length. "Take it off, take it off, before I tear it from your back!"

The lady who was passing the summer near Balcom's Works was sketching Editha's beauty, which lent itself wonderfully to the effects of a colorist. It had come to that confidence which is rather apt to grow between artist and sitter, and Editha had told her everything.

"To think of your having such a tragedy in your life!" the lady said. She added: "I suppose there are people who feel that way about war. But when you consider the good this war has done—how much it has done for the country! I can't understand such people, for my part. And when you had come all the way out there to console her—got up out of a sick-bed! Well!"

"I think," Editha said, magnanimously, "she wasn't quite in her right mind; and so did papa."

"Yes," the lady said, looking at Editha's lips in nature and then at her lips in art, and giving an empirical touch to them in the picture. "But how dreadful of her! How perfectly— excuse me—how *vulgar!*"

A light broke upon Editha in the darkness which she felt had been without a gleam of brightness for weeks and months. The mystery that had bewildered her was solved by the word; and from that moment she rose from grovelling in shame and self-pity, and began to live again in the ideal.

IV   The Winds of Doctrine: Defining Realism

An excellent brief discussion of realistic theory is to be found in Gordon S. Haight, "Realism Defined," in Spiller, *et al.*, *Literary History of the United States*, 1948, Chapter 54. Everett Carter, *Howells and the Age of Realism*, 1954, is a good extended study. F. O. Matthiessen, *Henry James: the Major Phase*, 1944, Leon Edel, *The Prefaces of Henry James*, 1931, Morris Roberts, *Henry James' Criticism*, 1929, and R. P. Blackmur (ed.), *The Art of the Novel*, 1934, all contain intensive examinations of James' critical theories. See also Robert Penn Warren (ed.), The Henry James Number, *Kenyon Rev.* (1943), V, 481-617, which contains a symposium of nine critical essays.

William Peirce Randel, *Edward Eggleston: Author of "The Hoosier Schoolmaster,"* 1946, is a full biographical and critical treatment. On Eggleston's theory and method, see Benjamin T. Spencer, "The New Realism and a National Literature," *PMLA* (1941), LVI, 1116-1132; and Charles Hirshfeld, "Edward Eggleston: Pioneer in Social History," in Eric F. Goldman (ed.), *Historiography and Urbanization: Essays in American History in Honor of W. Stull Holt*, 1941.

There is no biography of Garland, and no collected edition of his works. Fairly full discussion of his theory and practice as a writer of fiction may be found in Walter F. Taylor, *The Economic Novel in America*, 1942, pp. 148-183; in Carl Van Doren, *Contemporary American Novelists*, 1922, pp. 38-47; and in Claude Simpson, "Hamlin Garland's Decline," *Southwest Rev.* (1941), XXVI, 223-234. Garland elaborated the theories of *Crumbling Idols* in "The West in Literature," *Arena* (1892), VI, 669-676; "The Future of Fiction," *Arena* (1893), VII, 513-524; and "Productive Conditions of American Literature," *Forum* (1894), VII, 690-698.

Henry James

1843-1916

from PARTIAL PORTRAITS

THE ART OF FICTION
(1884)

I should not have affixed so comprehensive a title to these few remarks, necessarily wanting in any completeness upon a subject the full consideration of which would carry us far, did I not seem to discover a pretext for my temerity in the interesting pamphlet lately published under this name by Mr. Walter Besant. Mr. Besant's lecture at the Royal Institution—the original form of his pamphlet—appears to indicate that many persons are interested in the art of fiction, and are not indifferent to such remarks, as those who practice it may attempt to make about it. I am therefore anxious not to lose the benefit of this favourable association, and to edge in a few words under cover of the attention which Mr. Besant is sure to have excited. There is something very encouraging in his having put into form certain of his ideas on the mystery of story-telling.

It is a proof of life and curiosity—curiosity on the part of the brotherhood of novelists as well as on the part of their readers. Only a short time ago it might have been supposed that the English novel was not what the French call *discutable*. It had no air of having a theory, a conviction, a consciousness of itself behind it—of being the expression of an artistic faith, the result of choice and comparison. I do not say it was necessarily the worse for that: it would take much more courage than I possess to intimate that the form of the novel as Dickens and Thackeray (for instance) saw it had any taint of incompleteness. It was, however, *naïf* (if I may help myself out with another French word); and evidently if it be destined to suffer in any way for having lost its *naïveté* it has now an idea of making sure of the corresponding advantages. During the period I have alluded to there was a comfortable, good-humoured feeling abroad that a novel is a novel, as a pudding is a pudding, and that our only business with it could be to swallow it. But within a year or two, for some reason or other, there have been signs of returning animation—the era of discussion would appear to have been to a certain extent opened. Art lives upon discussion, upon experiment, upon curiosity, upon variety of attempt, upon the exchange of views and the comparison of standpoints; and there is a presumption that those times when no one has anything particular to say about it, and has no reason to give for practice or preference, though they may be times of honour, are not times of development— are times, possibly even, a little of dulness. The successful application of any art is a delightful spectacle, but the theory too is interesting; and though there is a great deal of the latter without the former I suspect there has never been a genuine success that has not had a latent core of conviction. Discussion, suggestion, formulation, these things are fertilizing when they are frank and sincere. Mr. Besant has set an excellent example in saying what he thinks, for his part, about the way in which fiction should be written, as well as about the way in which it should be published; for his view of the "art," carried on into an appendix, covers that too. Other labourers in the same field will doubtless take up the argument, they will give it the light of their experience, and the effect will surely be to make our interest in the novel a little more what it had for some time threatened to fail to be—a serious, active, inquiring interest, under protection of which this delightful study may, in moments of confidence, venture to say a little more what it thinks of itself.

It must take itself seriously for the public to take it so. The old superstition about fiction being "wicked" has doubtless died out in England; but the spirit of it lingers in a certain oblique regard directed toward any story which does not more or less admit that it is only a joke. Even the most jocular novel feels in some degree the weight of the proscription that was formerly directed against literary levity: the jocularity does not always succeed in passing for orthodoxy. It is still expected, though perhaps people are shamed to say it, that a production which is after all only a "make-believe" (for what else is a "story"?) shall be in some degree apologetic—shall renounce the pretension of attempting really to represent life. This, of course, any sensible, wide-awake story declines to do, for it quickly perceives that the tolerance granted to it on such a condition is only an attempt to stifle it disguised in the form of generosity. The old evangelical hostility to the novel, which was as explicit as it was narrow, and which regarded it as little less favourable to our immortal part than a stage-play, was in reality far less insulting. The only reason for the existence of a novel is that it does attempt to represent life. When it relinquishes this attempt, the same attempt that we see on the canvas of the painter, it will have arrived at a very strange pass. It is not expected of the picture that it will make itself humble in order to be forgiven; and the analogy between the art of the painter and the art of the novelist is, so far as I am able to see, complete. Their inspiration is the same, their process (allowing for the different quality of the vehicle) is the same, their success is the same. They may learn from each other, they may explain and sustain each other. Their cause is the same, and the honour of one is the honour of another. The Mohametans think a picture an unholy thing, but it is a long time since any Christian did, and it is therefore the more odd that in the Christian mind the traces (dissimulated though they may be) of a suspicion of the sister art should linger to this day. The only effectual way to lay it to rest is to emphasize the analogy to which I just alluded—to insist on the fact that as the picture is reality, so the novel is history. That is the only general description (which does it justice) that we may give of the novel. But history also is allowed to represent life; it is not, any more than painting, expected to apologize. The subject-matter of fiction is stored up likewise in documents and records, and if it will not give itself away, as they say in California, it must speak with assurance, with the tone of the historian. Certain accomplished novelists have a habit of giving themselves away which must often bring tears to the eyes of people who take their fiction seriously. I was lately struck, in reading over many pages of Anthony Trollope, with his want of discretion in this particular. In a digression, a parenthesis or an aside, he concedes to the reader that he and this trusting friend are only "making believe." He admits that the events he narrates have not really happened, and that he can give his narrative any turn the reader may like best. Such a betrayal of a sacred office seems to me, I confess, a terrible crime; it is what I mean by the attitude of apology, and it shocks me every whit as much in Trollope as it would have shocked me in Gibbon or Macaulay. It implies that the novelist is less occupied in looking for the truth (the truth, of course I mean, that he assumes, the premises that we must grant him, whatever they may be) than the historian, and in doing so it deprives him at a stroke of all his standing-room. To represent and illustrate the past, the actions of men, is the task of either writer, and the only difference that I can see is, in proportion as he succeeds, to the honour of the novelist, consisting as it does in his having more difficulty in collecting his evidence, which is so far from being purely literary. It seems to me to give him a great character, the fact that he has at once so much in common with the philosopher and the painter; this double analogy is a magnificent heritage.

It is of all this evidently that Mr. Besant is full when he insists upon the fact that fiction is one of the *fine* arts, deserving in its turn of all the honours and emoluments that have hitherto been reserved for the successful profession of music, poetry, painting, architecture. It is impossible to insist too much on so important a truth, and the place that Mr. Besant demands for the work of the novelist may be represented, a trifle less abstractly, by saying that he demands not only that it shall be reputed artistic, but that it shall be reputed very artistic indeed. It is excellent that he should have struck this note, for his doing so indicates that there was need of it, that his proposition may be to many people a novelty. One rubs one's eyes at the thought; but the rest of Mr. Besant's essay confirms the revelation. I suspect in truth that it would be possible to confirm it still further, and that one would not be far wrong in saying that in addition to the people to whom it has never occurred that a novel ought to be artistic, there are a great many others who, if this principle were urged upon them, would be filled with an indefinable mistrust. They would find it difficult to explain their repugnance, but it would operate strongly to put them on their guard. "Art," in our Protestant communities, where so many things have got so strangely twisted about, is supposed in certain circles to have some vaguely injurious effect upon those who make it an important consideration, who let it weigh in the balance. It is supposed to be opposed in some mysterious manner to morality, to amusement, to instruction. When it is embodied in the work of the painter (the sculptor is another affair!) you know what it is: it stands there before you, in the honesty of pink and green and a gilt frame; you can see the worst of it at a glance, and you can be on your guard. But when it is introduced into literature it becomes more insidious—there is danger of its hurting you before you know it. Literature should be either instructive or amusing, and there is in many minds an impression that these artistic preoccupations, the search for form, contribute to neither end, interfere indeed with both. They are too frivolous to be edifying, and too serious to be diverting; and they are moreover priggish and paradoxical and superfluous. That, I think, represents the manner in which the latent thought of many people who read novels as an exercise in skipping would explain itself if it were to become articulate. They would argue, of course, that a novel ought to be "good," but they would interpret this term in a fashion of their own, which indeed would vary considerably from one critic to another. One would say that being good means representing virtuous and aspiring characters, placed in prominent positions; another would say that it depends on a "happy ending," on a distribution at the last of prizes, pensions, husbands, wives, babies, millions, appended paragraphs, and cheerful remarks. Another still would say that it means being full of incident and movement, so that we shall wish to jump ahead, to see who was the mysterious stranger, and if the stolen will was ever found, and shall not be distracted from this pleasure by any tiresome analysis or "description." But they would all agree that the "artistic" idea would spoil some of their fun. One would hold it accountable for all the description, another would see it revealed in the absence of sympathy. Its hostility to a happy ending would be evident, and it might even in some cases render any ending at all impossible. The "ending" of a novel is, for many persons, like that of a good dinner, a course of dessert and ices, and the artist in fiction is regarded as a sort of meddlesome doctor who forbids agreeable aftertastes. It is therefore true that this conception of Mr. Besant's of the novel as a superior form encounters not only a negative but a positive indifference. It matters little that as a work of art it should really be as little or as much of its essence to supply happy endings, sympathetic characters, and an objective tone, as if it were a work of mechanics; the association of ideas, however incongruous, might easily be too much for it if an eloquent voice were not sometimes raised to call attention to the fact that it is at once as free and as serious a branch of literature as any other.

Certainly this might sometimes be doubted in presence of the enormous number of works of fiction that appeal to the credulity of our generation, for it might easily seem that there could be no great character in a commodity so quickly and easily produced. It must be admitted that good novels are much compromised by bad ones, and that the field at large suffers discredit from overcrowding. I think, however, that this injury is only superficial, and that the superabundance of written fiction proves nothing against the principle itself. It has been vulgarized, like all other kinds of literature, like everything else to-day, and it has proved more than some kinds accessible to vulgarization. But there is as much difference as there ever was between a good novel and a bad one: the bad is swept with all the daubed canvases and spoiled marble into some unvisited limbo, or infinite rubbish-yard beneath the back-windows of the world, and the good subsists and emits its light and stimulates our desire for perfection. As I shall take the liberty of making but a single criticism of Mr. Besant, whose tone is so full of the love of his art, I may as well have done with it at once. He seems to me to mistake in attempting to say so definitely beforehand what sort of an affair the good novel will be. To indicate the danger of such an error as that has been the purpose of these few pages; to suggest that certain traditions on the subject, applied *a priori*, have already had much to answer for, and that the good health of an art which undertakes so immediately to reproduce life must demand that it be perfectly free. It lives upon exercise, and the very meaning of exercise is freedom. The only obligation to which in advance we may hold a novel, without incurring the accusation of being arbitrary, is that it be interesting. That general responsibility rests upon it, but it is the only one I can think of. The ways in which it is at liberty to accomplish this result (of interesting us) strike me as innumerable, and such as can only suffer from being marked out or fenced in by prescription. They are as various as the temperament of man, and they are successful in proportion as they reveal a particular mind, different from others. A novel is in its broadest definition a personal, a direct impression of life: that, to begin with, constitutes its value, which is greater or less according to the intensity of the impression. But there will be no intensity at all, and therefore no value, unless there is freedom to feel and say. The tracing of a line to be followed, of a tone to be taken, of a form to be filled out, is a limitation of that freedom and a suppression of the very thing that we are most curious about. The form, it seems to me, is to be appreciated after the fact: then the author's choice has been made, his standard has been indicated; then we can follow lines and directions and compare tones and resemblances. Then in a word we can enjoy one of the most charming of pleasures, we can estimate quality, we can apply the test of execution. The execution belongs to the author alone; it is what is most personal to him, and we measure him by that. The advantage, the luxury, as well as the torment and responsibility of the novelist, is that there is no limit to what he may attempt as an executant—no limit to his possible experiments, efforts, discoveries, successes. Here it is especially that he works, step by step, like his brother of the brush, of whom we may always say that he has painted his picture in a manner best known to himself. His manner is his secret, not necessarily a jealous one. He cannot disclose it as a general thing if he would; he would be at a loss to teach it to others. I say this with a due recollection of having insisted on the community of method of the artist who paints a picture and the artist who writes a novel. The painter *is* able to teach the rudiments of his practice, and it is possible, from the study of good work (granted the aptitude), both to learn how to paint and to learn how to write. Yet it remains true, without injury to the *rapprochement*, that the literary artist would be obliged to say to his pupil much more than the other, "Ah, well, you must do it as you can!" It is a question of degree, a matter of delicacy. If there are exact sciences, there are also exact arts, and the grammer of painting is so much more definite that it makes the difference.

I ought to add, however, that if Mr. Besant says at the beginning of his essay that the "laws of fiction may be laid down and taught with as much precision and exactness as the laws of harmony, perspective, and proportion," he mitigates what might appear to be an extravagance by applying his remark to "general" laws, and by expressing most of these rules in a manner with which it would certainly be unaccommodating to disagree. That the novelist must write from his experience, that his "characters must be real and such as might be met with in actual life"; that "a young lady brought up in a quiet country village should avoid descriptions of garrison life," and "a writer whose friends and personal experience belong to the lower middle-class should carefully avoid introducing his characters into society"; that one should enter one's notes in a

common-place book; that one's figures should be clear in outline; that making them clear by some trick of speech or of carriage is a bad method, and "describing them at length" is a
worse one; that English Fiction should have a "conscious
moral purpose"; that "it is almost impossible to estimate too
highly the value of careful workmanship—that is, of style";
that "the most important point of all is the story," that "the
story is everything"; these are principles with most of which it
is surely impossible not to sympathize. That remark about the
lower middle-class writer and his knowing his place is perhaps
rather chilling; but for the rest I should find it difficult to dis-
sent from any one of these recommendations. At the same
time, I should find it difficult positively to assent to them,
with the exception, perhaps, of the injunction as to entering
one's notes in a common-place book. They scarcely seem to
me to have the quality that Mr. Besant attributes to the rules
of the novelist—the "precision and exactness" of "the laws of
harmony, perspective, and proportion." They are suggestive,
they are even inspiring, but they are not exact, though they
are doubtless as much so as the case admits of: which is a
proof of that liberty of interpretation for which I just contended. For the value of these different injunctions—so beautiful and so vague—is wholly in the meaning one attaches to
them. The characters, the situation, which strike one as real
will be those that touch and interest one most, but the measure of reality is very difficult to fix. The reality of Don Quixote
or of Mr. Micawber is a very delicate shade; it is a reality so
coloured by the author's vision that, vivid as it may be, one
would hesitate to propose it as a model: one would expose
one's self to some very embarrassing questions on the part of a
pupil. It goes without saying that you will not write a good
novel unless you possess the sense of reality; but it will be
difficult to give you a recipe for calling that sense into being.
Humanity is immense, and reality has a myriad forms; the
most one can affirm is that some of the flowers of fiction have
the odour of it, and others have not; as for telling you in advance how your nosegay should be composed, that is another

affair. It is equally excellent and inconclusive to say that one must write from experience; to our supposititious aspirant such a declaration might savour of mockery. What kind of experience is intended, and where does it begin and end? Experience is never limited, and it is never complete; it is an immense sensibility, a kind of huge spiderweb of the finest silken threads suspended in the chamber of consciousness, and catching every airborne particle in its tissue. It is the very atmosphere of the mind; and when the mind is imaginative—much more when it happens to be that of a man of genius—it takes to itself the faintest hints of life, it converts the very pulses of the air into revelations. The young lady living in a village has only to be a damsel upon whom nothing is lost to make it quite unfair (as it seems to me) to declare to her that she shall have nothing to say about the military. Greater miracles have been seen than that, imagination assisting, she should speak the truth about some of these gentlemen. I remember an English novelist, a woman of genius, telling me that she was much commended for the impression she had managed to give in one of her tales of the nature and way of life of the French Protestant youth. She had been asked where she learned so much about this recondite being, she had been congratulated on her peculiar opportunities. These opportunities consisted in her having once, in Paris, as she ascended a staircase, passed an open door where, in the household of a *pasteur*, some of the young Protestants were seated at table round a finished meal. The glimpse made a picture; it lasted only a moment, but that moment was experience. She had got her direct personal impression, and she turned out her type. She knew what youth was, and what Protestantism; she also had the advantage of having seen what it was to be French, so that she converted these ideas into a concrete image and produced a reality. Above all, however, she was blessed with the faculty which when you give it an inch takes an ell, and which for the artist is a much greater source of strength than any accident of residence or of place in the social scale. The power to guess the unseen from the seen, to trace the implication of things, to judge the whole piece by the pattern, the condition of feeling life in general so completely that you are well on your way to knowing any particular corner of it—this cluster of gifts may almost be said to constitute experience, and they occur in country and in town, and in the most differing stages of education. If experience consists of impressions, it may be said that impressions *are* experience, just as (have we not seen it?) they are the very air we breathe. Therefore, if I should certainly say to a novice, "Write from experience and experience only," I should feel that this was rather a tantalizing monition if I were not careful immediately to add, "Try to be one of the people on whom nothing is lost!"

I am far from intending by this to minimize the importance of exactness—of truth of detail. One can speak best from one's own taste, and I may therefore venture to say that the air of reality (solidity of specification) seems to me to be the supreme virtue of a novel—the merit on which all its other merits (including that conscious moral purpose of which Mr. Besant speaks) helplessly and submissively depend. If it be not there they are all as nothing, and if these be there, they owe their effect to the success with which the author has produced the illusion of life. The cultivation of this success, the study of this exquisite process, form, to my taste, the beginning and the end of the art of the novelist. They are his inspiration, his despair, his reward, his torment, his delight. It is here in very truth that he competes with life; it is here that he competes with his brother the painter in *his* attempt to render the look of things, the look that conveys their meaning, to catch the colour, the relief, the expression, the surface, the substance of the human spectacle. It is in regard to this that Mr. Besant is well inspired when he bids him take notes. He cannot possibly take too many, he cannot possibly take enough. All life solicits him, and to "render" the simplest surface, to produce the most momentary illusion, is a very complicated business. His case would be easier, and the rule would be more exact, if Mr. Besant had been able to tell him what notes to take. But this, I fear, he can never learn in any manual; it is the business of his life. He has to take a great many in order to select a few, he has to work them up as he can, and even the guides and philosophers who might have most to say to him must leave him alone when it comes to the application of precepts, as we leave the painter in communion with his palette. That his characters "must be clear in outline," as Mr. Besant says—he feels that down to his boots; but how he shall make them so is a secret between his good angel and himself. It would be absurdly simple if he could be taught that a great deal of "description" would make them so, or that on the contrary the absence of description and the cultivation of dialogue, or the absence of dialogue and the multiplication of "incident," would rescue him from his difficulties. Nothing, for instance, is more possible than that he be of a turn of mind for which this odd, literal opposition of description and dialogue, incident and description, has little meaning and light. People often talk of these things as if they had a kind of internecine distinctness, instead of melting into each other at every breath, and being intimately associated parts of one general effort of expression. I cannot imagine composition existing in a series of blocks, nor conceive, in any novel worth discussing at all, of a passage of description that is not in its intention narrative, a passage of dialogue that is not in its intention descriptive, a touch of truth of any sort that does not partake of the nature of incident, or an incident that derives its interest from any other source than the general and only source of the success of a work of art—that of being illustrative. A novel is a living thing, all one and continuous, like any other organism, and in proportion as it lives will it be found, I think, that in each of the parts there is something of each of the other parts. The critic who over the close texture of a finished work shall pretend to trace a geography of items will mark some frontiers as artificial, I fear, as any that have been known to history. There is an old-fashioned distinction between the novel of character and the novel of incident which must have cost many a smile to the intending fabulist who was keen about his work. It appears to me as little to the point as the equally celebrated distinction between the novel and the romance—to answer as little to any reality. There are

bad novels and good novels, as there are bad pictures and good
pictures; but that is the only distinction in which I see any
meaning, and I can as little imagine speaking of a novel of character as I can imagine speaking of a picture of character. When
one says picture one says of character, when one says novel one
says of incident, and the terms may be transposed at will. What
is character but the determination of incident? What is incident but the illustration of character? What is either a picture
or a novel that is not of character? What else do we seek in it
and find in it? It is an incident for a woman to stand up with
her hand resting on a table and look out at you in a certain way;
or if it be not an incident I think it will be hard to say what it
is. At the same time it is an expression of character. If you say
you don't see it (character in *that—allons donc!*), this is exactly
what the artist who has reasons of his own for thinking he *does*
see it undertakes to show you. When a young man makes up his
mind that he has not faith enough after all to enter the church
as he intended, that is an incident, though you may not hurry
to the end of the chapter to see whether perhaps he doesn't
change once more. I do not say that these are extraordinary or
startling incidents. I do not pretend to estimate the degree of
interest proceeding from them, for this will depend upon the
skill of the painter. It sounds almost puerile to say that some
incidents are intrinsically much more important than others,
and I need not take this precaution after having professed my
sympathy for the major ones in remarking that the only classification of the novel that I can understand is into that which
has life and that which has it not.

The novel and the romance, the novel of incident and that
of character—these clumsy separations appear to me to have
been made by critics and readers for their own convenience,
and to help them out of some of their occasional queer pre-
dicaments, but to have little reality or interest for the producer, from whose point of view it is of course that we are attempting to consider the art of fiction. The case is the same
with another shadowy category which Mr. Besant apparently
is disposed to set up—that of the "modern English novel";

unless indeed it be that in this matter he has fallen into an
accidental confusion of standpoints. It is not quite clear
whether he intends the remarks in which he alludes to it to be
didactic or historical. It is as difficult to suppose a person intending to write a modern English as to suppose him writing
an ancient English novel: that is a label which begs the question. One writes the novel, one paints the picture, of one's
language and of one's time, and calling it modern English will
not, alas! make the difficult task any easier. No more, unfortunately, will calling this or that work of one's fellow-artist a
romance—unless it be, of course, simply for the pleasantness
of the thing, as for instance when Hawthorne gave this head-
ing to his story of *Blithedale*. The French, who have brought
the theory of fiction to remarkable completeness, have but
one name for the novel, and have not attempted smaller
things in it, that I can see, for that. I can think of no obligation to which the "romancer" would not be held equally with
the novelist; the standard of execution is equally high for each.
Of course it is of execution that we are talking—that being
the only point of a novel that is open to contention. This is
perhaps too often lost sight of, only to produce interminable
confusions and cross-purposes. We must grant the artist his
subject, his idea, his *donnée*: our criticism is applied only to
what he makes of it. Naturally I do not mean that we
are bound to like it or find it interesting: in case we do not
our course is perfectly simple—to let it alone. We may believe that of a certain idea even the most sincere novelist can
make nothing at all, and the event may perfectly justify our
belief; but the failure will have been a failure to execute, and
it is in the execution that the fatal weakness is recorded. If we
pretend to respect the artist at all, we must allow him his freedom of choice, in the face, in particular cases, of innumerable
presumptions that the choice will not fructify. Art derives a
considerable part of its beneficial exercise from flying in the
face of presumptions, and some of the most interesting experiments of which it is capable are hidden in the bosom of common things. Gustave Flaubert has written a story about the

devotion of a servant-girl to a parrot, and the production, highly finished as it is, cannot on the whole be called a success. We are perfectly free to find it flat, but I think it might have been interesting; and I, for my part, am extremely glad he should have written it; it is a contribution to our knowledge of what can be done—or what cannot. Ivan Turgénieff has written a tale about a deaf and dumb serf and a lap-dog, and the thing is touching, loving, a little masterpiece. He struck the note of life where Gustave Flaubert missed it—he flew in the face of a presumption and achieved a victory. Nothing, of course, will ever take the place of the good old fashion of "liking" a work of art or not liking it: the most improved criticism will not abolish that primitive, that ultimate test. I mention this to guard myself from the accusation of intimating that the idea, the subject, of a novel or a picture, does not matter. It matters, to my sense, in the highest degree, and if I might put up a prayer it would be that artists should select none but the richest. Some, as I have already hastened to admit, are much more remunerative than others, and it would be a world happily arranged in which persons intending to treat them should be exempt from confusions and mistakes. This fortunate condition will arrive only, I fear, on the same day that critics become purged from error. Meanwhile, I repeat, we do not judge the artist with fairness unless we say to him,

"Oh, I grant you your starting-point, because if I did not I should seem to prescribe to you, and heaven forbid I should take that responsibility. If I pretend to tell you what you must not take, you will call upon me to tell you then what you must take; in which case I shall be prettily caught. Moreover, it isn't till I have accepted your data that I can begin to measure you. I have the standard, the pitch; I have no right to tamper with your flute and then criticize your music. Of course I may not like your idea at all; I may think it silly, or stale, or unclean; in which case I wash my hands of you altogether. I may content myself with believing that you will not have succeeded in being interesting, but I shall, of course, not attempt to demonstrate it, and you will be as indifferent to me as I am to you. I needn't remind you that there are all sorts of tastes: who can know it better? Some people, for excellent reasons, don't like to read about carpenters; others, for reasons even better, don't like to read about courtesans. Many object to Americans. Others (I believe they are mainly editors and publishers) won't look at Italians. Some readers don't like quiet subjects; others don't like bustling ones. Some enjoy a complete illusion, others the consciousness of large concessions. They choose their novels accordingly, and if they don't care about your idea they won't, *a fortiori*, care about your treatment."

So that it comes back very quickly, as I have said, to the liking: in spite of M. Zola, who reasons less powerfully than he represents, and who will not reconcile himself to this absoluteness of taste, thinking that there are certain things that people ought to like, and that they can be made to like. I am quite at a loss to imagine anything (at any rate in this matter of fiction) that people *ought* to like or to dislike. Selection will be sure to take care of itself, for it has a constant motive behind it. That motive is simply experience. As people feel life, so they will feel the art that is most closely related to it. This closeness of relation is what we should never forget in talking of the effort of the novel. Many people speak of it as a factitious, artificial form, a product of ingenuity, the business of which is to alter and arrange the things that surround us, to translate them into conventional, traditional moulds. This, however, is a view of the matter which carries us but a very short way, condemns the art to an eternal repetition of a few familiar *clichés*, cuts short its development, and leads us straight up to a dead wall. Catching the very note and trick, the strange irregular rhythm of life, that is the attempt whose strenuous force keeps Fiction upon her feet. In proportion as in what she offers us we see life *without* rearrangement do we feel that we are touching the truth; in proportion as we see it *with* rearrangement do we feel that we are being put off with a substitute, a compromise and convention. It is not uncommon to hear an extraordinary assurance of remark in regard to this matter of rearranging, which is often spoken of as if it were the last word of art. Mr. Besant seems to me in danger of falling into the great error with his rather unguarded talk about "selection." Art is essentially selection, but it is a selection whose main care is to be typical, to be inclusive. For many people art means rose-coloured windowpanes, and selection means picking a bouquet for Mrs. Grundy. They will tell you glibly that artistic considerations have nothing to do with the disagreeable, with the ugly; they will rattle off shallow commonplaces about the province of art and the limits of art till you are moved to some wonder in return as to the province and the limits of ignorance. It appears to me that no one can ever have made a seriously artistic attempt without becoming conscious of an immense increase—a kind of revelation—of freedom. One perceives in that case—by the light of a heavenly ray—that the province of art is all life, all feeling, all observation, all vision. As Mr. Besant so justly intimates, it is all experience. That is a sufficient answer to those who maintain that it must not touch the sad things of life, who stick into its divine unconscious bosom little prohibitory inscriptions on the end of sticks, such as we see in public gardens—"It is forbidden to walk on the grass; it is forbidden to touch the flowers; it is not allowed to introduce dogs or to remain after dark; it is requested to keep to the right." The young aspirant in the line of fiction whom we continue to imagine will do nothing without taste, for in that case his freedom would be of little use to him; but the first advantage of his taste will be to reveal to him the absurdity of the little sticks and tickets. If he have taste, I must add, of course he will have ingenuity, and my disrespectful reference to that quality just now was not meant to imply that it is useless in fiction. But it is only a secondary aid; the first is a capacity for receiving straight impressions.

Mr. Besant has some remarks on the question of "the story"

which I shall not attempt to criticize, though they seem to me to contain a singular ambiguity, because I do not think I understand them. I cannot see what is meant by talking as if there were a part of a novel which is the story and part of it which for mystical reasons is not—unless indeed the distinction be made in a sense in which it is difficult to suppose that any one should attempt to convey anything. "The story," if it represents anything, represents the subject, the idea, the *donnée* of the novel; and there is surely no "school"—Mr. Besant speaks of a school—which urges that a novel should be all treatment and no subject. There must assuredly be something to treat; every school is intimately conscious of that. This sense of the story being the idea, the starting-point, of the novel, is the only one that I see in which it can be spoken of as something different from its organic whole; and since in proportion as the work is successful the idea permeates and penetrates it, informs and animates it, so that every word and every punctuation-point contribute directly to the expression, in that proportion do we lose our sense of the story being a blade which may be drawn more or less out of its sheath. The story and the novel, the idea and the form, are the needle and thread, and I never heard of a guild of tailors who recommended the use of the thread without the needle, or the needle without the thread. Mr. Besant is not the only critic who may be observed to have spoken as if there were certain things in life which constitute stories, and certain others which do not. I find the same odd implication in an entertaining article in the *Pall Mall Gazette*, devoted, as it happens, to Mr. Besant's lecture. "The story is the thing!" says this graceful writer, as if with a tone of opposition to some other idea. I should think it was, as every painter who, as the time for "sending in" his picture looms in the distance, finds himself still in quest of a subject—as every belated artist not fixed about his theme will heartily agree. There are some subjects which speak to us and others which do not, but he would be a clever man who should undertake to give a rule—an *index expurgatorius*—by which the story and the no-story should be known apart. It is impossible (to me at least) to imagine any such rule which shall not be altogether arbitrary. The writer in the *Pall Mall* opposes the delightful (as I suppose) novel of *Margot la Balafrée* to certain tales in which "Bostonian nymphs" appear to have "rejected English dukes for psychological reasons." I am not acquainted with the romance just designated, and can scarcely forgive the *Pall Mall* critic for not mentioning the name of the author, but the title appears to refer to a lady who may have received a scar in some heroic adventure. I am inconsolable at not being acquainted with this episode, but am utterly at a loss to see why it is a story when the rejection (or acceptance) of a duke is not, and why a reason, psychological or other, is not a subject when a cicatrix is. They are all particles of the multitudinous life with which the novel deals, and surely no dogma which pretends to make it lawful to touch the one and unlawful to touch the other will stand for a moment on its feet. It is the special picture that must stand or fall, according as it seems to possess truth or to lack it. Mr. Besant does not, to my sense, light up the subject by intimating that a story must, under penalty of not being a story, consist of "adventures." Why of adventures more than of green spectacles? He mentions a category of impossible things, and among them he places "fiction without adventure." Why without adventure, more than without matrimony, or celibacy, or parturition, or cholera, or hydropathy, or Jansenism? This seems to me to bring the novel back to the hapless little *rôle* of being an artificial, ingenious thing—bring it down from its large, free character of an immense and exquisite correspondence with life. And what *is* adventure, when it comes to that, and by what sign is the listening pupil to recognize it? It is an adventure—an immense one—for me to write this little article; and for a Bostonian nymph to reject an English duke is an adventure only less stirring, I should say, than for an English duke to be rejected by a Bostonian nymph. I see dramas within dramas in that, and innumerable points of view. A psychological reason is, to my imagination, an object adorably pictorial; to catch the tint of its complexion—I feel as if that idea might inspire one to Titianesque efforts. There are few things more exciting to me, in short, than a psychological reason, and yet, I protest, the novel seems to me the most magnificent form of art. I have just been reading, at the same time, the delightful story of *Treasure Island*, by Mr. Robert Louis Stevenson, and, in a manner less consecutive, the last tale from M. Edmond de Goncourt, which is entitled *Chérie*. One of these works treats of murders, mysteries, islands of dreadful renown, hairbreadth escapes, miraculous coincidences and buried doubloons. The other treats of a little French girl who lived in a fine house in Paris, and died of wounded sensibility because no one would marry her. I call *Treasure Island* delightful, because it appears to me to have succeeded wonderfully in what it attempts; and I venture to bestow no epithet upon *Chérie*, which strikes me as having failed deplorably in what it attempts—that is, in tracing the development of the moral consciousness of a child. But one of these productions strikes me as exactly as much of a novel as the other, and as having a "story" quite as much. The moral consciousness of a child is as much a part of life as the islands of the Spanish Main, and the one sort of geography seems to me to have those "surprises" of which Mr. Besant speaks quite as much as the other. For myself (since it comes back in the last resort, as I say, to the preference of the individual), the picture of the child's experience has the advantage that I can at successive steps (an immense luxury, near to the "sensual pleasure" of which Mr. Besant's critic in the *Pall Mall* speaks) say Yes or No, as it may be, to what the artist puts before me. I have been a child in fact, but I have been on a quest for a buried treasure only in supposition, and it is a simple accident that with M. de Goncourt I should have for the most part to say No. With George Eliot, when she painted that country with a far other intelligence, I always said Yes.

The most interesting part of Mr. Besant's lecture is unfortunately the briefest passage—his very cursory allusion to the "conscious moral purpose" of the novel. Here again it is not very clear whether he be recording a fact or laying down a principle; it is a great pity that in the latter case he should not have developed his idea. This branch of the subject is of immense importance, and Mr. Besant's few words point to considerations of the widest reach, not to be lightly disposed of. He will have treated the art of fiction but superficially who is not prepared to go every inch of the way that these considerations will carry him. It is for this reason that at the beginning of these remarks I was careful to notify the reader that my reflections on so large a theme have no pretension to be exhaustive. Like Mr. Besant, I have left the question of the morality of the novel till the last, and at the last I find I have used up my space. It is a question surrounded with difficulties, as witness the very first that meets us, in the form of a definite question, on the threshold. Vagueness, in such a discussion, is fatal, and what is the meaning of your morality and your conscious moral purpose? Will you not define your terms and explain how (a novel being a picture) a picture can be either moral or immoral? You wish to paint a moral picture or carve a moral statue: will you not tell us how you would set about it? We are discussing the Art of Fiction; questions of art are questions (in the widest sense) of execution; questions of morality are quite another affair, and will you not let us see how it is that you find it so easy to mix them up? These things are so clear to Mr. Besant that he has deduced from them a law which he sees embodied in English Fiction, and which is "a truly admirable thing and a great cause for congratulation." It is a great cause for congratulation indeed when such thorny problems become as smooth as silk. I may add that in so far as Mr. Besant perceives that in point of fact English Fiction has addressed itself preponderantly to these delicate questions he will appear to many people to have made a vain discovery. They will have been positively struck, on the contrary, with the moral timidity of the usual English novelist; with his (or with her) aversion to face the difficulties with which on every side the treatment of reality bristles. He is apt to be extremely shy (whereas the picture that Mr. Besant draws is a picture of boldness), and the sign of his work, for the most part, is a cautious silence on certain subjects. In the English novel (by which of course I mean the American as well), more than in any other, there is a traditional difference between that which people know and that which they agree to admit that they know, that which they see and that which they speak of, that which they feel to be a part of life and that which they allow to enter into literature. There is the great difference, in short, between what they talk of in conversation and what they talk of in print. The essence of moral energy is to survey the whole field, and I should directly reverse Mr. Besant's remark and say not that the English novel has a purpose, but that it has a diffidence. To what degree a purpose in a work of art is a source of corruption I shall not attempt to inquire; the one that seems to me least dangerous is the purpose of making a perfect work. As for our novel, I may say lastly on this score that as we find it in England to-day it strikes me as addressed in a large degree to "young people," and that this in itself constitutes a presumption that it will be rather shy. There are certain things which it is generally agreed not to discuss, not even to mention, before young people. That is very well, but the absence of discussion is not a symptom of the moral passion. The purpose of the English novel—"a truly admirable thing, and a great cause for congratulation"—strikes me therefore as rather negative.

There is one point at which the moral sense and the artistic sense lie very near together; that is in the light of the very obvious truth that the deepest quality of a work of art will always be the quality of the mind of the producer. In proportion as that intelligence is fine will the novel, the picture, the statue partake of the substance of beauty and truth. To be constituted of such elements is, to my vision, to have purpose enough. No good novel will ever proceed from a superficial mind; that seems to me an axiom which, for the artist in fiction, will cover all needful moral ground: if the youthful aspirant take it to heart it will illuminate for him many of the mysteries of "purpose." There are many other useful things that might be said to him, but I have come to the end of my article, and can only touch them as I pass. The critic in the *Pall Mall Gazette*, whom I have already quoted, draws attention to the danger, in speaking of the art of fiction, of generalizing. The danger that he has in mind is rather, I imagine, that of particularizing, for there are some comprehensive remarks which, in addition to those embodied in Mr. Besant's suggestive lecture, might without fear of misleading him be addressed to the ingenuous student. I should remind him first of the magnificence of the form that is open to him, which offers to sight so few restrictions and such innumerable opportunities. The other arts, in comparison, appear confined and hampered; the various conditions under which they are exercised are so rigid and definite. But the only condition that I can think of attaching to the composition of the novel is, as I have already said, that it be sincere. This freedom is a splendid privilege, and the first lesson of the young novelist is to learn to be worthy of it. "Enjoy it as it deserves [I should say to him]; take possession of it, explore it to its utmost extent, publish it, rejoice in it. All life belongs to you, and do not listen either to those who would shut you up into corners of it and tell you that it is only here and there that art inhabits, or to those who would persuade you that this heavenly messenger wings her way outside of life altogether, breathing a superfine air, and turning away her head from the truth of things. There is no impression of life, no manner of seeing it and feeling it, to which the plan of the novelist may not offer a place; you have only to remember that talents so dissimilar as those of Alexandre Dumas and Jane Austen, Charles Dickens and Gustave Flaubert have worked in this field with equal glory. Do not think too much about optimism and pessimism; try and catch the colour of life itself. In France to-day we see a prodigious effort (that of Émile Zola, to whose solid and serious work no explorer of the capacity of the novel can allude without respect), we see an extraordinary effort vitiated by a spirit of pessimism on a narrow basis. M. Zola is magnificent, but he strikes an English reader as ignorant; he has an air of working in the dark; if he had as much light as energy, his results would be of the highest value. As for the aberrations of a shallow optimism, the ground (of English fiction especially) is strewn with their brittle particles as with broken glass. If you must indulge in conclusions, let them have the taste of a wide knowledge. Remember that your first duty is to be as complete as possible—to make as perfect a work. Be generous and delicate and pursue the prize."

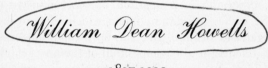

William Dean Howells

1837-1920

from CRITICISM AND FICTION

(1891)

Editor's Note: The text, with a few slight mechanical corrections, is from the Harper & Brothers edition of 1891. The present selection represents approximately half the book, which first appeared as essays in The Editor's Study of *Harper's Magazine* between 1886 and 1891. The discussion of realism and realistic fiction has been retained nearly intact; the omitted portions are primarily but not exclusively concerned with the functions of criticism and the nature of critics.

The question of a final criterion for the appreciation of art is one that perpetually recurs to those interested in any sort of aesthetic endeavor. Mr. John Addington Symonds, in a chapter of The Renaissance in Italy treating of the Bolognese school of painting, which once had so great cry, and was vaunted the supreme exemplar of the grand style, but which he now believes fallen into lasting contempt for its emptiness and soullessness, seeks to determine whether there can be an enduring criterion or not; and his conclusion is applicable to literature as to the other arts. "Our hope," he says, "with regard to the unity of taste in the future then is, that all sentimental or academical seekings after the ideal having been abandoned, momentary theories founded upon idiosyncratic or temporary partialities exploded, and nothing accepted but what is solid and positive, the scientific spirit shall make men progressively more and more conscious of these *bleibende Verhältnisse*, more and more capable of living in the whole; also, that in proportion as we gain a firmer hold upon our own place in the world, we shall come to comprehend with more instinctive certitude what is simple, natural, and honest, welcoming with gladness all artistic products that exhibit these qualities. The perception of the enlightened man will then be the task of a healthy person who has made himself acquainted with the laws of evolution in art and in society, and is able to test the excellence of work in any stage from immaturity to decadence by discerning what there is of truth, sincerity, and natural vigor in it."

I

That is to say, as I understand, that moods and tastes and fashions change; people fancy now this and now that; but what is unpretentious and what is true is always beautiful and good, and nothing else is so. This is not saying that fantastic and monstrous and artificial things do not please; everybody knows that they do please immensely for a time, and then, after the lapse of a much longer time, they have the charm of the rococo. Nothing is more curious than the charm that fashion has. Fashion in women's dress, almost every fashion, is somehow delightful, else it would never have been the fashion; but if any one will look through a collection of old fashion plates, he must own that most fashions have been ugly. A few, which could be readily instanced, have been very pretty, and even beautiful, but it is doubtful if these have pleased the greatest number of people. The ugly delights as well as the beautiful, and not merely because the ugly in fashion is associated with the young loveliness of the women who wear the ugly fashions, and wins a grace from them, not because the vast majority of mankind are tasteless, but for some cause that is not perhaps ascertainable. It is quite as likely to return in the fashions of our clothes and houses and furniture, and poetry and fiction and painting, as the beautiful, and it may be from an instinctive or a reasoned sense of this that some of the extreme naturalists have refused to make the old discrimination against it, or to regard the ugly as any less worthy of celebration in art than the beautiful; some of them, in fact, seem to regard it as rather more worthy, if anything. Possibly there is no absolutely ugly, no absolutely beautiful; or possibly the ugly contains always an element of the beautiful better adapted to the general appreciation than the more perfectly beautiful. This is a somewhat discouraging conjecture, but I offer it for no more than it is worth; and I do not pin my faith to the saying of one whom I heard denying, the other day, that a thing of beauty was a joy forever. He contended that Keats's line should have read, "Some things of beauty are sometimes joys forever," and that any assertion beyond this was too hazardous.

II

I should, indeed, prefer another line of Keats's, if I were to profess any formulated creed, and should feel much safer with his "Beauty is Truth, Truth Beauty," than even with my friend's reformation of the more quoted verse. It brings us back to the solid ground taken by Mr. Symonds, which is not essentially different from that taken in the great Mr. Burke's Essay on the Sublime and the Beautiful—a singularly modern book, considering how long ago it was wrote (as the great Mr. Steele would have written the participle a little longer ago), and full of a certain well-mannered and agreeable instruction. In some things it is of that droll little eighteenth-century world, when philosophy had got the neat little universe into the hollow of its hand, and knew just what it was, and what it was for; but it is quite without arrogance. "As for those called critics," the author says, "they have generally sought the rule of the arts in the wrong place; they have sought among poems, pictures, engravings, statues, and buildings; but art can never give the rules that make an art. This is, I believe, the reason why artists in general, and poets principally, have been confined in so narrow a circle; they have been rather imitators of one another than of nature. Critics follow them, and therefore can do little as guides. I can judge but poorly of anything while I measure it by no other standard than itself. The true standard of the arts is in every man's power; and an easy observation of the most common, sometimes of the meanest things, in nature will give the truest lights, where the greatest sagacity and industry that slights such observation must leave us in the dark, or, what is worse, amuse and mislead us by false lights."

If this should happen to be true—and it certainly commends itself to acceptance—it might portend an immediate danger to the vested interests of criticism, only that it was written a hundred years ago; and we shall probably have the "sagacity and industry that slights the observation" of nature long enough yet to allow most critics the time to learn some more useful trade than criticism as they pursue it. Nevertheless, I am in hopes that the communistic era in taste foreshadowed by Burke is approaching, and that it will occur within the lives of men now overawed by the foolish old superstition that literature and art are anything but the expression of life, and are to be judged by any other test than that of their fidelity to it. The time is coming, I hope, when each new author, each new artist, will be considered, not in his proportion to any other author or artist, but in his relation to the human nature, known to us all, which it is his privilege, his high duty, to interpret. "The true standard of the artist is in every man's power" already, as Burke says; Michelangelo's "light of the piazza," the glance of the common eye, is and always was the best light on a statue; Goethe's "boys and blackbirds" have in all ages been the real connoisseurs of berries; but hitherto the mass of common men have been afraid to apply their own simplicity, naturalness, and honesty to the appreciation of the beautiful. They have always cast about for the instruction of some one who professed to know better, and who browbeat wholesome common-sense into the self-distrust that ends in sophistication. They have fallen generally to the worst of this bad species, and have been "amused and misled" (how pretty that quaint old use of amuse is!) "by the false lights" of critical vanity and self-righteousness. They have been taught to compare what they see and what they read, not with the things that they have observed and known, but with the things that some other artist or writer has done. Especially if they have themselves the artistic impulse in any direction they are taught to form themselves, not upon life, but upon the masters who became masters only by forming themselves upon life. The seeds of death are planted in them, and they can produce only the still-born, the academic. They are not told to take their work into the public square and see if it seems true to the chance passer, but to test it by the work of the very men who refused and decried any other test of their own work. The young writer who attempts to report the phrase and carriage of every-day life, who tries to tell just how he has heard men talk and seen them look, is made to feel guilty of something low and unworthy by the stupid people who would like to have him show how Shakespeare's men talked and looked, or Scott's, or Thackeray's, or Balzac's, or Hawthorne's, or Dickens's; he is instructed to idealize his personages, that is, to take the life-likeness out of them, and put the book-likeness into them. He is approached in the spirit of the wretched pedantry into which learning, much or little, always decays when it withdraws itself and stands apart from experience in an attitude of imagined superiority, and which would say with the same confidence to the scientist: "I see that you are looking at a grasshopper there which you have found in the grass, and I suppose you intend to describe it. Now don't waste your time and sin against culture in that way. I've got a grasshopper here, which has been evolved at considerable pains and expense out of the grasshopper in general; in fact, it's a type.

It's made up of wire and card-board, very prettily painted in a conventional tint, and it's perfectly indestructible. It isn't very much like a real grasshopper, but it's a great deal nicer, and it's served to represent the notion of a grasshopper ever since man emerged from barbarism. You may say that it's artificial. Well, it is artificial; but then it's ideal too; and what you want to do is to cultivate the ideal. You'll find the books full of my kind of grasshopper, and scarcely a trace of yours in any of them. The thing that you are proposing to do is commonplace; but if you say that it isn't commonplace, for the very reason that it hasn't been done before, you'll have to admit that it's photographic."

As I said, I hope the time is coming when not only the artist, but the common, average man, who always "has the standard of the arts in his power," will have also the courage to apply it, and will reject the ideal grasshopper wherever he finds it, in science, in literature, in art, because it is not "simple, natural, and honest," because it is not like a real grasshopper. But I will own that I think the time is yet far off, and that the people who have been brought up on the ideal grasshopper, the heroic grasshopper, the impassioned grasshopper, the self-devoted, adventureful, good old romantic cardboard grasshopper, must die out before the simple, honest, and natural grasshopper can have a fair field. I am in no haste to compass the end of these good people, whom I find in the meantime very amusing. It is delightful to meet one of them, either in print or out of it—some sweet elderly lady or excellent gentleman whose youth was pastured on the literature of thirty or forty years ago—and to witness the confidence with which they preach their favorite authors as all the law and the prophets. They have commonly read little or nothing since, or, if they have, they have judged it by a standard taken from these authors, and never dreamed of judging it by nature; they are destitute of the documents in the case of the later writers; they suppose that Balzac was the beginning of realism, and that Zola is its wicked end; they are quite ignorant, but they are ready to talk you down, if you differ from them, with an assumption of knowledge sufficient for any occasion. The horror, the resentment, with which they receive any question of their literary saints is genuine; you descend at once very far in the moral and social scale, and anything short of offensive personality is too good for you; it is expressed to you that you are one to be avoided, and put down even a little lower than you have naturally fallen.

These worthy persons are not to blame; it is part of their intellectual mission to represent the petrifaction of taste, and to preserve an image of a smaller and cruder and emptier world than we now live in, a world which was feeling its way towards the simple, the natural, the honest, but was a good deal "amused and misled" by lights now no longer mistakable for heavenly luminaries. They belong to a time, just passing away, when certain authors were considered authorities in certain kinds, when they must be accepted entire and not questioned in any particular. Now we are beginning to see and to say that no author is an authority except in those moments when he held his ear close to Nature's lips and caught her very accent. These moments are not continuous with any authors in the past, and they are rare with all. Therefore I am not afraid to say now that the greatest classics are sometimes not at all great, and that we can profit by them only when we hold them, like our meanest contemporaries, to a strict accounting, and verify their work by the standard of the arts which we all have in our power, the simple, the natural, and the honest.

Those good people, those curious and interesting if somewhat musty back-numbers, must always have a hero, an idol of some sort, and it is droll to find Balzac, who suffered from their sort such bitter scorn and hate for his realism while he was alive, now become a fetich in his turn, to be shaken in the faces of those who will not blindly worship him. But it is no new thing in the history of literature: whatever is established is sacred with those who do not think. At the beginning of the century, when romance was making the same fight against effete classicism which realism is making today against effete romanticism, the Italian poet Monti declared that "the romantic was the cold grave of the Beautiful," just as the realistic is now supposed to be. The romantic of that day and the real of this are in certain degree the same. Romanticism then sought, as realism seeks now, to widen the bounds of sympathy, to level every barrier against aesthetic freedom, to escape from the paralysis of tradition. It exhausted itself in this impulse; and it remained for realism to assert that fidelity to experience and probability of motive are essential conditions of a great imaginative literature. It is not a new theory, but it has never before universally characterized literary endeavor. When realism becomes false to itself, when it heaps up facts merely, and maps life instead of picturing it, realism will perish too. Every true realist instinctively knows this, and it is perhaps the reason why he is careful of every fact, and feels himself bound to express or to indicate its meaning at the risk of over-moralizing. In life he finds nothing insignificant; all tells for destiny and character; nothing that God has made is contemptible. He cannot look upon human life and declare this thing or that thing unworthy of notice, any more than the scientist can declare a fact of the material world beneath the dignity of his inquiry. He feels in every nerve the equality of things and the unity of men; his soul is exalted, not by vain shows and shadows and ideals, but by realities, in which alone the truth lives. In criticism it is his business to break the images of false gods and misshapen heroes, to take away the poor silly toys that many grown people would still like to play with. He cannot keep terms with Jack the Giant-killer or Puss in Boots, under any name or in any place, even when they reappear as the convict Vautrec, or the Marquis de Montrivaut, or the Sworn Thirteen Noblemen. He must say to himself that Balzac, when he imagined these monsters, was not Balzac, he was Dumas; he was not realistic, he was romantic.

IV

In the beginning of any art even the most gifted worker must be crude in his methods, and we ought to keep this fact always in mind when we turn, say, from the purblind worshippers of Scott to Scott himself, and recognize that he often wrote a style cumbrous and diffuse; that he was tediously analytical where the modern novelist is dramatic, and evolved his characters by means of long-winded explanation and commentary; that, except in the case of his lower-class personages, he made them talk as seldom man and never woman talked; that he was tiresomely descriptive; that on the simplest occasions he went about half a mile to express a thought that could be uttered in ten paces across lots; and that he trusted his readers' intuitions so little that he was apt to rub in his appeals to them. He was probably right; the generation which he wrote for was duller than this; slower-witted, aesthetically untrained, and in maturity not so apprehensive of an artistic intention as the children of to-day. All this is not saying Scott was not a great man; he was a great man, and a very great novelist as compared with the novelists who went before him. He can still amuse young people, but they ought to be instructed how false and mistaken he often is, with his mediaeval ideals, his blind Jacobitism, his intense devotion to aristocracy and royalty; his acquiescence in the division of men into noble and ignoble, patrician and plebeian, sovereign and subject, as if it were the law of God; for all which, indeed, he is not to blame as he would be if he were one of our contemporaries. Something of this is true of another master, greater than Scott in being less romantic, and inferior in being more German, namely, the great Goethe himself. He taught us, in novels otherwise now antiquated, and always full of German clumsiness, that it was false to good art—which is never anything but the reflection of life—to pursue and round the career of the persons introduced, whom he often allowed to appear and disappear in our knowledge as people in the actual world do. This is a lesson which the writers able to profit by it can never be too grateful for; and it is equally a benefaction to readers; but there is very little else in the conduct of the Goethean novels which is in advance of their time; this remains almost their sole contribution to the science of fiction. They are very primitive in certain characteristics, and unite with their calm, deep insight, an amusing helplessness in dramatization. "Wilhelm retired to his room, and indulged in the following reflections," is a mode of analysis which would not be practised nowadays; and all that fancifulness of nomenclature in Wilhelm Meister is very drolly sentimental and feeble. The adventures with robbers seem as if dreamed out of books of chivalry, and the tendency to allegorization affects me like an endeavor on the author's part to escape from the unrealities which he must have felt harassingly, German as he was. Mixed up with the shadows and illusions are honest, wholesome, every-day people, who have the air of wandering homelessly about among them, without definite direction; and the mists are full of a luminosity which, in spite of them, we know for common-sense and poetry. What is useful in any review of Goethe's methods is the recognition of the fact, which it must bring, that the greatest master cannot produce a masterpiece in a new kind. The novel was too recently invented in Goethe's day not to be, even in his hands, full of the faults of apprentice work.

V

In fact, a great master may sin against the "modesty of nature" in many ways, and I have felt this painfully in reading Balzac's romance—it is not worthy the name of novel—Le Père Goriot, which is full of a malarial restlessness, wholly alien to healthful art. After that exquisitely careful and truthful setting of his story in the shabby boarding-house, he fills the scene with figures jerked about by the exaggerated passions and motives of the stage. We cannot have a cynic reasonably wicked, disagreeable, egoistic; we must have a lurid villain of melodrama, a disguised convict, with a vast criminal organization at his command, and

> "So dyèd double red"

in deed and purpose that he lights up the faces of the horrified spectators with his glare. A father fond of unworthy children, and leading a life of self-denial for their sake, as may probably and pathetically be, is not enough; there must be an imbecile, trembling dotard, willing to promote even the liaisons of his daughters to give them happiness and to teach the sublimity of the paternal instinct. The hero cannot sufficiently be a selfish young fellow, with alternating impulses of greed and generosity; he must superfluously intend a career of iniquitous splendor, and be swerved from it by nothing but the most cataclysmal interpositions. It can be said that without such personages the plot could not be transacted; but so much the worse for the plot. Such a plot had no business to be; and while actions so unnatural are imagined, no mastery can save fiction from contempt with those who really think about it. To Balzac it can be forgiven, not only because in his better mood he gave us such biographies as Eugénie Grandet, but because he wrote at a time when fiction was just beginning to verify the externals of life, to portray faithfully the outside of men and things. It was still held that in order to interest the reader the characters must be moved by the old romantic ideals; we were to be taught that "heroes" and "heroines" existed all around us, and that these abnormal beings needed only to be discovered in their several humble disguises, and then we should see every-day people actuated by the fine frenzy of the creatures of the poets. How false that notion was few but the critics, who are apt to be rather belated, need now be told. Some of these poor fellows, however, still contend that it ought to be done, and that human feelings and motives, as God made them and as men know them, are not good enough for novel readers . . .

XIII

In fine, I would beseech the literary critics of our country to disabuse themselves of the mischievous notion that they are essential to the progress of literature in the way critics have vainly imagined. Canon Farrar confesses that with the best will in the world to profit by the many criticisms of his books, he has never profited in the least by any of them; and this is almost the universal experience of authors. It is not always the fault of the critics. They sometimes deal honestly and fairly by a book, and not so often they deal adequately. But in making a book, if it is at all a good book, the author has learned all that is knowable about it, and every strong point and every weak point in it, far more accurately than any one else can possibly learn them. He has learned to do better than well for the future; but if his book is bad, he cannot be taught anything about it from the outside. It will perish; and if he has not the root of literature in him, he will perish as an author with it.

But what is it that gives tendency in art, then? What is it makes people like this at one time, and that at another? Above all, what makes a better fashion change for a worse; how can the ugly come to be preferred to the beautiful; in other words, how can an art decay?

This question came up in my mind lately with regard to English fiction and its form, or rather its formlessness. How, for instance, could people who had once known the simple verity, the refined perfection of Miss Austen, enjoy anything less refined and less perfect?

With her example before them, why should not English novelists have gone on writing simply, honestly, artistically, ever after? One would think it must have been impossible for them to do otherwise, if one did not remember, say, the lamentable behavior of the actors who support Mr. Jefferson, and their theatricality in the very presence of his beautiful naturalness. It is very difficult, that simplicity, and nothing is so hard as to be honest, as the reader, if he has ever happened to try it, must know. "The big bow-wow I can do myself, like any one going," said Scott, but he owned that the exquisite touch of Miss Austen was denied him; and it seems certainly to have been denied in greater or less measure to all her successors. But though reading and writing come by nature, as Dogberry justly said, a taste in them may be cultivated, or once cultivated, it may be preserved; and why was it not so among those poor islanders? One does not ask such things in order to be at the pains of answering them one's self, but with the hope that some one else will take the trouble to do so, and I propose to be rather a silent partner in the enterprise, which I shall leave mainly to Señor Armando Palacio Valdés. This delightful author will, however, only be able to answer my question indirectly from the essay on fiction with which he prefaces one of his novels, the charming story of The Sister of San Sulphizo, and I shall have some little labor in fitting his saws to my instances. It is an essay which I wish every one intending to read, or even to write, a novel, might acquaint himself with; for it contains some of the best and clearest things which have been said of the art of fiction in a time when nearly all who practise it have turned to talk about it.

Señor Valdés is a realist, but a realist according to his own conception of realism; and he has some words of just censure for the French naturalists, whom he finds unnecessarily, and suspects of being sometimes even mercenarily, nasty. He sees the wide difference that passes between this naturalism and the realism of the English and Spanish; and he goes somewhat further than I should go in condemning it. "The French naturalism represents only a moment, and an insignificant part of life . . . It is characterized by sadness and narrowness. The prototype of this literature is the Madame Bovary of Flaubert. I am an admirer of this novelist, and especially of this novel; but often in thinking of it I have said, How dreary would literature be if it were no more than this! There is something antipathetic and gloomy and limited in it, as there is in modern French life;" but this seems to me exactly the best possible reason for its being. I believe with Señor Valdés that "no literature can live long without joy," not because of its mistaken aesthetics, however, but because no civilization can live long without joy. The expression of French life will change when French life changes; and French naturalism is better at its worst than French unnaturalism at its best. "No one," as Señor Valdés truly says, "can rise from the perusal of a naturalistic book . . . without a vivid desire to escape" from the wretched world depicted in it, "and a purpose, more or less vague, of helping to better the lot and morally elevate the ab-

ject beings who figure in it. Naturalistic art, then, is not immoral in itself, for then it would not merit the name of art; for
though it is not the business of art to preach morality, still I
think that, resting on a divine and spiritual principle, like the
idea of the beautiful, it is perforce moral. I hold much more
immoral other books which, under a glamour of something
spiritual and beautiful and sublime, portray the vices in which
we are allied to the beasts. Such, for example, are the works of
Octave Feuillet, Arséne Houssaye, Georges Ohnet, and other
contemporary novelists much in vogue among the higher
classes of society."

But what is this idea of the beautiful which art rests upon,
and so becomes moral? "The man of our time," says Señor
Valdés, "wishes to know everything and enjoy everything: he
turns the objective of a powerful equatorial towards the heavenly spaces where gravitate the infinitude of the stars, just as
he applies the microscope to the infinitude of the smallest in-
sects; for their laws are identical. His experience, united with
intuition, has convinced him that in nature there is neither
great nor small; all is equal. All is equally grand, all is equally
just, all is equally beautiful, because all is equally divine." But
beauty, Señor Valdés explains, exists in the human spirit, and
is the beautiful effect which it receives from the true meaning
of things; it does not matter what the things are, and it is the
function of the artist who feels this effect to impart it to
others. I may add that there is no joy in art except this perception of the meaning of things and its communication;
when you have felt it, and portrayed it in a poem, a sym-
phony, a novel, a statue, a picture, an edifice, you have fulfilled
the purpose for which you were born an artist.

The reflection of exterior nature in the individual spirit,
Señor Valdés believes to be the fundamental of art. "To say,
then, that the artist must not copy but create is nonsense, because he can in no wise copy, and in no wise create. He who
sets deliberately about modifying nature, shows that he has
not felt her beauty, and therefore cannot make others feel it.
The puerile desire which some artists without genius manifest

to go about selecting in nature, not what seems to them beautiful, but what they think will seem beautiful to others, and rejecting what may displease them, ordinarily produces cold and insipid works. For, instead of exploring the illimitable fields of reality, they cling to the forms invented by other artists who have succeeded, and they make statues of statues, poems of poems, novels of novels. It is entirely false that the great romantic, symbolic, or classic poets modified nature; such as they have expressed her they felt her; and in this view they are as much realists as ourselves. In like manner if in the realistic tide that now bears us on there are some spirits who feel nature in another way, in the romantic way, or the classic way, they would not falsify her in expressing her so. Only those falsify her who, without feeling classic wise or romantic wise, set about being classic or romantic, wearisomely reproducing the models of former ages; and equally those who, without sharing the sentiment of realism, which now prevails, force themselves to be realists merely to follow the fashion."

The pseudo-realists, in fact, are the worse offenders, to my thinking, for they sin against the living; whereas those who continue to celebrate the heroic adventures of Puss in Boots and the hairbreadth escapes of Tom Thumb, under various aliases, only cast disrespect upon the immortals who have passed beyond these noises.

XIV

"The principal cause," our Spaniard says, "of the decadence of contemporary literature is found, to my thinking, in the vice which has been very graphically called effectism, or the itch of awaking at all cost in the reader vivid and violent emotions, which shall do credit to the invention and originality of the writer. This vice has its roots in human nature itself, and more particularly in that of the artist; he has always something feminine in him, which tempts him to coquet with the reader, and display qualities that he thinks will astonish him, as women laugh for no reason, to show their teeth when they have them white and small and even, or lift their dresses to show their feet when there is no mud in the street . . . What many writers nowadays wish, is to produce an effect, grand and immediate, to play the part of geniuses. For this they have learned that it is only necessary to write exaggerated works in any sort, since the vulgar do not ask that they shall be quietly made to think and feel, but that they shall be startled; and among the vulgar, of course, I include the great part of those who write literary criticism, and who constitute the worst vulgar, since they teach what they do not know . . . There are many persons who suppose that the highest proof an artist can give of his fantasy is the invention of a complicated plot, spiced with perils, surprises, and suspenses; and that anything else is the sign of a poor and tepid imagination. And not only people who seem cultivated, but are not so, suppose this, but there are sensible persons, and even sagacious and intelligent critics, who sometimes allow themselves to be hoodwinked by the dramatic mystery and the surprising and fantastic scenes of a novel. They own it is all false; but they admire the imagination, what they call the 'power' of the author. Very well; all I have to say is that the 'power' to dazzle with strange incidents, to entertain with complicated plots and impossible characters, now belongs to some hundreds of writers in Europe; while there are not much above a dozen who know how to interest with the ordinary events of life, and with the portrayal of characters truly human. If the former is a talent, it must be owned that it is much commoner than the latter . . . If we are to rate novelists according to their fecundity, or the riches of their invention, we must put Alexander Dumas above Cervantes. Cervantes wrote a novel with the simplest plot, without belying much or little the natural and logical course of events. This novel, which was called Don Quixote, is perhaps the greatest work of human wit. Very well; the same Cervantes, mischievously influenced afterwards by the ideas of the vulgar, who were then what they are now and always will be, attempted to please them by a work giving a lively proof of his inventive talent, and wrote the Persiles and Sigismunda, where the strange incidents, the vivid complications, the surprises, the pathetic scenes, succeed one another so rapidly and constantly that it really fatigues you . . . But in spite of this flood of invention, imagine," says Señor Valdés, "the place that Cervantes would now occupy in the heaven of art, if he had never written Don Quixote, but only Persiles and Sigismunda!"

From the point of view of modern English criticism, which likes to be melted, and horrified, and astonished, and blood-curdled, and goose-fleshed, no less than to be "chippered up" in fiction, Señor Valdés were indeed incorrigible. Not only does he despise the novel of complicated plot, and everywhere prefer Don Quixote to Persiles and Sigismunda, but he has a lively contempt for another class of novels much in favor with the gentilities of all countries. He calls their writers "novelists of the world," and he says that more than any others they have the rage of effectism. "They do not seek to produce effect by novelty and invention in plot . . . they seek it in character. For this end they begin by deliberately falsifying human feelings, giving them a paradoxical appearance completely inadmissible . . . Love that disguises itself as hate, incomparable energy under the cloak of weakness, virginal innocence under the aspect of malice and impudence, wit masquerading as folly, etc., etc. By this means they hope to make an effect of which they are incapable through the direct, frank, and conscientious study of character." He mentions Octave Feuillet as the greatest offender in this sort among the French, and Bulwer among the English; but Dickens is full of it (Boffin in Our Mutual Friend will suffice for all example), and the present loathsome artistic squalor of the English drama is witness of the result of this effectism when allowed full play.

But what, then, if he is not pleased with Dumas, or with the effectists who delight genteel people at all the theatres, and in most of the romances, what, I ask, will satisfy this extremely difficult Spanish gentleman? He would pretend, very little. Give him simple, life-like character; that is all he wants. "For me, the only condition of character is that it be human, and that is enough. If I wished to know what was human, I should study humanity."

But, Señor Valdés, Señor Valdés! Do not you know that this small condition of yours implies in its fulfillment hardly less than the gift of the whole earth, with a little gold fence round it? You merely ask that the character portrayed in fiction be human; and you suggest that the novelist should study humanity if he would know whether his personages are human. This appears to me the cruelest irony, the most sarcastic affectation of humility. If you had asked that character in fiction be superhuman, or subterhuman, or preterhuman, or intrahuman, and had bidden the novelist go, not to humanity, but the humanities, for the proof of his excellence, it would have been all very easy. The books are full of those "creations," of every pattern, of all ages, of both sexes; and it is so much handier to get at books than to get at men; and when you have portrayed "passion" instead of feeling, and used "power" instead of common-sense, and shown yourself a "genius" instead of an artist, the applause is so prompt and the glory so cheap, that really anything else seems wickedly wasteful of one's time. One may not make one's reader enjoy or suffer nobly, but one may give him the kind of pleasure that arises from conjuring, or from a puppetshow, or a modern stage play, and leave him, if he is an old fool, in the sort of stupor that comes from hitting the pipe; or if he is a young fool, half crazed with the spectacle of qualities and impulses like his own in an apotheosis of achievement and fruition far beyond any earthly experience.

But apparently Señor Valdés would not think this any great artistic result. "Things that appear ugliest in reality to the spectator who is not an artist, are transformed into beauty and poetry when the spirit of the artist possesses itself of them. We all take part every day in a thousand domestic scenes, every day we see a thousand pictures in life, that do not make any impression upon us, or if they make any it is one of repugnance; but let the novelist come, and without betraying the truth, but painting them as they appear to his vision, he produces a most interesting work, whose perusal enchants us. That which in life left us indifferent, or repelled us, in art delights us. Why? Simply because the artist has made us see the idea that resides in it. Let not the novelists, then, endeavor to add anything to reality, to turn it and twist it, to restrict it. Since nature has endowed them with this precious gift of discovering ideas in things, their work will be beautiful if they paint these as they appear. But if the reality does not impress them, in vain will they strive to make their work impress others."

XV

Which brings us again, after this long way about, to the divine Jane and her novels, and that troublesome question about them. She was great and they were beautiful, because she and they were honest, and dealt with nature nearly a hundred years ago as realism deals with it today. Realism is nothing more and nothing less than the truthful treatment of material, and Jane Austen was the first and the last of the English novelists to treat material with entire truthfulness. Because she did this, she remains the most artistic of the English novelists, and alone worthy to be matched with the great Scandinavian and Slavic and Latin artists. It is not a question of intellect, or not wholly that. The English have mind enough; but they have not taste enough; or, rather, their taste has been perverted by their false criticism, which is based upon personal preference, and not upon principle; which instructs a man to think that what he likes is good, instead of teaching him first to distinguish what is good before he likes it. The art of fiction, as Jane Austen knew it, declined from her through Scott, and Bulwer, and Dickens, and Charlotte Brontë, and Thackeray, and even George Eliot, because the mania of romanticism had seized upon all Europe, and these great writers could not escape the taint of their time; but it has shown few signs of recovery in England, because English criticism, in the presence of the Continental masterpieces, has continued provincial and special and personal, and has expressed a love and a hate which had to do with the quality of the artist rather than the character of his work. It was inevitable that in their time the English romanticists should treat, as Señor Valdés says, "the barbarous customs of the Middle Ages, softening and disfiguring them, as Walter Scott and his kind did;" that they should "devote themselves to falsifying nature, refining and subtilizing sentiment, and modifying psychology after their own fancy," like Bulwer and Dickens, as well as like Rousseau and Madame de Staël, not to mention Balzac, the worst of all that sort at his worst. This was the natural course of the disease; but it really seems as if it were their criticism that was to blame for the rest: not, indeed, for the performance of this writer or that, for criticism can never affect the actual doing of a thing; but for the esteem in which this writer or that is held through the perpetuation of false ideals. The only observer of English middle-class life since Jane Austen worthy to be named with her was not George Eliot, who was first ethical and then artistic, who transcended her in everything but the form and method most essential to art, and there fell hopelessly below her. It was Anthony Trollope who was most like her in simple honesty and instinctive truth, as unphilosophized as the light of common day; but he was so warped from a wholesome ideal as to wish at times to be like the caricaturist Thackeray, and to stand about in his scene, talking it over with his hands in his pockets, interrupting the action, and spoiling the illusion in which alone the truth of art resides. Mainly, his instinct was too much for his ideal, and with a low view of life in its civic relations and a thoroughly bourgeois soul, he yet produced works whose beauty is surpassed only by the effect of a more poetic writer in the novels of Thomas Hardy. Yet if a vote of English criticism even at this late day, when all continental Europe has the light of aesthetic truth, could be taken, the majority against these artists would be overwhelmingly in favor of a writer who had so little artistic sensibility, that he never hesitated on any occasion, great or small, to make a foray among his characters, and catch them up to show them to the reader and tell him how beautiful or ugly they were; and cry out over their amazing properties.

Doubtless the ideal of those poor islanders will be finally changed. If the truth could become a fad it would be accepted by all their "smart people," but truth is something rather too large for that; and we must await the gradual advance of civilization among them. Then they will see that their criticism has misled them; and that it is to this false guide they owe, not precisely the decline of fiction among them, but its continued debasement as an art.

XVI

"How few materials," says Emerson, "are yet used by our arts! The mass of creatures and of qualities are still hid and expectant," and to break new ground is still one of the uncommonest and most heroic of the virtues. The artists are not alone to blame for the timidity that keeps them in the old furrows of the worn-out field; most of those whom they live to please, or live by pleasing, prefer to have them remain there; it wants rare virtue to appreciate what is new, as well as to invent it; and the "easy things to understand" are the conventional things. This is why the ordinary English novel, with its hackneyed plot, scenes, and figures, is more comfortable to the ordinary American than an American novel, which deals, at its worst, with comparatively new interests and motives. To adjust one's self to the enjoyment of these costs an intellectual effort, and an intellectual effort is what no ordinary person likes to make. It is only the extraordinary person who can say, with Emerson: "I ask not for the great, the remote, the romantic . . . I embrace the common; I sit at the feet of the familiar and the low . . . Man is surprised to find that things near are not less beautiful and wondrous than things remote . . . The perception of the worth of the vulgar is fruitful in discoveries . . . The foolish man wonders at the unusual, but the wise man at the usual . . . Today always looks mean to the thoughtless; but today is a king in disguise . . .

Banks and tariffs, the newspaper and caucus, Methodism and Unitarianism, are flat and dull to dull people, but rest on the same foundations of wonder as the town of Troy and the temple of Delphos."

Perhaps we ought not to deny their town of Troy and their temple of Delphos to the dull people; but if we ought, and if we did, they would still insist upon having them. An English novel, full of titles and rank, is apparently essential to the happiness of such people; their weak and childish imagination is at home in its familiar environment; they know what they are reading; the fact that it is hash many times warmed over reassures them; whereas a story of our own life, honestly studied and faithfully represented, troubles them with varied misgiving. They are not sure that it is literature; they do not feel that it is good society; its characters, so like their own, strike them as commonplace; they say they do not wish to know such people.

Everything in England is appreciable to the literary sense, while the sense of the literary worth of things in America is still faint and weak with most people, with the vast majority who "ask for the great, the remote, the romantic," who cannot "embrace the common," cannot "sit at the feet of the familiar and the low," in the good company of Emerson. We are all, or nearly all, struggling to be distinguished from the mass, and to be set apart in select circles and upper classes like the fine people we have read about. We are really a mixture of the plebeian ingredients of the whole world; but that is not bad; our vulgarity consists in trying to ignore "the worth of the vulgar," in believing that the superfine is better.

XVIII

In General Grant's confession of novel-reading there is a sort of inference that he had wasted his time, or else the guilty conscience of the novelist in me imagines such an inference. But however this may be, there is certainly no question concerning the intention of a correspondent who once wrote to me after reading some rather bragging claims I had made for fiction as a mental and moral means. "I have very grave doubts," he said, "as to the whole list of magnificent things that you seem to think novels have done for the race, and can witness in myself many evil things which they have done for me. Whatever in my mental make-up is wild and visionary, whatever is untrue, whatever is injurious, I can trace to the perusal of some work of fiction. Worse than that, they beget such high-strung and super-sensitive ideas of life that plain industry and plodding perseverance are despised, and matter-of-fact poverty, or every-day, commonplace distress, meets with no sympathy, if indeed noticed at all, by one who has wept over the impossibly accumulated sufferings of some gaudy hero or heroine."

I am not sure that I had the controversy with this correspondent that he seemed to suppose; but novels are now so fully accepted by everyone pretending to cultivated taste—and they really form the whole intellectual life of such immense numbers of people, without question of their influence, good or bad, upon the mind—that it is refreshing to have them frankly denounced, and to be invited to revise one's ideas and feelings in regard to them. A little honesty, or a great deal of honesty, in this quest will do the novel, as we hope yet to have it, and as we have already begun to have it, no harm; and for my own part I will confess that I believe fiction in the past to have been largely injurious, as I believe the stage play to be still almost wholly injurious, through its falsehood, its folly, its wantonness, and its aimlessness. It may be safely assumed that most of the novel-reading which people fancy an intellectual pastime is the emptiest dissipation, hardly more related to thought or the wholesome exercise of the mental faculties than opium-eating; in either case the brain is drugged, and left weaker and crazier for the debauch. If this may be called the negative result of the fiction habit, the positive injury that most novels work is by no means so easily to be measured in the case of young men whose character they help so much to form or deform, and the women of all ages whom they keep so much in ignorance of the world they misrepresent. Grown men have little harm from them, but in the other cases, which are the vast majority, they hurt because they are not true—not because they are malevolent, but because they are idle lies about human nature and the social fabric, which it behooves us to know and to understand, that we may deal justly with ourselves and with one another. One need not go so far as our correspondent, and trace to the fiction habit "whatever is wild and visionary, whatever is untrue, whatever is injurious," in one's life; bad as the fiction habit is it is probably not responsible for the whole sum of evil in its victims, and I believe that if the reader will use care in choosing from this fungus-growth with which the fields of literature teem every day, he may nourish himself as with the true mushroom, at no risk from the poisonous species.

The tests are very plain and simple, and they are perfectly infallible. If a novel flatters the passions, and exalts them above the principles, it is poisonous; it may not kill, but it will certainly injure; and this test will alone exclude an entire class of fiction, of which eminent examples will occur to all. Then the whole spawn of so-called unmoral romances, which imagine a world where the sins of sense are unvisited by the penalties following, swift or slow, but inexorably sure, in the real world, are deadly poison: these do kill. The novels that merely tickle our prejudices and lull our judgment, or that coddle our sensibilities or pamper our gross appetite for the marvelous are not so fatal, but they are innutritious, and clog the soul with unwholesome vapors of all kinds. No doubt they too help to weaken the moral fibre, and make their readers indifferent to "plodding perseverance and plain industry," and to "matter-of-fact poverty and commonplace distress."

Without taking them too seriously, it still must be owned that the "gaudy hero and heroine" are to blame for a great deal of harm in the world. That heroine long taught by example, if not precept, that Love, or the passion or fancy she mistook for it, was the chief interest of a life, which is really concerned with a great many other things; that it was lasting in the way she knew it; that it was worthy of every sacrifice, and was altogether a finer thing than prudence, obedience, reason; that love alone was glorious and beautiful, and these were mean and ugly in comparison with it. More lately she has begun to idolize and illustrate Duty, and she is hardly less mischievous in this new role, opposing duty, as she did love, to prudence, obedience, and reason. The stock hero, who, if we met him, we could not fail to see was a most deplorable person, has undoubtedly imposed himself upon the victims of the fiction habit as admirable. With him, too, love was and is the great affair, whether in its old romantic phase of chivalrous achievement or manifold suffering for love's sake, or its more recent development of the "virile," the bullying, and the brutal, or its still more recent agonies of self-sacrifice, as idle and useless as the moral experiences of the insane asylums. With his vain posturings and his ridiculous splendor he is really a painted barbarian, the prey of his passions and his delusions, full of obsolete ideals, and the motives and ethics of a savage, which the guilty author of his being does his best—or his worst—in spite of his own light and knowledge, to foist upon the reader as something generous and noble. I am not merely bringing this charge against that sort of fiction which is beneath literature and outside of it, "the shoreless lakes of ditch-water," whose miasms fill the air below the empyrean where the great ones sit; but I am accusing the work of some of the most famous, who have, in this instance or in that, sinned against the truth, which can alone exalt and purify men. I do not say that they have constantly done so, or even commonly done so; but that they have done so at all marks them as of the past, to be read with the due historical allowance for their epoch and their conditions. For I believe that, while inferior writers will and must continue to imitate them in their foibles and their errors, no one hereafter will be able to achieve greatness who is false to humanity, either in its facts or its duties. The light of civilization has already broken even upon the novel, and no conscientious man can now set about painting an image of life without perpetual question of the verity of his work, and without feeling bound to distinguish so clearly that no reader of his may be misled, between what is right and what is wrong, what is noble and what is base, what is health and what is perdition, in the actions and the characters he portrays.

The fiction that aims merely to entertain—the fiction that is to serious fiction as the opera-bouffe, the ballet, and the panto-mime are to the true drama—need not feel the burden of this obligation so deeply; but even such fiction will not be gay or trivial to any reader's hurt, and criticism will hold it to account if it passes from painting to teaching folly.

More and more not only the criticism which prints its opin-ions, but the infinitely vaster and powerfuler criticism which thinks and feels them merely, will make this demand. I confess that I do not care to judge any work of the imagination with-out first of all applying this test to it. We must ask ourselves before we ask anything else, Is it true?—true to the motives, the impulses, the principles that shape the life of actual men and women? This truth, which necessarily includes the highest morality and the highest artistry—this truth given, the book cannot be wicked and cannot be weak; and without it all graces of style and feats of invention and cunning of construction are so many superfluities of naughtiness. It is well for the truth to have all these, and shine in them, but for falsehood they are merely meretricious, the bedizenment of the wanton; they atone for nothing, they account for nothing. But in fact they come naturally of truth, and grace it without solicitation; they are added unto it. In the whole range of fiction we know of no true picture of life—that is, of human nature—which is not also a masterpiece of literature, full of divine and natural beauty. It may have no touch or tint of this special civilization or of that; it had better have this local color well ascertained; but the truth is deeper and finer than aspects, and if the book is true to what men and women know of one another's souls it will be true enough, and it will be great and beautiful. It is the conception of literature as something apart from life, superfinely aloof, which makes it really unimportant to the great mass of mankind, without a message or a meaning for them; and it is the notion that a novel may be false in its portrayal of causes and effects that makes literary art contemptible even to those whom it amuses, that forbids them to regard the novelist as a serious or right-minded person. If they do not in some moment of indignation cry out against all novels, as my correspondent does, they remain besotted in the fume of the delusions purveyed to them, with no higher feeling for the author than such maudlin affection as the habitué of an opium-joint perhaps knows for the attendant who fills his pipe with the drug.

Or, as in the case of another correspondent who writes that in his youth he "read a great many novels, but always regarded it as an amusement, like horse-racing and card-playing," for which he had no time when he entered upon the serious business of life, it renders them merely contemptuous. His view of the matter may be commended to the brotherhood and sisterhood of novelists as full of wholesome if bitter suggestion; and we urge them not to dismiss it with high literary scorn as that of some Boeotian dull to the beauty of art. Refuse it as we may, it is still the feeling of the vast majority of people for whom life is earnest, and who find only a distorted and misleading likeness of it in our books. We may fold ourselves in our scholars' gowns, and close the doors of our studies, and affect to despise this rude voice; but we cannot shut it out. It comes to us from wherever men are at work, from wherever they are truly living, and accuses us of unfaithfulness, of triviality, of mere stage-play; and none of us can escape conviction except he prove himself worthy of his time—a time in which the great masters have brought literature back to life, and filled its ebbing veins with the red tides of reality. We cannot all equal them; we need not copy them; but we can all go to the sources of their inspiration and their power; and to draw from these no one need go far—no one need really go out of himself.

Fifty years ago, Carlyle, in whom the truth was always alive, but in whom it was then unperverted by suffering, by celebrity, and by despair, wrote in his study of Diderot: "Were it not reasonable to prophesy that this exceeding great multitude of novel-writers and such like must, in a new generation, gradually do one of two things: either retire into the nurseries, and work for children, minors, and semi-fatuous persons of both sexes, or else, what were far better, sweep their novel-fabric into the dust-cart, and betake themselves with such faculty as they have to understand and record what is true, of which surely there is, and will forever be, a whole infinitude unknown to us of infinite importance to us? Poetry, it will more and more come to be understood, is nothing but higher knowledge; and the genuine Romance (for grown persons), Reality."

If, after half a century, fiction still mainly works for "children, minors, and semi-fatuous persons of both sexes," it is nevertheless one of the hopefulest signs of the world's progress that it has begun to work for "grown persons," and if not exactly in the way that Carlyle might have solely intended in urging its writers to compile memoirs instead of building the "novel-fabric," still it has, in the highest and widest sense, already made Reality its Romance. I cannot judge it, I do not even care for it, except as it has done this; and I can hardly conceive of a literary self-respect in these days compatible with the old trade of make-believe, with the production of the kind of fiction which is too much honored by classification with card-playing and horse-racing. But let fiction cease to lie about life; let it portray men and women as they are, actuated by the motives and the passions in the measure we all know; let it leave off painting dolls and working them by springs and wires; let it show the different interests in their true proportions; let it forbear to preach pride and revenge, folly and insanity, egotism and prejudice, but frankly own these for what they are, in whatever figures and occasions they appear; let it not put on fine literary airs; let it speak the dialect, the language, that most Americans know—the language of unaffected people everywhere—and there can be no doubt of an unlimited future, not only of delightfulness but of usefulness, for it.

XXI

It is no doubt such work as Mr. James's that an English essay-
ist (Mr. E. Hughes) has chiefly in mind, in a study of the
differences of the English and American novel. He defines the
English novel as working from within outwardly, and the
American novel as working from without inwardly. The definition is very surprisingly accurate; and the critic's discovery of
this fundamental difference is carried into particulars with a
distinctness which is as unfailing as the courtesy he has in
recognizing the present superiority of American work. He
seems to think, however, that the English principle is the
better, though why he should think so he does not make so
clear. It appears a belated and rather voluntary effect of pa-
triotism, disappointing in a philosopher of his degree; but it
does not keep him from very explicit justice to the best characteristics of our fiction. "The American novelist is distinguished for the intellectual grip which he has of his characters. . . . He penetrates below the crust, and he recognizes
no necessity of the crust to anticipate what is beneath. . . .
He utterly discards heroics; he often even discards anything
like a plot. . . . His story proper is often no more than a
natural predicament. . . . It is no stage view we have of his
characters, but one behind the scenes. . . . We are brought
into contact with no strained virtues, illumined by strained
lights upon strained heights of situation. . . . Whenever he
appeals to the emotions it would seem to be with an appeal to
the intellect too. . . . because he weaves his story of the finer,
less self-evident though common threads of human nature,
seldom calling into play the grosser and more powerful strain.
. . . Everywhere in his pages we come across acquaintances
undisguised. . . . The characters in an American novel are
never unapproachable to the reader. . . . The naturalness,
with the every-day atmosphere which surrounds it, is one great
charm of the American novel. . . . It is throughout examina-
tive, discursory, even more—quizzical. Its characters are undergoing, at the hands of the author, calm, interested obser-

vation. . . . He is never caught identifying himself with them; he must preserve impartiality at all costs . . . but . . . the touch of nature is always felt, the feeling of kinship always follows. . . . The strength of the American novel is its optimistic faith. . . . If out of this persistent hopefulness it can evolve for men a new order of trustfulness, a tenet that between man and man there should be less suspicion, more confidence, since human nature sanctions it, its mission will have been more than an aesthetic, it will have been a moral one."

Not all of this will be found true of Mr. James, but all that relates to artistic methods and characteristics will, and the rest is true of American novels generally. For the most part in their range and tendency they are admirable. I will not say they are all good, or that any of them is wholly good; but I find in nearly every one of them a disposition to regard our life without the literary glasses so long thought desirable, and to see character, not as it is in other fiction, but as it abounds outside of all fiction. This disposition sometimes goes with poor enough performance, but in some of our novels it goes with performance that is excellent; and at any rate it is for the present more valuable than evenness of performance. It is what relates American fiction to the only living movement in imaginative literature, and distinguishes by a superior freshness and authenticity any group of American novels from a similarly accidental group of English novels, giving them the same good right to be as the like number of recent Russian novels, French novels, Spanish novels, Italian novels, Norwegian novels.

It is the difference of the American novelist's ideals from those of the English novelist that gives him his advantage, and seems to promise him the future. The love of the passionate and the heroic, as the Englishman has it, is such a crude and unwholesome thing, so deaf and blind to all the most delicate and important facts of art and life, so insensible to the subtle values in either that its presence or absence makes the whole difference, and enables one who is not obsessed by it to thank Heaven that he is not as that other man is.

There can be little question that many refinements of thought and spirit which every American is sensible of in the fiction of this continent, are necessarily lost upon our good kin beyond seas, whose thumb-fingered apprehension requires something gross and palpable for its assurance of reality. This is not their fault, and I am not sure that it is wholly their misfortune: they are made so as not to miss what they do not find, and they are simply content without those subtleties of life and character which it gives us so keen a pleasure to have noted in literature. If they perceive them at all it is as something vague and diaphanous, something that filmily wavers before their sense and teases them, much as the beings of an invisible world might mock one of our material frame by intimations of their presence. It is with reason, therefore, on the part of an Englishman, that Mr. Henley complains of our fiction as a shadow-land, though we find more and more in it the faithful report of our life, its motives and emotions, and all the comparatively etherealized passions and ideals that influence it.

In fact, the American who chooses to enjoy his birthright to the full, lives in a world wholly different from the Englishman's, and speaks (too often through his nose) another language: he breathes a rarefied and nimble air full of shining possibilities and radiant promises which the fog-and-soot-clogged lungs of those less-favored islanders struggle in vain to fill themselves with. But he ought to be modest in his advantage, and patient with the coughing and sputtering of his cousin who complains of finding himself in an exhausted receiver on plunging into one of our novels. To be quite just to the poor fellow, I have had some such experience as that myself in the atmosphere of some of our more attenuated romances. Yet every now and then I read a book with perfect comfort and much exhilaration, whose scenes the average Englishman would gasp in. Nothing happens; that is, nobody murders or debauches anybody else; there is no arson or pillage of any sort; there is not a ghost, or a ravening beast, or a hairbreadth escape, or a shipwreck, or a monster of self-sacrifice, or a lady five thousand years old in the whole course of the story; "no promenade, no band of music, nossing!" as Mr. Du Maurier's Frenchman said of the meet for a fox-hunt. Yet it is all alive with the keenest interest for those who enjoy the study of individual traits and general conditions as they make themselves known to American experience.

These conditions have been so favorable hitherto (though they are becoming always less so) that they easily account for the optimistic faith of our novel which Mr. Hughes notices. It used to be one of the disadvantages of the practice of romance in America, which Hawthorne more or less whimsically lamented, that there were so few shadows and inequalities in our broad level of prosperity; and it is one of the reflections suggested by Dostoievsky's novel, The Crime and the Punishment, that whoever struck a note so profoundly tragic in American fiction would do a false and mistaken thing—as false and mistaken in its way as dealing in American fiction with certain nudities which the Latin peoples seem to find edifying. Whatever their deserts, very few American novelists have been led out to be shot, or finally exiled to the rigors of a winter at Duluth; and in a land where journeymen carpenters and plumbers strike for four dollars a day the sum of hunger and cold is comparatively small, and the wrong from class to class has been almost inappreciable, though all this is changing for the worse. Our novelists, therefore, concern themselves with the more smiling aspects of life, which are the more American, and seek the universal in the individual rather than the social interests. It is worth while, even at the risk of being called commonplace, to be true to our well-to-do actualities; the very passions themselves seem to be softened and modified by conditions which formerly at least could not be said to wrong anyone, to cramp endeavor, or to cross lawful desire. Sin and suffering and shame there must always be in the world, I suppose, but I believe that in this new world of ours it is still mainly from one to another one, and oftener still from one to one's self. We have death too in America, and a great deal of disagreeable and painful disease, which the multiplicity of our patent medicines does not seem to cure; but this is tragedy that comes in the very nature of things, and is not peculiarly American, as the large, cheerful average of health and success and happy life is. It will not do to boast, but it is well to be true to the facts, and to see that, apart from these purely mortal troubles, the race here has enjoyed conditions in which most of the ills that have darkened its annals might be averted by honest work and unselfish behavior . . .

XXII

An interesting fact in regard to the different varieties of the short story among us is that the sketches and studies by the women seem faithfuler and more realistic than those of the men, in proportion to their number. Their tendency is more distinctly in that direction, and there is a solidity, an honest observation, in the work of such women as Mrs. Cooke, Miss Murfree, Miss Wilkins and Miss Jewett, which often leaves little to be desired. I should, upon the whole, be disposed to rank American short stories only below those of such Russian writers as I have read, and I should praise rather than blame their free use of our different local parlances, or "dialects," as people call them. I like this because I hope that our inherited English may be constantly freshened and revived from the native sources which our literary decentralization will help to keep open, and I will own that as I turn over novels coming from Philadelphia, from New Mexico, from Boston, from Tennessee, from rural New England, from New York, every local flavor of diction gives me courage and pleasure. M. Alphonse Daudet, in a conversation which Mr. H. H. Boyesen has set down in a recently recorded interview with him, said, in speaking of Tourguéneff: "What a luxury it must be to have a great big untrodden barbaric language to wade into! We poor fellows who work in the language of an old civilization, we must sit and chisel our little verbal felicities, only to find in the end that it is a borrowed jewel we are polishing. The crown jewels of our French tongue have passed through the hands of so many generations of monarchs that it seems like presumption on the part of any late-born pretender to attempt to wear them.". . . It will never do to allow that we are at such a desperate pass in English, but something of this divine despair we may feel too in thinking of "the spacious times of great Elizabeth," when the poets were trying the stops of the young language, and thrilling with the surprises of their own music. We may comfort ourselves, however, unless we prefer a luxury of grief, by remembering that no language is ever old on the lips of those who speak it, no matter how decrepit it drops from the pen. We have only to leave our studies, editorial and other, and go into the shops and fields to find the "spacious times" again; and from the beginning Realism, before she had put on her capital letter, had divined this near-at-hand truth along with the rest. Mr. Lowell, almost the greatest and finest realist who ever wrought in verse, showed us that Elizabeth was still Queen where he heard Yankee farmers talk. One need not invite slang into the company of its betters, though perhaps slang has been dropping its "s" and becoming language ever since the world began, and is certainly sometimes delightful and forcible beyond the reach of the dictionary. I would not have anyone go about for new words, but if one of them came aptly, not to reject its help. For our novelists to try to write Americanly, from any motive, would be a dismal error, but being born Americans, I would have them use "Americanisms" whenever these serve their turn; and when their characters speak, I should like to hear them speak true American, with all the varying Tennessean, Philadelphian, Bostonian, and New York accents. If we bother ourselves to write what the critics imagine to be "English," we shall be priggish and artificial, and still more if we make our Americans talk "English." There is also this serious disadvantage about "English," that if we wrote the best "English" in the world, probably the English themselves would not know it, or, if they did, certainly would not own it. It has always been supposed by grammarians and purists that a language can be kept as they find it; but languages, while they live, are perpetually changing. God apparently meant them for the common people—whom Lincoln believed God liked because he had made so many of them; and the common people will use them freely as they use other gifts of God. On their lips our continental English will differ more and more from the insular English, and I believe that this is not deplorable, but desirable.

In fine, I would have our American novelists be as American as they unconsciously can. Matthew Arnold complained that he found no "distinction" in our life, and I would gladly persuade all artists intending greatness in any kind among us that the recognition of the fact pointed out by Mr. Arnold ought to be a source of inspiration to them, and not discouragement. We have been now some hundred years building up a state on the affirmation of the essential equality of men in their rights and duties, and whether we have been right or wrong the gods have taken us at our word, and have responded to us with a civilization in which there is no "distinction" perceptible to the eye that loves and values it. Such beauty and such grandeur as we have is common beauty, common grandeur, or the beauty and grandeur in which the quality of solidarity so prevails that neither distinguishes itself to the disadvantage of anything else. It seems to me that these conditions invite the artist to the study and the appreciation of the common, and to the portrayal in every art of those finer and higher aspects which unite rather than sever humanity, if he would thrive in our new order of things. The talent that is robust enough to front the every-day world and catch the charm of its work-worn, care-worn, brave, kindly face, need not fear the encounter, though it seems terrible to the sort nurtured in the superstition of the romantic, the bizarre, the heroic, the distinguished, as the things alone worthy of painting or carving or writing. The arts must become democratic, and then we shall have the expression of America in art; and the reproach which Mr. Arnold was half right in making us shall have no justice in it any longer; we shall be "distinguished."

XXIV

One of the great newspapers the other day invited the prominent American authors to speak their minds upon a point in the theory and practice of fiction which had already vexed some of them. It was the question of how much or how little the American novel ought to deal with certain facts of life which are not usually talked of before young people, and especially young ladies. Of course the question was not decided, and I forget just how far the balance inclined in favor of a larger freedom in the matter. But it certainly inclined that way; one or two writers of the sex which is somehow supposed to have purity in its keeping (as if purity were a thing that did not practically concern the other sex, preoccupied with serious affairs) gave it a rather vigorous tilt to that side. In view of this fact it would not be the part of prudence to make an effort to dress the balance; and indeed I do not know that I was going to make any such effort. But there are some things to say, around and about the subject, which I should like to have some one else say, and which I may myself possibly be safe in suggesting.

One of the first of these is the fact, generally lost sight of by those who censure the Anglo-Saxon novel for its prudishness, that it is really not such a prude after all; and that if it is sometimes apparently anxious to avoid those experiences of life not spoken of before young people, this may be an appearance only. Sometimes a novel which has this shuffling air, this effect of truckling to propriety, might defend itself, if it could speak for itself, by saying that such experiences happened not to come within its scheme, and that, so far from maiming or mutilating itself in ignoring them, it was all the more faithfully representative of the tone of modern life in dealing with love that was chaste, and with passion so honest that it could be openly spoken of before the tenderest society bud at dinner. It might say that the guilty intrigue, the betrayal, the extreme flirtation even, was the exceptional thing in life, and unless the scheme of the story necessarily involved it, that it would be bad art to lug it in, and as bad taste as to introduce such topics in a mixed company. It could say very justly that the novel in our civilization now always addresses a mixed company, and that the vast majority of the company are ladies, and that very many, if not most, of these ladies are young girls. If the novel were written for men and for married women alone, as in continental Europe, it might be altogether different. But the simple fact is that it is not written for them alone among us, and it is a question of writing, under cover of our universal acceptance, things for young girls to read which you would be put out-of-doors for saying to them; or of frankly giving notice of your intention, and so cutting yourself off from the pleasure— and it is a very high and sweet one—of appealing to these vivid, responsive intelligences, which are none the less brilliant and admirable because they are innocent.

One day a novelist who liked, after the manner of other men, to repine at his hard fate, complained to his friend, a critic, that he was tired of the restriction he had put upon himself in this regard; for it is a mistake, as can be readily shown, to suppose that others impose it. "See how free those French fellows are!" he rebelled. "Shall we always be shut up to our tradition of decency?"

"Do you think it's much worse than being shut up to their tradition of indecency?" said his friend.

Then that novelist began to reflect, and he remembered how sick the invariable motive of the French novel made him. He perceived finally that, convention for convention, ours was not only more tolerable, but on the whole was truer to life, not only to its complexion, but also to its texture. No one will pretend that there is not vicious love beneath the surface of our society; if he did, the fetid explosions of the divorce trials would refute him; but if he pretended that it was in any just sense characteristic of our society, he could be still more easily refuted. Yet it exists, and it is unquestionably the material of tragedy, the stuff from which intense effects are wrought. The question, after owning this fact, is whether these intense effects are not rather cheap effects. I incline to think they are, and I will try to say why I think so, if I may do so without offence. The material itself, the mere mention of it, has an instant fascination; it arrests, it detains, till the last word is said, and while there is anything to be hinted. This is what makes a love intrigue of some sort all but essential to the popularity of any fiction. Without such an intrigue the intellectual equipment of the author must be of the highest, and then he will succeed only with the highest class of readers. But any author who will deal with a guilty love intrigue holds all readers in his hand, the highest with the lowest, as long as he hints the slightest hope of the smallest potential naughtiness. He need not at all be a great author; he may be a very shabby wretch, if he has but the courage or the trick of that sort of thing. The critics will call him "virile" and "passionate;" decent people will be ashamed to have been limed by him; but the low average will only ask another chance of flocking into his net. If he happens to be an able writer, his really fine and costly work will be unheeded, and the lure to the appetite will be chiefly remembered. There may be other qualities which make reputations for other men, but in his case they will count for nothing. He pays this penalty for his success in that kind; and every one pays some such penalty who deals with some such material. It attaches in like manner to the triumphs of the writers who now almost form a school among us, and who may be said to have established themselves in an easy popularity simply by the study of erotic shivers and fervors. They may find their account in the popularity, or they may not; there is no question of the popularity.

But I do not mean to imply that their case covers the whole ground. So far as it goes, though, it ought to stop the mouths of those who complain that fiction is enslaved to propriety among us. It appears that of a certain kind of impropriety it is free to give us all it will, and more. But this is not what serious men and women writing fiction mean when they rebel against the limitations of their art in our civilization. They have no desire to deal with nakedness, as painters and sculptors freely do in the worship of beauty; or with certain facts of life, as the stage does, in the service of sensation. But they ask why, when the conventions of the plastic and histrionic arts liberate their followers to the portrayal of almost any phase of the physical or of the emotional nature, an American novelist may not write a story on the lines of Anna Karenina or Madame Bovary. Sappho they put aside, and from Zola's work they avert their eyes. They do not condemn him or Daudet, necessarily, or accuse their motives; they leave them out of the question; they do not want to do that kind of thing. But they do sometimes wish to do another kind, to touch one of the most serious and sorrowful problems of life in the spirit of Tolstoi and Flaubert, and they ask why they may not. At one time, they remind us, the Anglo-Saxon novelist did deal with such problems—De Foe in his spirit, Richardson in his, Goldsmith in his. At what moment did our fiction lose this privilege? In what fatal hour did the Young Girl arise and seal the lips of Fiction, with a touch of her finger, to some of the most vital interests of life?

Whether I wished to oppose them in their aspiration for greater freedom, or whether I wished to encourage them, I should begin to answer them by saying that the Young Girl had never done anything of the kind. The manners of the novel have been improving with those of its readers; that is all. Gentlemen no longer swear or fall drunk under the table, or abduct young ladies and shut them up in lonely country-houses, or so habitually set about the ruin of their neighbors' wives, as they once did. Generally, people now call a spade an agricultural implement; they have not grown decent without having also grown a little squeamish, but they have grown comparatively decent; there is no doubt about that. They require of a novelist whom they respect unquestionable proof of his seriousness, if he proposes to deal with certain phases of life; they require a sort of scientific decorum. He can no longer expect to be received on the ground of entertainment only; he assumes a higher function, something like that of a physician or a priest, and they expect him to be bound by laws as sacred as those of such professions; they hold him solemnly pledged not to betray them or abuse their confidence. If he will accept the conditions, they give him their confidence, and he may then treat to his greater honor, and not at all to his disadvantage, of such experiences, such relations of men and women as George Eliot treats in Adam Bede, in Daniel Deronda, in Romola, in almost all her books; such as Hawthorne treats in the Scarlet Letter; such as Dickens treats in David Copperfield; such as Thackeray treats in Pendennis, and glances at in every one of his fictions; such as most of the masters of English fiction have at some time treated more or less openly. It is quite false or quite mistaken to suppose that our novels have left untouched these most important realities of life. They have only not made them their stock in trade; they have kept a true perspective in regard to them; they have relegated them in their pictures of life to the space and place they occupy in life itself, as we know it in England and America. They have kept a correct proportion, knowing perfectly well that unless the novel is to be a map, with everything scrupulously laid down in it, a faithful record of life in far the greater extent could be made to the exclusion of guilty love and all its circumstances and consequences.

I justify them in this view not only because I hate what is cheap and meretricious, and hold in particular loathing the cant of the critics who require "passion" as something in itself admirable and desirable in a novel, but because I prize fidelity in the historian of feeling and character. Most of these critics who demand "passion" would seem to have no conception of any passion but one. Yet there are several other passions: the passion of grief, the passion of avarice, the passion of pity, the passion of ambition, the passion of hate, the passion of envy, the passion of devotion, the passion of friendship; and all these have a greater part in the drama of life than the passion of love, and infinitely greater than the passion of guilty love. Wittingly or unwittingly, English fiction and American fiction have recognized this truth, not fully, not in the measure it merits, but in greater degree than most other fiction.

Edward Eggleston

1837-1902

Preface to the Library Edition of

THE HOOSIER SCHOOL-MASTER

Being the History of a Story

(1892)

"The Hoosier School-Master" was written and printed in the autumn of 1871. It is therefore now about twenty-one years old, and the publishers propose to mark its coming of age by issuing a library edition. I avail myself of the occasion to make some needed revisions, and to preface the new edition with an account of the origin and adventures of the book. If I should seem to betray unbecoming pride in speaking of a story that has passed into several languages and maintained an undiminished popularity for more than a score of years, I count on receiving the indulgence commonly granted to paternal vanity when celebrating the majority of a first-born. With all its faults on its head, this little tale has become a classic, in the bookseller's sense at least; and a public that has shown so constant a partiality for it has a right to feel some curiosity regarding its history.

I persuade myself that additional extenuation for this biography of a book is to be found in the relation which "The Hoosier School-Master" happens to bear to the most significant movement in American literature in our generation. It is the file-leader of the procession of American dialect novels. Before the appearance of this story, the New England folk-speech had long been employed for various literary purposes, it is true; and after its use by Lowell, it had acquired a standing that made it the classic *lingua rustica* of the United States. Even Hoosiers and Southerners when put into print, as they sometimes were in rude burlesque stories, usually talked about "huskin' bees" and "apple-parin' bees" and used many other expressions foreign to their vernacular. American literature hardly touched the speech and life of the people outside of New England; in other words, it was provincial in the narrow sense.

I can hardly suppose that "The Hoosier School-Master" bore any causative relation to that broader provincial movement in our literature which now includes such remarkable productions as the writings of Mr. Cable, Mr. Harris, Mr. Page, Miss Murfree, Mr. Richard Malcom Johnson, Mr. Howe, Mr. Garland, some of Mrs. Burnett's stories and others quite worthy of inclusion in this list. The taking up of life in this regional way has made our literature really national by the only process possible. The Federal nation has at length manifested a consciousness of the continental diversity of its forms of life. The "great American novel," for which prophetic critics yearned so fondly twenty years ago, is appearing in sections. I may claim for this book the distinction, such as it is, of being the first of the dialect stories that depict a life quite beyond New England influence. Some of Mr. Bret Harte's brief and powerful tales had already foreshadowed this movement toward a larger rendering of our life. But the romantic character of Mr. Harte's delightful stories and the absence of anything that can justly be called dialect in them mark them as rather forerunners than beginners of the prevailing school. For some years after the appearance of the present novel, my own stories had to themselves the field of provincial realism (if, indeed, there be any such thing as realism) before there came the succession of fine productions which have made the last fourteen years notable.

Though it had often occurred to me to write something

in the dialect now known as Hoosier—the folk-speech of the southern part of Ohio, Indiana, and Illinois of forty years ago —I had postponed the attempt indefinitely, probably because the only literary use that had been made of the allied speech of the Southwest had been in the books of the primitive humorists of that region. I found it hard to dissociate in my own mind the dialect from the somewhat coarse boisterousness which seemed inseparable from it in the works of these rollicking writers. It chanced that in 1871 Taine's lectures on "Art in the Netherlands," or rather Mr. John Durand's translation of them, fell into my hands as a book for editorial review. These discourses are little else than an elucidation of the thesis that the artist of originality will work courageously with the materials he finds in his own environment. In Taine's view, all life has matter for the artist, if only he have eyes to see.

Many years previous to the time of which I am now speaking, while I was yet a young man, I had projected a lecture on the Hoosier folk-speech, and had even printed during the war a little political skit in that dialect in a St. Paul paper. So far as I know, nothing else had ever been printed in the Hoosier. Under the spur of Taine's argument, I now proceeded to write a short story wholly in the dialect spoken in my childhood by rustics on the north side of the Ohio River. This tale I called "The Hoosier School-Master." It consisted almost entirely of an autobiographical narration in dialect by Mirandy Means of the incidents that form the groundwork of the present story. I was the newly installed editor of a weekly journal, *Hearth and Home*, and I sent this little story in a new dialect to my printer. It chanced that one of the proprietors of the paper saw a part of it in proof. He urged me to take it back and make a longer story out of the materials, and he expressed great confidence in the success of such a story. Yielding to his suggestion, I began to write this novel from week to week as it appeared in the paper, and thus found myself involved in the career of a novelist, which had up to that time formed no part of my plan of life. In my inexperience I worked at a white-heat, completing the book in ten weeks. Long before these weeks of eager toil were over, it was a question among my friends whether the novel might not write *finis* to me before I should see the end of it.

The sole purpose I had in view at first was the resuscitation of the dead-and-alive newspaper of which I had ventured to take charge. One of the firm of publishers thought much less favorably of my story than his partner did. I was called into the private office and informed with some severity that my characters were too rough to be presentable in a paper so refined as ours. I confess they did seem somewhat too robust for a sheet so anæmic as *Hearth and Home* had been in the months just preceding. But when, the very next week after this protest was made, the circulation of the paper increased some thousands at a bound, my employer's critical estimate of the work underwent a rapid change—a change based on what seemed to him better than merely literary considerations. By the time the story closed, at the end of fourteen instalments, the subscription list had multiplied itself four or five fold. It is only fair to admit, however, that the original multiplicand had been rather small.

Papers in Canada and in some of the other English colonies transferred the novel bodily to their columns, and many of the American country papers helped themselves to it quite freely. It had run some weeks of its course before it occurred to any one that it might profitably be reprinted in book form. The publishers were loath to risk much in the venture. The newspaper type was rejustified to make a book page and barely two thousand copies were printed for a first edition. I remember expressing the opinion that the number was too large.

"The Hoosier School-Master" was pirated with the utmost promptitude by the Messrs. Routledge, in England, for that was in the barbarous days before international copyright, when English publishers complained of the unscrupulousness of American reprinters, while they themselves pounced upon every line of American production that promised some shillings of profit. "The Hoosier School-Master" was brought out in England in a cheap, sensational form. The edition of ten thou-

sand has long been out of print. For this large edition and for
the editions issued in the British colonies and in continental
Europe I have never received a penny. A great many men have
made money out of the book, but my own returns have been
comparatively small. For its use in serial form I received nothing beyond my salary as editor. On the copyright edition I have
received the moderate royalty allowed to young authors at the
outset of their work. The sale of the American edition in the
first twenty years amounted to seventy thousand copies. The
peculiarity of this sale is its steadiness. After twenty years,
"The Hoosier School-Master" is selling at the average rate of
more than three thousand copies per annum. During the last
half-dozen years the popularity of the book has apparently increased, and its twentieth year closed with a sale of twenty-one
hundred in six months. Only those who are familiar with the
book trade and who know how brief is the life of the average
novel will understand how exceptional is this long-continued
popularity.

Some of the newspaper reviewers of twenty years ago were a
little puzzled to know what to make of a book in so question-
able a shape, for the American dialect novel was then a newcomer. But nothing could have given a beginner more genuine
pleasure than the cordial commendation of the leading professional critic of the time, the late Mr. George Ripley, who
wrote an extended review of this book for the *Tribune*. The
monthly magazines all spoke of "The Hoosier School-Master"
in terms as favorable as it deserved. I cannot pretend that I
was content with these notices at the time, for I had the sen-
sitiveness of a beginner. But on looking at the reviews in the
magazines of that day, I am amused to find that the faults
pointed out in the work of my prentice hand are just those I
should be disposed to complain of now, if it were any part of
my business to tell the reader wherein I might have done
better.

The Nation, then in its youth, honored "The Hoosier
School-Master" by giving it two pages, mostly in discussion of

its dialect, but dispensing paradoxical praise and censure in that condescending way with which we are all familiar enough. According to its critic, the author had understood and described the old Western life, but he had done it "quite sketchily, to be sure." Yet it was done "with essential truth and some effectiveness." The critic, however, instantly stands on the other foot again and adds that the book "is not a captivating one." But he makes amends in the very next sentence by an allusion to "the faithfulness of its transcript of the life it depicts," and then instantly balances the account on the adverse side of the ledger by assuring the reader that "it has no interest of passion or mental power." But even this fatal conclusion is diluted by a dependent clause. "Possibly," says the reviewer, "the good feeling of the intertwined love story may conciliate the good-will of some of the malcontent." One could hardly carry further the fine art of oscillating between moderate commendation and parenthetical damnation—an art that lends a factitious air of judicial impartiality and mental equipoise. Beyond question, *The Nation* is one of the ablest weekly papers in the world; the admirable scholarship of its articles and reviews in departments of special knowledge might well be a subject of pride to any American. But its inadequate reviews of current fiction add nothing to its value, and its habitual tone of condescending depreciation in treating imaginative literature of indigenous origin is one of the strongest discouragements to literary production.

The main value of good criticism lies in its readiness and penetration in discovering and applauding merit not before recognized, or imperfectly recognized. This is a conspicuous trait of Sainte-Beuve, the greatest of all newspaper critics. He knew how to be severe upon occasion, but he saw talent in advance of the public and dispensed encouragement heartily, so that he made himself almost a foster-father to the literature of his generation in France. But there is a class of anonymous reviewers in England and America who seem to hold a traditional theory that the function of a critic toward new-born talent is analogous to that of Pharaoh toward the infant Jewish population.[1]

During the first year after its publication "The Hoosier School-Master" was translated into French and published in a condensed form in the *Revue des Deux Mondes*. The translator was the writer who signs the name M. Th. Bentzon, and who is well known to be Madame Blanc. This French version afterward appeared in book form in the same volume with one of Mr. Thomas Bailey Aldrich's stories and some other stories of mine. In this latter shape I have never seen it. The title given to the story by Madame Blanc was "Le Maître d'École de Flat Creek." It may be imagined that the translator found it no easy task to get equivalents in French for expressions in a dialect new and strange. "I'll be dog-on'd" appears in French as "devil take me" (*"diable m'emporte"*), which is not bad; the devil being rather a jolly sort of fellow, in French. "The Church of the Best Licks" seems rather unrenderable, and I do not see how the translator could have found a better phrase for it than *"L'Eglise des Raclées,"* though *"raclées"* does not convey the double sense of "licks." *"Jim epelait vite comme l'eclair"* is not a good rendering of "Jim spelled like lightning," since it is not the celerity of the spelling that is the main consideration. *"Concours d'epellation"* is probably the best equivalent for "spelling-school," but it seems something more stately in its French dress. When Bud says, with reference to Hannah, "I never took no shine that air way," the phrase is rather too idiomatic for the French tongue, and it becomes "I

---

[1] Since writing the passage in the text, I have met with the following in *The Speaker*, of London: "Everybody knows that when an important work is published in history, philosophy, or any branch of science, the editor of a respectable paper employs an expert to review it; . . . indeed, the more abstruse the subject of the book, the more careful and intelligent you will find the review. . . . It is equally well known that works of fiction and books of verse are not treated with anything like the same care. . . . A good poem, play, or novel is at least as fine an achievement as a good history; yet the history gets the benefit of an expert's judgment and two columns of thoughtful praise or censure, while the poem, play, or novel is treated to ten skittish lines by the hack who happens to be within the nearest call when the book comes in."

haven't run after that hare" (*"Je n'ai pas chassé ce lièvre-la"*).
Perhaps the most sadly amusing thing in the translation is the
way the meaning of the nickname Shocky is missed in an
explanatory foot-note. It is, according to the translator, an
abbreviation or corruption of the English word "shocking,"
which expresses the shocking ugliness of the child—*"qui ex-
prime la laideur choquante de l'enfant."*

A German version of "The Hoosier School-Master" was
made about the time of the appearance of the French translation, but of this I have never seen a copy. I know of it only
from the statement made to me by a German professor, that
he had read it in German before he knew any English. What
are the equivalents in High German for "right smart" and
"dog-on" I cannot imagine.

Several years after the publication of "The Hoosier School-
Master" it occurred to Mr. H. Hansen, of Kjöge, in Denmark,
to render it into Danish. Among the Danes the book enjoyed
a popularity as great, perhaps, as it has had at home. The circulation warranted Mr. Hansen and his publisher in bringing
out several other novels of mine. The Danish translator was the
only person concerned in the various foreign editions of this
book who had the courtesy to ask the author's leave. Under
the old conditions in regard to international copyright, an author came to be regarded as one not entitled even to common civilities in the matter of reprinting his works—he was to
be plundered without politeness. As I look at the row of my
books in the unfamiliar Danish, I am reminded of that New
England mother who, on recovering her children carried away
by the Canadian Indians, found it impossible to communicate
with a daughter who spoke only French and a son who knew
nothing but the speech of his savage captors. Mr. Hansen was
thoughtful enough to send me the reviews of my books in the
Danish newspapers; and he had the double kindness to translate these into English and to leave out all but those that were
likely to be agreeable to my vanity. Of these I remember but a
single sentence, and that because it was expressed with felicity.
The reviewer said of the fun in "The Hoosier School-Master":

"This is humor laughing to keep from bursting into tears."

A year or two before the appearance of "The Hoosier School-Master," a newspaper article of mine touching upon American dialect interested Mr. Lowell, and he urged me to "look for the foreign influence" that has affected the speech of the Ohio River country. My reverence for him as the master in such studies did not prevent me from feeling that the suggestion was a little absurd. But at a later period I became aware that North Irishmen used many of the pronunciations and idioms that distinctly characterized the language of old-fashioned people on the Ohio. Many Ulster men say "wair" for were and "air" for are, for example. Connecting this with the existence of a considerable element of Scotch-Irish names in the Ohio River region, I could not doubt that here was one of the keys the master had bidden me look for. While pursuing at a later period a series of investigations into the culture-history of the American people in the seventeenth and eighteenth centuries, I became much interested in the emigration to America from the north of Ireland, a movement that waxed and waned as the great Irish-linen industry of the last century declined or prospered. The first American home of these Irish was Pennsylvania. A portion of them were steady-going, psalm-singing, money-getting people, who in course of time made themselves felt in the commerce, politics, and intellectual life of the nation. There was also a dare-devil element, descended perhaps from those rude borderers who were deported to Ireland more for the sake of the peace of North Britain than for the benefit of Ireland. In this rougher class there was perhaps a larger dash of the Celtic fire that came from the wild Irish women whom the first Scotch settlers in Ulster made the mothers of their progeny. Arrived in the wilds of Pennsylvania, these Irishmen built rude cabins, planted little patches of corn and potatoes, and distilled a whiskey that was never suffered to grow mellow. The forest was congenial to men who spent much the larger part of their time in boisterous sport of one sort or another. The manufacture of the rifle was early brought to Lancaster, in Pennsylvania, direct from the land of its invention by Swiss emigrants, and in the adventurous Scotch-Irishman of the Pennsylvania frontier the rifle found its fellow. Irish settlers became hunters of wild beasts, explorers, pioneers, and warriors against the Indians, upon whom they avenged their wrongs with relentless ferocity. Both the Irish race and the intermingled Pennsylvania Dutch were prolific, and the up-country of Pennsylvania soon overflowed. Emigration was held in check to the westward for a while by the cruel massacres of the French and Indian wars, and one river of population poured itself southward into the fertile valleys of the Virginia mountain country; another and larger flood swept still farther to the south along the eastern borders of the Appalachian range until it reached the uplands of Carolina. When the militia of one county in South Carolina was mustered during the Revolution, it was found that every one of the thirty-five hundred men enrolled were natives of Pennsylvania. These were mainly sons of North Irishmen, and from the Carolina Irish sprang Calhoun, the most aggressive statesman that has appeared in America, and Jackson, the most brilliant military genius in the whole course of our history. Before the close of the Revolution this adventurous race had begun to break over the passes of the Alleghanies into the dark and bloody ground of Kentucky and Tennessee. Soon afterward a multitude of Pennsylvanians of all stocks—the Scotch-Irish and those Germans, Swiss, and Hollanders who are commonly classed together as the Pennsylvania Dutch, as well as a large number of people of English descent—began to migrate down the Ohio Valley. Along with them came professional men and people of more or less culture, chiefly from eastern Virginia and Maryland. There came also into Indiana and Illinois, from the border States and from as far south as North Carolina and Tennessee, a body of "poor whites." These semi-nomadic people, descendants of the colonial bond-servants, formed, in the second quarter of the nineteenth century, the lowest rank of Hoosiers. But as early as 1845 there was a considerable exodus of these to Missouri. From Pike County, in that State, they wended their way to California, to appear in Mr. Bret Harte's stories as "Pikes." The movement of this class out of Indiana went on with augmented volume in the fifties. The emigrants of this period mostly sought the States lying just west of the Mississippi, and the poorer sort made the trip in little one-horse wagons of the sorriest description, laden mainly with white-headed children and followed by the yellow curs that are the one luxury indispensable to a family of this class. To this migration and to a liberal provision for popular education Indiana owes a great improvement in the average intelligence of her people. As early as 1880, I believe, the State had come to rank with some of the New England States in the matter of literacy.

The folk-speech of the Ohio River country has many features in common with that of the eastern Middle States, while it received but little from the dignified eighteenth-century English of eastern Virginia. There are distinct traces of the North-Irish in the idioms and in the peculiar pronunciations. One finds also here and there a word from the "Pennsylvania Dutch," such as "waumus," for a loose jacket, from the German *wamms*, a doublet, and "smearcase" for cottage cheese, from the German *schmierkäse*. The only French word left by the old *voyageurs*, so far as I now remember, is "cordelle," to tow a boat by a rope carried along the shore.

Substantially the same folk-speech exists wherever the Pennsylvania migration formed the main element of the primitive settlement. I have heard the same dialect in the South Carolina uplands that one gets from a Posey County Hoosier, or rather that one used to get in the old days before the vandal school-master had reduced the vulgar tongue to the monotonous propriety of what we call good English.

In drawing some of the subordinate characters in this tale a little too baldly from the model, I fell into an error common to inexperienced writers. It is amusing to observe that these portrait characters seem the least substantial of all the figures in the book. Dr. Small is a rather unrealistic villain, but I knew him well and respected him in my boyish heart for a most exemplary Christian of good family at the very time that, according to testimony afterward given, he was diversifying his pursuits as a practising physician by leading a gang of burglars. More than one person has been pointed out as the original of Bud Means, and I believe there are one or two men each of whom flatters himself that he posed for the figure of the first disciple of the Church of the Best Licks. Bud is made up of elements found in some of his race, but not in any one man. Not dreaming that the story would reach beyond the small circulation of *Hearth and Home*, I used the names of people in Switzerland and Decatur counties, in Indiana, almost without being aware of it. I have heard that a young man bearing the surname given to one of the rudest families in this book had to suffer many gibes while a student at an Indiana college. I here do public penance for my culpable indiscretion.

"Jeems Phillips," name and all, is a real person whom at the time of writing this story I had not seen since I was a lad of nine and he a man of nearly forty. He was a mere memory to me, and was put into the book with some slighting remarks which the real Jeems did not deserve. I did not know that he was living, and it did not seem likely that the story would have vitality enough to travel all the way to Indiana. But the portion referring to Phillips was transferred to the county paper circulating among Jeems' neighbors. For once the good natured man was, as they say in Hoosier, "mad," and he threatened to thrash the editor. "Do you think he means you?" demanded the editor. "To be sure he does," said the champion speller. "Can you spell?" "I can spell down any master that ever came to our district," he replied. As time passed on, Phillips found himself a lion. Strangers desired an introduction to him as a notability, and invited the champion to dissipate with them at the soda fountain in the village drug store. It became a matter of pride with him that he was the most famous speller in the world. Two years ago, while visiting the town of my nativity, I met upon the street the aged Jeems Phillips, whom I had not seen for more than forty years. I would go far to hear him "spell down" a complacent schoolmaster once more.

The publication of this book gave rise to an amusing revival of the spelling-school as a means of public entertainment, not in rustic regions alone, but in towns also. The furor extended to the great cities of New York and London, and reached at last to farthest Australia, spreading to every region in which English is spelled or spoken. But the effect of the chapter on the spelling-school was temporary and superficial; the only organization that came from the spelling-school mania, so far as I know, was an association of proof-readers in London to discuss mooted points. The sketch of the Church of the Best Licks, however, seems to have made a deep and enduring impression upon individuals and to have left some organized results. I myself endeavored to realize it, and for five years I was the pastor of a church in Brooklyn, organized on a basis almost as simple as that in the Flat Creek school-house. The name I rendered into respectable English, and the Church of the Best Licks became the Church of Christian Endeavor. It was highly successful in doing that which a church ought to do, and its methods of work have been widely copied. After my work as a minister had been definitely closed, the name and the underlying thought of this church were borrowed for a young people's society; and thus the little story of good endeavor in Indiana seems to have left a permanent mark on the ecclesiastical organization of the time.

If any one, judging by the length of this preface, should conclude that I hold my little book in undue esteem, let him know that I owe it more than one grudge. It is said that Thomas Campbell, twenty years after the appearance of his best-known poem, was one day introduced as "the author of 'The Pleasures of Hope.' " "Confound 'The Pleasures of Hope,' " he protested; "can't I write anything else?" So, however much I may prefer my later work, more carefully wrought in respect of thought, structure, and style, this initial novel, the favorite of the larger public, has become inseparably associated with my name. Often I have mentally applied Campbell's imprecation on "The Pleasures of Hope" to this story. I could not write in this vein now if I would, and twenty-one years have made so many changes in me that I dare not make any but minor changes in this novel. The author of "The Hoosier School-Master" is distinctly not I; I am but his heir and executor; and since he is a more popular writer than I, why should I meddle with his work? I have, however, ventured to make some necessary revision of the diction, and have added notes, mostly with reference to the dialect.

A second grudge against this story is that somehow its readers persist in believing it to be a bit of my own life. Americans are credulous believers in that miracle of the imagination whom no one has ever seen in the flesh—the self-made man. Some readers of "The Hoosier School-Master" have settled it for a certainty that the author sprang from the rustic class he has described. One lady even wrote to inquire whether my childhood were not represented in Shocky, the little lad out of the poor-house. A biographical sketch of me in Italian goes so far as to state that among the hard resorts by which I made a living in my early life was the teaching of a Sunday-school in Chicago.

No one knows so well as I the faults of immaturity and inexperience that characterize this book. But perhaps after all the public is right in so often preferring an author's first book. There is what Emerson would have called a "central spontaneity" about the work of a young man that may give more delight to the reader than all the precision of thought and perfection of style for which we strive as life advances.

JOSHUA'S ROCK ON LAKE GEORGE, 1892.

Hamlin Garland

1860-1940

from CRUMBLING IDOLS

(1894)

New Fields: The secret of every lasting success in art or literature lies, I believe, in a powerful, sincere, emotional concept of life first, and, second, in the acquired power to convey that concept to others. This leads necessarily to individuality in authorship and to freedom from past models . . .

It is a settled conviction with me that each locality must produce its own literary record, each special phase of life utter its own voice. There is no other way for a true local expression to embody itself. The sun of truth strikes each part of the earth at a little different angle; it is this angle which gives life and infinite variety to literature. It is the subtle differences which life presents in California and Oregon, for example, which will produce, and justify, a Pacific-Coast literature . . .

The mere fact that a writer happens to live in California or Oregon will not make him a part of that literature, any more than Stevenson's life in Samoa will make him a Samoan author. A nation, in the early part of its literary history, is likely to sweep together all that can, by any construction, be called its literature; but as it grows rich in real utterances, it eliminates one after the other all those writings which its clearer judgment perceives to be exotics . . .

Veritism, as I understand it, puts aside all models, even living writers. Whatever he may do unconsciously, the artist must consciously stand alone before nature and before life. Nature and life have changed since Miller and Harte wrote. The California of today is quite different. The creative writer today, if true to himself, finds himself interested in other subjects, and finds himself believing in a different treatment of the same material.

There is no necessity of treating the same material, however. Vast changes, already in progress, invite the writer. The coming in of horticulture, the immigration of farmers from all the Eastern States; the mingling of races; the feudalistic ownership of lands; the nomadic life of the farm-hands, the growth of cities, the passing Spanish civilization—these are a few of the subjects which occur to me as worthy the best work of novelist and dramatist.

Being "a farmer by birth and a novelist by occupation," I saw most clearly the literary possibilities of the farmer's life in the valleys of California and in the stupendous forests of Oregon.

I saw children moving along to school in the shadow of the most splendid mountains; I saw a youth plowing—behind him rose a row of palms, against which he stood like a figure of bronze in relief; I saw young men and maidens walking down aisles of green and crimson pepper-trees, and the aisles led to blue silhouetted mountains; I saw men herding cattle where the sun beat with hot radiance, and strange cacti held out wild arms; I saw children playing about cabins, setting at defiance the illimitable width and sunless depths of the Oregon forests—and I thought, "Perhaps one of these is the novelist or painter of the future."

Perhaps the future poet of these spaces is plowing somewhere like that, because it must be that from the splendor and dramatic contrast of such scenes the poet will rise. He always has, and he always will. His feet will be on the soil like Whittier's, and like Miller's; his song will differ from theirs because he will be an individual soul, and because his time and his environment will not be the same.

Why should the Western artists and poets look away to Greece and Rome and Persia for themes? I have met Western people who were writing blank-verse tragedies of the Middle

Ages and painting pictures of sirens and cherubs, and still considered themselves Western artists and Western writers. The reason is not hard to find. They had not risen to the perception of the significant and beautiful in their own environment, or they were looking for effects, without regard to their sincere conviction. They were poets of books, not of life.

This insincerity is fatal to any great work of art. A man must be moved by something higher than money, by something higher than hope of praise; he must have a sleepless love in his heart urging him to re-create in the image the life he has loved. He must be burdened and without rest until he has given birth to his conception. He will not be questioned when he comes; he will be known as a product of some one time and place, a voice speaking the love of his heart . . .

A new literature will come with the generation just coming to manhood and womanhood on the Coast. If rightly educated, their eyes will turn naturally to the wheat-fields, the forests, the lanes of orange trees, the ranges of unsurpassed mountains. They will try to express in the novel, the drama, in painting and in song, the love and interest they take in the things close at hand.

This literature will not deal with crime and abnormalities, nor with diseased persons. It will deal, I believe, with the wholesome love of honest men for honest women, with the heroism of labor, the comradeship of men,—a drama of average types of character, infinitely varied, but always characteristic . . . It will be a literature such as no other locality could produce, a literature that could not have been written in any other time, or among other surroundings. That is the test of a national literature.

The Local Novel: The local novel seems to be the heir apparent to the kingdom of poesy. It is already the most prominent of all literary attempts today; certainly it is the most sincere. It seems but beginning its work. It is "hopelessly contemporaneous;" that is its strength. It is (at its best) unaffected, natural, emotional. It is sure to become all-powerful.

It will redeem American literature, as it has already redeemed the South from its conventional and highly-wrought romanticism . . .

In the North the novel will continue local for some time to come. It will delineate the intimate speech and life of every section of our enormous and widely-scattered republic. It will catch and fix in charcoal the changing, assimilating races . . . each wonderful locality in our Nation of Nations will yet find its native utterance. The superficial work of the tourist and outsider will not do. The real novelist of these sections is walking behind the plow or trudging to school in these splendidly potential environments.

This local movement will include the cities as well, and St. Louis, Chicago, San Francisco, will be delineated by artists born of each city, whose work will be so true that it could not have been written by anyone from the outside. The real utterance of a city or a locality can only come when a writer is born out of its intimate heart. To such an one, nothing will be "strange" or "picturesque;" all will be familiar, and full of significance or beauty. The novel of the slums must be written by one who has played there as a child, and taken part in all its amusements; not out of curiosity, but out of pleasure-seeking. It cannot be done from above nor from the outside. It must be done out of a full heart and without seeking for effect . . .

Both drama and novel will be colloquial. This does not mean that they will be exclusively in the dialects, but the actual speech of the people of each locality will unquestionably be studied more closely than ever before. Dialect is the life of a language, precisely as the common people of the nation form the sustaining power of its social life and art.

And so in the novel, in the short story, and in the drama— by the work of a multitude of loving artists, not by the work of an over-topping personality—will the intimate social, individual life of the nation be depicted. Before this localism shall pass away, such a study will have been made of this land and people as has never been made by any other age or social group—a literature from the plain people, reflecting their unrestrained outlook on life, subtle in speech and color, humane beyond precedent, humorous, varied, simple in means, lucid as water, searching as sunlight.

To one who believes each age to be its own best interpreter, the idea of "decay of fiction" never comes. That which the absolutist takes for decay is merely change. The conservative fears change; the radical welcomes it. The conservative tries to argue that fundamentals cannot change; that they are the same yesterday, today, and tomorrow. If that were true, then a sorrowful outlook on the future would be natural. Life means change . . .

To the veritist, therefore, the present is the vital theme. The past is dead, and the future can be trusted to look after itself. The young men and maidens of that time will find the stars of their present brighter than the stars of '92, the people around them more absorbing than books, and their own outlook on life more reasonable than that of dead men. Their writing and painting, in proportion to its vitality and importance, will reflect this, their natural attitude, toward life and history.

Literary Centres: . . . The blight upon the literature of the West, like that of all provinces, has been its timidity, its tendency to work in accepted modes, its childish desire to write for the applause of its masters in the East. This has been, in fact, the weakness of the entire output of American literature. The West only emphasizes the fact. In material things, America has boundless self-assertion, but in the arts it has imitated because of its failure to perceive its proper relation to the literature of the world. The West, reckoning itself an annex of the East, has imitated imitations.

Because the East considered itself English in general character, the West, so far as most of its writers are concerned, has acquiesced. As a matter of fact, the West is not English. The Northwest is more largely Teutonic and Scandinavian, and the people of Indiana, Ohio, and Illinois are far removed from England and from English conceptions of life; and this distance is sure to find its statement in literature. Wisconsin, Iowa, Minnesota, Dakota, and other Western states are half composed of men and women of Germanic or Scandinavian extraction. The literature rising from these people will not be English. It will be something new; it will be, and ought to be, American—that is to say, a new composite.

The centre of this literature of national scope, therefore, cannot be in the East. It will not be dominated by the English idea . . . The judgment of the East should take rank merely among other judgments; it should not be held all-important.

The purpose of this writing is not merely to combat literary centralization, but also to build up local centres. Wherever a human being is moved by genuine love of nature and of men to the conscientious and faithful study of the expression of his emotions, there is a literary centre. Around him are grouped minds whose candid criticism can aid and direct him; but this criticism must not evade, nor demand conformity to tradition; it must demand of the young writer truth, sincerity, and individuality.

Let the critics of the local centres remember Mistral and Whitcomb Riley, who won their way among the people before the critical journals would take count of them. It is the man who has no knowledge of accepted forms, and who therefore refers every work back to nature, who is quickest to respond to the literature of life . . .

Let them keep close to the local life, developing the best— that is, the simplest and most natural—talent of their region, making their appeal constantly to the unspoiled yet discerning taste of the middle-conditioned people, and they will succeed . . . Taste is rising, Culture is broadening swiftly. A new generation is coming on—a generation of veritists.

Yours not to worship crumbling idols; your privilege and pleasure should be to face life and the material earth in a new way—moulding old forms of government into new shapes, catching from earth and sea and air, new songs to sing, new thoughts to frame, new deeds to dare.

Mark Twain

1835-1910

FENIMORE COOPER'S
LITERARY OFFENCES

(1895)

The Pathfinder and *The Deerslayer* stand at the head of Cooper's novels as artistic creations. There are others of his works which contain parts as perfect as are to be found in these, and scenes even more thrilling. Not one can be compared with either of them as a finished whole.

The defects in both of these tales are comparatively slight. They were pure works of art.—*Prof. Lounsbury.*

The five tales reveal an extraordinary fulness of invention.

. . . One of the very greatest characters in fiction, Natty Bumppo . . .

The craft of the woodsman, the tricks of the trapper, all the delicate art of the forest, were familiar to Cooper from his youth up.—*Prof. Brander Matthews.*

Cooper is the greatest artist in the domain of romantic fiction yet produced by America.—*Wilkie Collins.*

It seems to me that it was far from right for the Professor of English Literature in Yale, the Professor of English Literature in Columbia, and Wilkie Collins to deliver opinions on Cooper's literature without having read some of it. It would have been much more decorous to keep silent and let persons talk who have read Cooper.

Cooper's art has some defects. In one place in *Deerslayer*, and in the restricted space of two-thirds of a page, Cooper has scored 114 offences against literary art out of a possible 115. It breaks the record.

There are nineteen rules governing literary art in the domain of romantic fiction—some say twenty-two. In *Deerslayer* Cooper violated eighteen of them. These eighteen require:

1. That a tale shall accomplish something and arrive somewhere. But the *Deerslayer* tale accomplishes nothing and arrives in the air.

2. They require that the episodes of a tale shall be necessary parts of the tale, and shall help to develop it. But as the *Deerslayer* tale is not a tale, and accomplishes nothing and arrives nowhere, the episodes have no rightful place in the work, since there was nothing for them to develop.

3. They require that the personages in a tale shall be alive, except in the case of corpses, and that always the reader shall be able to tell the corpses from the others. But this detail has often been overlooked in the *Deerslayer* tale.

4. They require that the personages in a tale, both dead and alive, shall exhibit a sufficient excuse for being there. But this detail also has been overlooked in the *Deerslayer* tale.

5. They require that when the personages of a tale deal in conversation, the talk shall sound like human talk, and be talk such as human beings would be likely to talk in the given circumstances, and have a discoverable meaning, also a discoverable purpose, and a show of relevancy, and remain in the neighborhood of the subject in hand, and be interesting to the reader, and help out the tale, and stop when the people cannot think of anything more to say. But this requirement has been ignored from the beginning of the *Deerslayer* tale to the end of it.

6. They require that when the author describes the character of a personage in his tale, the conduct and conversation of that personage shall justify said description. But this law gets little or no attention in the *Deerslayer* tale, as Natty Bumppo's case will amply prove.

7. They require that when a personage talks like an illustrated, gilt-edged, tree-calf, hand-tooled, seven-dollar Friend-

ship's Offering in the beginning of a paragraph, he shall not talk like a negro minstrel in the end of it. But this rule is flung down and danced upon in the *Deerslayer* tale.

8. They require that crass stupidities shall not be played upon the reader as "the craft of the woodsman, the delicate art of the forest," by either the author or the people in the tale. But this rule is persistently violated in the *Deerslayer* tale.

9. They require that the personages of a tale shall confine themselves to possibilities and let miracles alone; or, if they venture a miracle, the author must so plausibly set it forth as to make it look possible and reasonable. But these rules are not respected in the *Deerslayer* tale.

10. They require that the author shall make the reader feel a deep interest in the personages of his tale and in their fate; and that he shall make the reader love the good people in the tale and hate the bad ones. But the reader of the *Deerslayer* tale dislikes the good people in it, is indifferent to the others, and wishes they would all get drowned together.

11. They require that the characters in a tale shall be so clearly defined that the reader can tell beforehand what each will do in a given emergency. But in the *Deerslayer* tale this rule is vacated.

In addition to these large rules there are some little ones. These require that the author shall

12. Say what he is proposing to say, not merely come near it.

13. Use the right word, not its second cousin.

14. Eschew surplusage.

15. Not omit necessary details.

16. Avoid slovenliness of form.

17. Use good grammar.

18. Employ a simple and straightforward style.

Even these seven are coldly and persistently violated in the *Deerslayer* tale.

Cooper's gift in the way of invention was not a rich endowment; but such as it was he liked to work it, he was pleased with the effects, and indeed he did some quite sweet things with it. In his little box of stage properties he kept six or eight cunning devices, tricks, artifices for his savages and woodsmen to deceive and circumvent each other with, and he was never so happy as when he was working these innocent things and seeing them go. A favorite one was to make a moccasined person tread in the tracks of the moccasined enemy, and thus hide his own trail. Cooper wore out barrels and barrels of moccasins in working that trick. Another stage-property that he pulled out of his box pretty frequently was his broken twig. He prized his broken twig above all the rest of his effects, and worked it the hardest. It is a restful chapter in any book of his when somebody doesn't step on a dry twig and alarm all the reds and whites for two hundred yards around. Every time a Cooper person is in peril, and absolute silence is worth four dollars a minute, he is sure to step on a dry twig. There may be a hundred handier things to step on, but that wouldn't satisfy Cooper. Cooper requires him to turn out and find a dry twig; and if he can't do it, go and borrow one. In fact, the Leather Stocking Series ought to have been called the Broken Twig Series.

I am sorry there is not room to put in a few dozen instances of the delicate art of the forest, as practised by Natty Bumppo and some of the other Cooperian experts. Perhaps we may venture two or three samples. Cooper was a sailor—a naval officer; yet he gravely tells us how a vessel, driving towards a lee shore in a gale, is steered for a particular spot by her skipper because he knows of an *undertow* there which will hold her back against the gale and save her. For just pure woodcraft, or sailorcraft, or whatever it is, isn't that neat? For several years Cooper was daily in the society of artillery, and he ought to have noticed that when a cannon-ball strikes the ground it either buries itself or skips a hundred feet or so; skips again a hundred feet or so—and so on, till finally it gets tired and rolls. Now in one place he loses some "females"— as he always calls women—in the edge of a wood near a plain at night in a fog, on purpose to give Bumppo a chance to show off the delicate art of the forest before the reader. These mislaid people are hunting for a fort. They hear a cannon-blast, and a cannon-ball presently comes rolling into the wood and stops at their feet. To the females this suggests nothing. The case is very different with the admirable Bumppo. I wish I may never know peace again if he doesn't strike out promptly and *follow the track* of that cannon-ball across the plain through the dense fog and find the fort. Isn't it a daisy? If Cooper had any real knowledge of Nature's ways of doing things, he had a most delicate art in concealing the fact. For instance: one of his acute Indian experts, Chingachgook (pronounced Chicago, I think), has lost the trail of a person he is tracking through the forest. Apparently that trail is hopelessly lost. Neither you nor I could ever have guessed out the way to find it. It was very different with Chicago. Chicago was not stumped for long. He turned a running stream out of its course, and there, in the slush in its old bed, were that person's moccasin-tracks. The current did not wash them away, as it would have done in all other like cases—no, even the eternal laws of Nature have to vacate when Cooper wants to put up a delicate job of woodcraft on the reader.

We must be a little wary when Brander Matthews tells us that Cooper's books "reveal an extraordinary fulness of invention." As a rule, I am quite willing to accept Brander Matthews's literary judgments and applaud his lucid and graceful phrasing of them; but that particular statement needs to be taken with a few tons of salt. Bless your heart, Cooper hadn't any more invention than a horse; and I don't mean a high-class horse, either; I mean a clothes-horse. It would be very difficult to find a really clever "situation" in Cooper's books, and still more difficult to find one of any kind which he has failed to render absurd by his handling of it. Look at the episodes of "the caves"; and at the celebrated scuffle between Maqua and those others on the table-land a few days later; and at Hurry Harry's queer water-transit from the castle to the ark; and at Deerslayer's half-hour with his first corpse; and at the quarrel between Hurry Harry and Deerslayer later; and at —but choose for yourself; you can't go amiss.

If Cooper had been an observer his inventive faculty would have worked better; not more interestingly, but more rationally, more plausibly. Cooper's proudest creations in the way of "situations" suffer noticeably from the absence of the observer's protecting gift. Cooper's eye was splendidly inaccurate. Cooper seldom saw anything correctly. He saw nearly all things as through a glass eye, darkly. Of course a man who cannot see the commonest little every-day matters accurately is working at a disadvantage when he is constructing a "situation." In the *Deerslayer* tale Cooper has a stream which is fifty feet wide where it flows out of a lake; it presently narrows to twenty as it meanders along for no given reason, and yet when a stream acts like that it ought to be required to explain itself. Fourteen pages later the width of the brook's outlet from the lake has suddenly shrunk thirty feet, and become "the narrowest part of the stream." This shrinkage is not accounted for. The stream has bends in it, a sure indication that it has alluvial banks and cuts them; yet these bends are only thirty and fifty feet long. If Cooper had been a nice and punctilious observer he would have noticed that the bends were oftener nine hundred feet long than short of it.

Cooper made the exit of that stream fifty feet wide, in the first place, for no particular reason; in the second place, he narrowed it to less than twenty to accommodate some Indians. He bends a "sapling" to the form of an arch over this narrow passage, and conceals six Indians in its foliage. They are "laying" for a settler's scow or ark which is coming up the stream on its way to the lake; it is being hauled against the stiff current by a rope whose stationary end is anchored in the lake; its rate of progress cannot be more than a mile an hour. Cooper describes the ark, but pretty obscurely. In the matter of dimensions "it was little more than a modern canal-boat." Let us guess, then, that it was about one hundred and forty feet long. It was of "greater breadth than common." Let us guess, then, that it was about sixteen feet wide. This leviathan had been prowling down bends which were but a third as long as itself, and scraping between banks where it had only two feet of space to spare on each side. We cannot too much admire this miracle. A low-roofed log dwelling occupies "two-thirds of the ark's length"—a dwelling ninety feet long and sixteen feet wide, let us say—a kind of vestibule train. The dwelling has two rooms—each forty-five feet long and sixteen feet wide, let us guess. One of them is the bedroom of the Hutter girls, Judith and Hetty; the other is the parlor in the daytime, at night it is papa's bedchamber. The ark is arriving at the stream's exit now, whose width has been reduced to less than twenty feet to accommodate the Indians—say to eighteen. There is a foot to spare on each side of the boat. Did the Indians notice that there was going to be a tight squeeze there? Did they notice that they could make money by climbing down out of that arched sapling and just stepping aboard when the ark scraped by? No, other Indians would have noticed these things, but Cooper's Indians never notice anything. Cooper thinks they are marvelous creatures for noticing, but he was almost always in error about his Indians. There was seldom a sane one among them.

The ark is one hundred and forty feet long; the dwelling is ninety feet long. The idea of the Indians is to drop softly and secretly from the arched sapling to the dwelling as the ark creeps along under it at the rate of a mile an hour, and butcher the family. It will take the ark a minute and a half to pass under. It will take the ninety foot dwelling a minute to pass under. Now, then, what did the six Indians do? It would take you thirty years to guess, and even then you would have to give it up, I believe. Therefore, I will tell you what the Indians did. Their chief, a person of quite extraordinary intellect for a Cooper Indian, warily watched the canal-boat as it squeezed along under him, and when he had got his calculations fined down to exactly the right shade, as he judged, he let go and dropped. And *missed the house!* That is actually what he did. He missed the house, and landed in the stern of the scow. It was not much of a fall, yet it knocked him silly. He lay there unconscious. If the house had been ninety-seven feet long he would have made the trip. The fault was Cooper's, not his. The error lay in the construction of the house. Cooper was no architect.

There still remained in the roost five Indians. The boat has passed under and is now out of their reach. Let me explain what the five did—you would not be able to reason it out for yourself. No. 1 jumped for the boat, but fell in the water astern of it. Then No. 2 jumped for the boat, but fell in the water still farther astern of it. Then No. 3 jumped for the boat, and fell a good way astern of it. Then No. 4 jumped for the boat, and fell in the water *away* astern. Then even No. 5 made a jump for the boat—for he was a Cooper Indian. In the matter of intellect, the difference between a Cooper Indian and the Indian that stands in front of the cigar-shop is not spacious. The scow episode is really a sublime burst of invention; but it does not thrill, because the inaccuracy of the details throws a sort of air of fictitiousness and general improbability over it. This comes of Cooper's inadequacy as an observer.

The reader will find some examples of Cooper's high talent for inaccurate observation in the account of the shooting-match in *The Pathfinder*.

"A common wrought nail was driven lightly into the target, its head having been first touched with paint."

The color of the paint is not stated—an important omission, but Cooper deals freely in important omissions. No, after all, it was not an important omission; for this nail-head is *a hundred yards from* the marksmen, and could not be seen by them at that distance, no matter what its color might be. How far can the best eyes see a common house-fly? A hundred yards? It is quite impossible. Very well; eyes that cannot see a house-fly that is a hundred yards away cannot see an ordinary nail-head at that distance, for the size of the two objects is the same. It takes a keen eye to see a fly or a nailhead at fifty yards—one hundred and fifty feet. Can the reader do it?

The nail was lightly driven, its head painted, and game

called. Then the Cooper miracles began. The bullet of the
first marksman chipped an edge of the nail-head; the next
man's bullet drove the nail a little way into the target—and
removed all the paint. Haven't the miracles gone far enough
now? Not to suit Cooper; for the purpose of this whole
scheme is to show off his prodigy, Deerslayer-Hawkeye-Long-
Rifle-Leather-Stocking-Pathfinder-Bumppo before the ladies.

" 'Be all ready to clench it, boys!' cried out Pathfinder, stepping
into his friend's tracks the instant they were vacant. 'Never mind a
new nail; I can see that, though the paint is gone, and what I can
see I can hit at a hundred yards, though it were only a mosquito's
eye. Be ready to clench!'
"The rifle cracked, the bullet sped its way, and the head of the
nail was buried in the wood, covered by the piece of flattened lead."

There, you see, is a man who could hunt flies with a rifle,
and command a ducal salary in a Wild West show to-day if we
had him back with us.

The recorded feat is certainly surprising just as it stands;
but it is not surprising enough for Cooper. Cooper adds a
touch. He has made Pathfinder do this miracle with another
man's rifle; and not only that, but Pathfinder did not have
even the advantage of loading it himself. He had everything
against him, and yet he made that impossible shot; and not
only made it, but did it with absolute confidence, saying, "Be
ready to clench." Now a person like that would have undertaken that same feat with a brickbat, and with Cooper to help
he would have achieved it, too.

Pathfinder showed off handsomely that day before the ladies. His very first feat was a thing which no Wild West show
can touch. He was standing with the group of marksmen, observing—a hundred yards from the target, mind; one Jasper
raised his rifle and drove the centre of the bull's-eye. Then
the Quartermaster fired. The target exhibited no result this
time. There was a laugh. "It's a dead miss," said Major Lun-
die. Pathfinder waited an impressive moment or two; then

said, in that calm, indifferent, know-it-all way of his, "No, Major, he has covered Jasper's bullet, as will be seen if any one will take the trouble to examine the target."

Wasn't it remarkable! How *could* he see that little pellet fly through the air and enter that distant bullet-hole? Yet that is what he did; for nothing is impossible to a Cooper person. Did any of those people have any deep-seated doubts about this thing? No; for that would imply sanity, and these were all Cooper people.

"The respect for Pathfinder's skill and for his *quickness and accuracy of sight*" (the italics are mine) "was so profound and general, that the instant he made this declaration the spectators began to distrust their own opinions, and a dozen rushed to the target in order to ascertain the fact. There, sure enough, it was found that the Quartermaster's bullet had gone through the hole made by Jasper's, and that, too, so accurately as to require a minute examination to be certain of the circumstance, which, however, was soon clearly established by discovering one bullet over the other in the stump against which the target was placed."

They made a "minute" examination; but never mind, how could they know that there were two bullets in that hole without digging the latest one out? for neither probe nor eyesight could prove the presence of any more than one bullet. Did they dig? No; as we shall see. It is the Pathfinder's turn now; he steps out before the ladies, takes aim, and fires.

But, alas! here is a disappointment; an incredible, an unimaginable disappointment—for the target's aspect is unchanged; there is nothing there but that same old bullet-hole!

" 'If one dared to hint at such a thing,' cried Major Duncan, 'I should say that the Pathfinder has also missed the target!' "

As nobody had missed it yet, the "also" was not necessary; but never mind about that, for the Pathfinder is going to speak.

" 'No, no, Major,' said he, confidently, 'that *would* be a risky declaration. I didn't load the piece, and can't say what was in it; but if it was lead, you will find the bullet driving down those of the Quartermaster and Jasper, else is not my name Pathfinder.'

"A shout from the target announced the truth of this assertion."

Is the miracle sufficient as it stands? Not for Cooper. The Pathfinder speaks again, as he "now slowly advances towards the stage occupied by the females":

" 'That's not all, boys, that's not all; if you find the target touched at all, I'll own to a miss. The Quartermaster cut the wood, but you'll find no wood cut by that last messenger."

The miracle is at last complete. He knew—doubtless *saw*— at the distance of a hundred yards—that his bullet had passed into the hole *without fraying the edges*. There were now three bullets in that one hole—three bullets embedded processionally in the body of the stump back of the target. Everybody knew this—somehow or other—and yet nobody had dug any of them out to make sure. Cooper is not a close observer, but he is interesting. He is certainly always that, no matter what happens. And he is more interesting when he is not noticing what he is about than when he is. This is a considerable merit.

The conversations in the Cooper books have a curious sound in our modern ears. To believe that such talk really ever came out of people's mouths would be to believe that there was a time when time was of no value to a person who thought he had something to say; when it was the custom to spread a two-minute remark out to ten; when a man's mouth was a rolling-mill, and busied itself all day long in turning four-foot pigs of thought into thirty-foot bars of conversational railroad iron by attenuation; when subjects were seldom faithfully stuck to, but the talk wandered all around and arrived nowhere; when conversations consisted mainly of irrelevancies, with here and there a relevancy, a relevancy with an embarrassed look, as not being able to explain how it got there.

Cooper was certainly not a master in the construction of dialogue. Inaccurate observation defeated him here as it defeated him in so many other enterprises of his. He even failed to notice that the man who talks corrupt English six days in the week must and will talk it on the seventh, and can't help himself. In the *Deerslayer* story he lets Deerslayer talk the showiest kind of book-talk sometimes, and at other times the basest of base dialects. For instance, when some one asks him if he has a sweetheart, and if so, where she abides, this is his majestic answer:

" 'She's in the forest—hanging from the boughs of the trees, in a soft rain—in the dew on the open grass—the clouds that float about in the blue heavens—the birds that sing in the woods—the sweet springs where I slake my thirst—and in all the other glorious gifts that come from God's Providence!' "

And he preceded that, a little before, with this:

" 'It consarns me as all things that touches a fri'nd consarns a fri'nd.' "

And this is another of his remarks:

" 'If I was Injin born, now, I might tell of this, or carry in the scalp and boast of the expl'ite afore the whole tribe; or if my inimy had only been a bear' "—and so on.

We cannot imagine such a thing as a veteran Scotch Commander-in-Chief comporting himself in the field like a windy melodramatic actor, but Cooper could. On one occasion Alice and Cora were being chased by the French through a fog in the neighborhood of their father's fort:

" '*Point de quartier aux coquins!*' cried an eager pursuer, who seemed to direct the operations of the enemy.
" 'Stand firm and be ready, my gallant 6oths!' suddenly ex-

claimed a voice above them; 'wait to see the enemy; fire low, and sweep the glacis.'

" 'Father! father!' exclaimed a piercing cry from out the mist; 'it is I! Alice! thy own Elsie! spare, O! save your daughters!'

" 'Hold!' shouted the former speaker, in the awful tones of parental agony, the sound reaching even to the woods, and rolling back in solemn echo. ' 'Tis she! God has restored me my children! Throw open the sally-port; to the field, 6oths, to the field! pull not a trigger, lest ye kill my lambs! Drive off these dogs of France with your steel!' "

Cooper's word-sense was singularly dull. When a person has a poor ear for music he will flat and sharp right along without knowing it. He keeps near the tune, but it is *not* the tune. When a person has a poor ear for words, the result is a literary flatting and sharping; you perceive what he is intending to say, but you also perceive that he doesn't *say* it. This is Cooper. He was not a word-musician. His ear was satisfied with the *approximate* word. I will furnish some circumstantial evidence in support of this charge. My instances are gathered from half a dozen pages of the tale called *Deerslayer*. He uses "verbal," for "oral"; "precision," for "facility"; "phenomena," for "marvels"; "necessary," for "predetermined"; "unsophisticated," for "primitive"; "preparation," for "expectancy"; "rebuked," for "subdued"; "dependent on," for "resulting from"; "fact," for "condition"; "fact," for "conjecture"; "precaution," for "caution"; "explain," for "determine"; "mortified," for "disappointed"; "meretricious," for "factitious"; "materially," for "considerably"; "decreasing," for "deepening"; "increasing," for "disappearing"; "embedded," for "enclosed"; "treacherous," for "hostile"; "stood," for "stooped"; "softened," for "replaced"; "rejoined," for "remarked"; "situation," for "condition"; "different," for "differing"; "insensible," for "unsentient"; "brevity," for "celerity"; "distrusted," for "suspicious"; "mental imbecility," for "imbecility"; "eyes," for "sight"; "counteracting," for "opposing"; "funeral obsequies," for "obsequies."

There have been daring people in the world who claimed

that Cooper could write English, but they are all dead now—all dead but Lounsbury. I don't remember that Lounsbury makes the claim in so many words, still he makes it, for he says that *Deerslayer* is a "pure work of art." Pure, in that connection, means faultless—faultless in all details—and language is a detail. If Mr. Lounsbury had only compared Cooper's English with the English which he writes himself—but it is plain that he didn't; and so it is likely that he imagines until this day that Cooper's is as clean and compact as his own. Now I feel sure, deep down in my heart, that Cooper wrote about the poorest English that exists in our language, and that the English of *Deerslayer* is the very worst that even Cooper ever wrote.

I may be mistaken, but it does seem to me that *Deerslayer* is not a work of art in any sense; it does seem to me that it is destitute of every detail that goes to the making of a work of art; in truth, it seems to me that *Deerslayer* is just simply a literary *delirium tremens*.

A work of art? It has no invention; it has no order, system, sequence, or result; it has no life-likeness, no thrill, no stir, no seeming of reality; its characters are confusedly drawn, and by their acts and words they prove that they are not the sort of people the author claims that they are; its humor is pathetic; its pathos is funny; its conversations are—oh! indescribable; its love-scenes odious; its English a crime against the language.

Counting these out, what is left is Art. I think we must all admit that.

Rinehart Editions

Selected American Prose

1841-1900

THE REALISTIC MOVEMENT

EDITED WITH AN INTRODUCTION BY

WALLACE STEGNER

Holt, Rinehart and Winston

NEW YORK · CHICAGO · SAN FRANCISCO

TORONTO · LONDON

28120-0118

Fifth Printing, April 1964

Introduction and notes © 1958 by Wallace Stegner
Typography Design by Stefan Salter
Library of Congress Card Number: 58-6436